Liquid Fuels from Oil Shale and Tar Sands 1972

John McDermott

Thirty-Six Dollars

NOYES DATA CORPORATION
Noyes Building
Park Ridge, New Jersey 07656, U.S.A.

FOREWORD

The detailed, descriptive information in this book is based on U.S. patents since 1960 relating to the production of liquid fuels from oil shale and tar sands. Where it was necessary to round out the complete technological picture, some earlier, but very relevant patents were included.

This book serves a double purpose in that it supplies detailed technical information and can be used as a guide to the U.S. patent literature in this field. By indicating all the information that is significant, and eliminating legalistic phraseology, this book presents an advanced commercially oriented review of the production of liquid fuels from oil shale and tar sands. By virtue of its similar arrangement it becomes a companion volume to our "Liquid Fuels from Coal."

The U.S. patent literature is the largest and most comprehensive collection of technical information in the world. There is more practical, commercial, timely process information assembled here than is available from any other source. The technical information obtained from a patent is extremely reliable and comprehensive; sufficient information must be included to avoid rejection for "insufficient disclosure."

The patent literature covers a substantial amount of information not available in the journal literature. The patent literature is a prime source of basic commercially useful information. This information is overlooked by those who rely primarily on the periodical journal literature. It is realized that there is a lag between a patent application on a new process development and the granting of a patent, but it is felt that this may roughly parallel or even anticipate the lag in putting that development into commercial practice.

Many of these patents are being utilized commercially. Whether used or not, they offer opportunities for technological transfer. Also, a major purpose of this book is to describe the number of technical possibilities available, which may open up profitable areas of research and development.

The Table of Contents is organized in such a way as to serve as a subject index. Other indexes by company, inventor, and patent number help in providing easy access to the information contained in this book.

CONTENTS AND SUBJECT INDEX

Contents and Subject Index

INTRODUCTION

Shale oil is basically a viscous organic liquid obtained by pyrolyzing oil shale. The organic portion of oil shale, termed "kerogen", is a mixture of complex chemical compounds and is considered to be one of the primary sources of liquid fuel to future generations. Deposits of oil shale are found in many parts of the world, varying widely in composition, with the inorganic material consisting mainly of clay, fine sand, calcite, dolomite and iron compounds.

A generalized formulation for the kerogen composition is, in percent, carbon, 66 to 88; hydrogen, 7.1 to 12.8; nitrogen, 0.1 to 3.0; sulfur, 0.1 to 8.8; and oxygen, 0.75 to 27.4. Destructive pyrolysis of the crushed shale at atmospheric pressure and temperatures of about 900°F. yields shale oil. Under these conditions disproportionation of the carbon and hydrogen structures occurs to give high conversion to liquid hydrocarbons, light gases and a carbon rich residue which remains on the inorganic matrix.

The recovery of oil from shale was underway in the 1850's in America and Scotland. The interest in shale oil has closely paralleled the price of conventional crude. For example, in the early twenties, some 200 companies were actively considering mining shale, but the discovery of the large Texas oil fields in 1930 dropped the price of conventional crude to ten cents a barrel and shale work was discontinued.

Today, with a pending world-wide energy crisis, and our dependence on oil from the Middle East, it appears that the cost of conventional operations will approach the cost of manufacturing oil from shale. Colony Development Corp. (Oil Shale Corp., Atlantic Richfield, Cleveland Cliffs and Standard of Ohio), working with the hot balls system of retorting are operating a 1,000-barrel-a-day shale mine and retort. These four companies have spent some $45 million on shale technology. Colony is considering building a $200 million plant which will turn out about 55,000 barrels of oil in a day.

The list of companies finding an interest in mining and retorting of oil shale includes Equity Oil, Austrol Oil, Western Oil Shale, Oil Shale Corp. and many major petroleum companies such as Shell, Mobil, Superior, Sun, American Petrofina, Texaco, Atlantic Richfield, Ohio Standard and Standard of California. Many of the holdings of these companies are in Scotland, Germany, Australia and Thailand, but the most extensive deposit is in the Green River formation in the Colorado-Wyoming-Utah triangle. Government owned lands were opened up to private drillers for the first time in 1971.

Introduction

It is estimated that by 1980, synthetic crude from shale will add some 200,000 barrels per day to the United States petroleum supply.

Vast reserves of oil are also found in tar sands such as the Athabasca deposits in Canada. Oil from tar sands must be mined with huge shovels and separated from the sands by water-based techniques. Sun Oil Co. is running a 44,000 barrels per day plant in Alberta through its Great Canadian Sands Ltd. venture which started in 1968.

All of these synthetic liquid fuel processes required extensive efficiency and conservation of energy values to get the price per barrel competitive with conventional crudes. The research and development in this area has been very extensive over the years and has largely been conducted by the major petroleum companies.

This book describes 101 processes related to the retorting and refining of oil shale and the separation of oil from tar sands.

OIL SHALE RETORTING

GAS COMBUSTION

Multistage Thermal Processes

N.P. Peet; U.S. Patent 3,384,569; May 21, 1968; assigned to Esso Research and Engineering Company describes a method for retorting oil shale in a plural stage thermal operation in which shale oil is recovered from crushed oil shale. The plural stage comprises preheating, retorting, burning and cooling zones in which the crushed shale moves serially through the zones and in which shale fines, flue gas and shale oil are formed. In the method, the shale fines are separately removed from each of the zones with the fines removed from the burning and cooling zones being substantially oil-free and discarded. The fines removed from the preheating and retorting zones are substantially oil-rich and are introduced into the burning zone to provide a source of fuel. Also introduced into the burning zone is a free oxygen-containing gas such as air. The oil-rich fines may be mixed with the free oxygen-containing gas and the free oxygen-containing gas thus serves as a carrier for the oil-rich fines.

Introduced into the retorting and cooling zones is a combustible gas, such as a high Btu content gas, which is preferably separated from the shale oil in a later stage in the process, but which may originate outside the system. Natural gas may be used as the combustible gas having a high Btu content. High Btu content as used means a Btu value of about 500 to 2,500. Preferably, a Btu value for the gas may range from about 800 to 1,200 Btu. Gas from the cooling zone is introduced into the preheating zone as a preheating fluid while flue gas from the burning zone is introduced into the retorting zone into indirect heat exchange with oil shale therein. Shale oil is recovered from the preheating and retorting zone by virtue of an operation such as briefly described. High overall thermal efficiency is achieved by recovery of heat, and carbonaceous material in the oil shale is substantially completely utilized in the operation.

The shale oil is recovered in vaporous form and cooled exteriorly of the preheating and retorting zones and thus, is not available for recycling in the several stages which ordinarily in the prior art processes results in consumption of oil and lowering of yield.

The high Btu gas is separated from the shale oil after cooling and condensing of the vaporous shale oil. The fines removed from the preheating and retorting zones are separated from vaporous shale oil before being introduced into the burning zone, and the fines removed from the burning and cooling zones are separated from flue gas before being discarded. The flue gas which is introduced into the retorting zone in indirect heat exchange is withdrawn from the retorting zone and may be discarded such as through a waste heat boiler for recovery of heat or may be reheated either in a separate vessel or other heating means and reintroduced for indirect heat exchange into the retorting zone.

Referring to Figure 1.1, shown on the following page, 11 indicates a charge line or conduit by way of which fresh crushed oil shale is introduced into the system from a source not shown. Line 11 leads into a preheat vessel or zone 12 provided with a distribution means or spider 13 connected to line 10 which introduces hot gas at a temperature of about 1000°F. The oil shale and hot gas flow countercurrently to each other in zone 12 with the preheated shale discharging by line 14 into a vessel comprising a retorting zone 15.

The vaporous and gaseous materials from zone 12 are discharged by line 16 into a separator 17 which may suitably be a cyclone separator from where the gaseous material and vaporous material may leave by line 18. The vaporous and gaseous materials in lines 16 and 18 are at a temperature of 250°F. and are therefore routed by line 19 containing a cooler-condenser 20 into a separator 21 wherein the condensed hydrocarbons shown as body 22 are separated from water 23 in leg 24 of separator 21, the water being discharged by line 25 and the hydrocarbons by line 26. High Btu content gas is withdrawn from separator 21 by line 27a part of which is recycled, in a manner which will be described, by line 28 while the remainder may be recovered by line 29 for further use as may be desired.

Returning to the retorting zone 15, this zone is provided with internal tubes 27 for indirect heat exchange with the preheated shale flowing downward through zone 15 from zone 12. In zone 15, the preheated shale contacts the high Btu content gas from line 29 which is introduced into retorting zone 15 by branch line 30 connecting to distribution means such as spider 31. The preheated shale in zone 15 is retorted by heat supplied indirectly to the internal tubes 27 by line 32, with the flue gas leaving the tubes 27 by line 33.

This flue gas which is at a temperature of 700°F. may be reheated by circulation through a furnace or other heating means or by heat exchange with material in the process at a higher temperature. The flue gas introduced in line 32 may be at a temperature of about 1800°F. The shale after being retorted in zone 15 leaves zone 15 by line 34 and is introduced into a vessel providing a burning zone 35. The retorted shale introduced into burning zone 35 may be at a temperature of about 1000°F. and is contacted with a free oxygen-containing gas such as air introduced by line 36 at a temperature of 80°F. from a source not shown, through a distribution means such as spider 37. Mixed with the air in line 36 for introduction into line 38 are oil-rich fines recovered from preheating zone 12 in cyclone separator 17. These recovered oil-rich fines are introduced into line 36 by line 38.

The vaporous shale oil which may also be in the form of a mist with entrained liquid shale oil is withdrawn from zone 15 by line 39 and discharged at a temperature of 900°F. into separator 40 which may be a cyclone separator. The products separated from the fines in separator 40 are introduced by line 41 into branch line 19 for recovery of hydrocarbons and high Btu gas. The oil-rich fines separated from the mist or vaporous shale oil are withdrawn from separator 40 by line 42 for introduction into line 36 in a mixture with the air for

FIGURE 1.1: MULTISTAGE THERMAL PROCESS

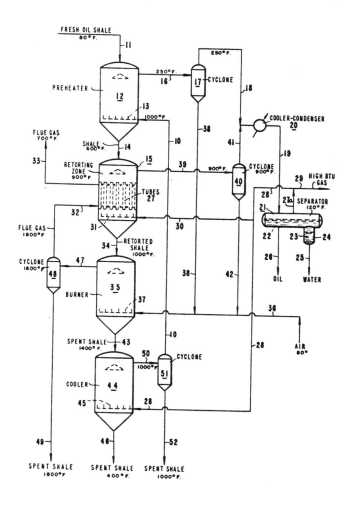

Source: N.P. Peet; U.S. Patent 3,384,569; May 21, 1968

ultimate injection into burning zone 35. The spent shale from burning zone 35 is with-drawn by line 43 at a temperature of 1400°F., and introduced thereby into a vessel defin-ing a cooling zone 44 into which there is introduced by line 28, which connects to distribu-tion means such as spider 45, the high Btu content gas recovered from separator 21. The spent shale at a temperature of 400°F. is discharged by line 46 from the system.

The flue gas from burning zone 35 discharges by line 47 into a separator such as a cyclone 48 from where the flue gas is withdrawn by line 32 for use in zone 15 with the spent shale fines, being substantially oil-free, being discharged by line 49 from the system. Likewise, the flue gas from zone 44 is discharged by line 50 into a separator 51 which may be a cy-clone separator from where the gases by line 10 are introduced into zone 12. Substantially oil-free fines are discharged from zone 51 from the system by lines 52. Since the spent shale fines in lines 49 and 52 are at temperatures, respectively 1800° and 1000°F., this material may be passed into heat exchange either with the flue gas in line 33 or the fresh oil shale in line 11.

In a process described by C.E. Hemminger; U.S. Patent 3,484,364; December 16, 1969; assigned to Esso Research and Engineering Company oil shale is contacted with hot hydrogen in a fluidized system under conditions to conserve heat, to give increased yields and to produce products which are susceptible to removal of nitrogen. The hot hydrogen containing gas is produced from the cracking of a heavy residue recycle in the presence of the hydrogen containing gas. The cracking takes place in a separate zone and supplies at least a portion of the heat necessary for the retorting of the shale.

B.L. Schulman and H.P. Dengler; U.S. Patent 3,520,795; July 14, 1970; assigned to Esso Research and Engineering Company have found that in retorting of crushed oil shale in a retorting system having in a single vessel preheating, retorting and cooling zones and the crushed shale flows serially through, a temperature below carbonate decomposition and below shale oil cracking temperature can be maintained by introducing vaporous water into the system adjacent or into the retorting zone and liquid water into the cooling zone, whereby introduction of cooling gas into the cooling zone is reduced, oil and gas yields are improved and gas heating value is enhanced.

Isolation of Retort Zone to Utilize Flue Gases

In a process described by D.D. MacLaren; U.S. Patent 3,475,319; October 28, 1969; assigned to Esso Research and Engineering Company oil shale is retorted serially downward through a preheating zone, a retorting zone and a combustion zone. Flue gas generated from burning carbonaceous material on the spent oil shale is withdrawn from the combustion zone and introduced into the preheating zone. The sensible heat of the flue gas is further utilized to raise the temperature of product gas which is introduced into the retorting zone as the source of retorting heat, consensibles having been previously removed from the product gas.

In the process, the several zones including the preheating zone, the retorting zone, and the combustion zone are isolated from each other to prevent vapor from the zone below entering the zone above. A sufficient amount of seal gas is employed to displace other gases in the interstices of the oil shale thereby preventing these gases from being carried along with the oil shale such that there is no net flow of seal gas upward into the zone above. Seal gas approximately equal in volume to the interstices flows downward. The zones may be isolated from each other by providing a restriction between the zones and introducing into the restriction upward a seal gas which may be steam or other gas such as, but not limited to, product gas, and the like. Steam is the preferred seal gas, since it does not dilute the product gas since the steam is condensed with the liquid product. Steam simply adds to the water generated by burning carbon from the spent shale. The amount of seal gas introduced into the restriction area may range from 5 to 20 standard cubic feet/ton of raw oil shale introduced into the system.

By sealing the zones from each other to prevent commingling of gaseous material in one zone from gaseous material in another zone, it is possible to withdraw product vapors substantially uncontaminated with flue gases within the system, and it is possible thereby to recover a recycle gas which comprises about 50 to 55% hydrogen with the remainder light hydrocarbons such as methane, ethane and propane, and other gaseous and perhaps normally liquid materials. This enhances the calorific value of the gas and provides a gas having a Btu value within the range from 500 to 750 Btu/scf. Also, by virtue of the high hydrogen content of the recycle product gas, this gas may be used if desired, in hydrogenating the shale oil to remove nitrogen compounds, sulfur, and other deleterious materials. Also, by isolating or sealing the zones from each other, the flue gas may be withdrawn from the combustion zone to bypass the retorting zone and be introduced into the preheating zone to provide heat for use in preheating the raw oil shale introduced into the system. Also, the recycle product gas introduced into the retorting zone may be suitably heated by passage in indirect heat exchange with the withdrawn flue gas, thus conserving heat and allowing the oil shale to be retorted with a mixture of principally hydrogen and hydrocarbons.

Referring to Figure 1.2, shown on the following page, 11 designates a retorting system provided with a preheating zone 12, a retorting zone 13, a combustion zone 14, and a cooling zone 15. The several zones are isolated from each other by restrictions 16, 17 and 18.

The raw oil shale 19, having particle diameters ranging from 1/4 up to 3 inches, is introduced into the system by means of a lock hopper device 20, provided with a control mechanism 21 for maintenance of the retorting system 11 under pressure, as will be described further. The raw oil shale 19 is introduced into preheating zone 12 where it is contacted with the hot flue gas at a temperature of 650°F. introduced by a distribution means 22 connected to line 23. The raw oil shale is preheated in zone 12 to a temperature of 600°F., and then the preheated oil shale flows through distribution means 24 connected to line 25. A flue gas stream is withdrawn from the preheating zone 12 by line 26.

The preheated oil shale flows downward through restriction 16 into retorting zone 13 where it is contacted with the heated gaseous product introduced into zone 13 through distribution means 27a connected to line 27 and introduced from a source which will be described further. The temperature at the bottom of the retorting zone 11 is suitably about 1100°F. and by virtue of contact with the heated gaseous product, the kerogen in the raw oil shale is decomposed to shale oil which is withdrawn as a vaporous product from zone 13 by line 28. The withdrawn vaporous product is cooled and condensed in condenser-cooler 29, and then introduced by line 30 into a collection or demisting drum 31, where a separation is made among the gaseous product, shale oil and water obtained in the operation. The water may be withdrawn by line 32 and the shale oil may be withdrawn by line 33 for further refining such as by hydrogenation. The off gas, comprised of gaseous product and recycle product gas, is withdrawn from collection drum 31 by line 34. An amount equal to the gaseous product produced is withdrawn through valve 37 and line 38. The rest is recycled by compresser 53 to heat exchanger 36 where it is preheated before injection through distributor 27a into zone 13.

The retorted oil shale then discharges through restriction 17 into which a seal gas is introduced through distribution means 39 from line 40 which prevents commingling of gaseous material from zone 14 with the product in zone 13, but permits passage downward of the retorted oil shale into combustion zone 14. In combustion zone 14, where a maximum temperature of 2100°F. may prevail, an oxygen-containing gas is introduced through distribution means 41, connected to line 42.

FIGURE 1.2: ISOLATION OF RETORT ZONE IN SERIALLY DOWNWARD REACTOR

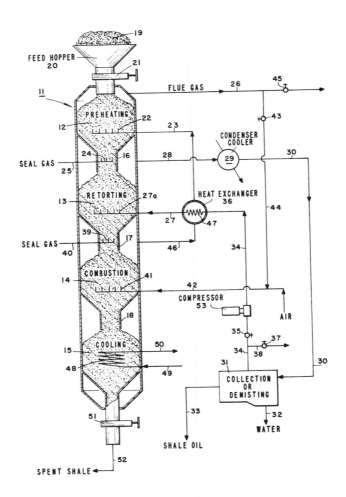

Source: D.D. MacLaren; U.S. Patent 3,475,319; October 28, 1969

Flue gas from line 26 is introduced into line 42 by opening valve 43 in branch line 44 which connects to line 42. Flue gas not introduced into zone 14 is discharged from the system by opening valve 45 in line 26. The flue gas is withdrawn from zone 14 through line 46 which connects to heat exchanger 36, and this withdrawn flue gas at a temperature of 2100°F. passes in indirect heat exchange with the gaseous product introduced into heat exchanger 36 by line 34 and which passes through coil 47. Passage of the flue gas through heat exchanger 36 cools it to temperatures within the range from 500° to 800°F.

In combustion zone 14, the free oxygen-containing gas, such as air, causes combustion of carbonaceous material, such as coke, on the oil shale and generates heat for the retorting operation. The oil shale, after being suitably burned, discharges through restriction 18 into cooling zone 15 which is provided with a cooling coil 48 through which cooling medium is circulated by line 49 and discharged by line 50.

The cooled oil shale is then withdrawn through a suitable lock means 51 and withdrawn to a waste pile by line 52 connected to the lock means 51. The spent shale will comprise from 75 to 90% by weight of raw oil shale fed into the system. By virtue of the operation described, the gases and products in the system are prevented from commingling with each other and yields are enhanced allowing the production of increased amounts of products and gaseous material of greater utility and increased value than previously.

In the process, the yields may be increased from 5 to 30%, while the nitrogen and sulfur content of the product may be decreased by 5 to 25% before subsequent hydrogenation. Furthermore, the Btu value of the gas is increased rrom 80 to 650 Btu/scf, which is quite substantial.

In a process described by J.E. Lawson, Jr.; U.S. Patent 3,440,162; April 22, 1969; assigned to Esso Research and Engineering Company independent control of the retorting of crushed oil shale is provided in a unitary operation by flowing the crushed shale downward through preheating, retorting and combustion-cooling zones with vaporous product being removed separately and fractionated. Shale oil bottoms are introduced into the retorting zone and inert heated gas is used to preheat the oil shale with the inert gas being recycled to the burning-cooling zone to cool the discarded shale. Air and combustible gas are introduced into the retorting zone while air may be introduced into the burning-cooling zone.

Increased Residence Time in Retort Zone

R.E. Biddick, C.E. Jahnig and C.W. Tyson; U.S. Patent 3,297,562; January 10, 1967; assigned to Esso Research and Engineering Company describe a method for increasing the time of residence of the shale lumps in the retorting zone to improve the recovery of oil.

Channels or tubes are provided for by-passing the combustion gases around at least a portion of the solid shale particles in the retorting zone. The tubes or channels may be mounted internally or externally of the retorting zone. The solid shale particles pass down around the tubes when mounted internally but some of the gas and/or vapor by-passes the shale solids and passes up through the tubes in the shale solids moving bed to a higher region. In this way the heated oil shale particles from the preheat zone are allowed to spend a longer time at desired retorting temperatures of 800° to 1200°F. before entering the combustion zone. In other words, a soaking zone is provided between the preheat and combustion zones to assure complete retorting and maximize oil recovery. Without it, independent control of retorting time and temperature is not possible, since the temperature profile in the bed is set by the relative flow rates of gas and solids.

Increased residence time at the selected desired temperature permits heat diffusion to the inner portions of the large lumps of shale which would otherwise pass into the combustion or hot zone before being fully retorted. This unretorted oil would be lost by combustion or be severely cracked to gas and coke. The channels or tubes in effect increase the length of the retorting zone and in this way increase the time of retorting.

Referring to Figure 1.3a, shown on the following page, 10 designates a cylindrical shale treating apparatus made up of superimposed vessels or zones in vertical alignment and which may if desired, be enclosed in a single exterior vessel.

FIGURE 1.3: RETORTING PROCESS

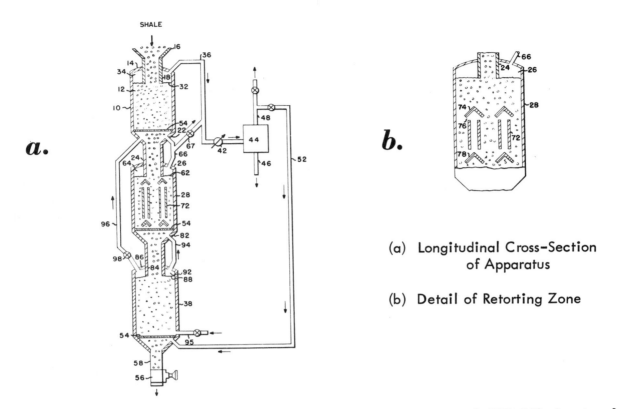

a.

SHALE

b.

(a) Longitudinal Cross-Section
of Apparatus

(b) Detail of Retorting Zone

Source: R.E. Biddick, C.E. Jahnig and C.W. Tyson; U.S. Patent 3,297,562; January 10,
1967

The top zone or vessel 12 is a shale preheating zone which has a dome-shaped top 14 through which extends a funnel-shaped inlet 16 having its lower cylindrical end 18 extending into the zone 12 a short distance and having its funnel end above the zone 12 for receiving shale particles to be treated. The bottom of preheating zone 12 is formed as an inverted truncated cone 22 with a cylindrical or tubular lower end 24 which extends through the dome-shaped top 26 of retorting zone or section 28 for conducting shale particles from preheating zone 12 to retorting zone 28.

The shale particles are not fluidized in any of the zones of the apparatus 10. The lower end 18 of funnel-shaped inlet 16 determines the level 32 of the shale solids in preheating zone 12 to leave an annular space 34 surrounding lower end 18 for collecting vapors and gases passing up through the downward moving shale particles in preheating zone 12. These vapors and gases are product gaseous material formed by retorting shale and include hydro-carbon vapors and gases and combustion gases which are removed from annular space 34 through line or pipe 36. These product gases and vapors will also contain water or steam and other gases if such gases are introduced in any of the zones forming the shale treating apparatus and including preheating zone or vessel 12, retorting zone or vessel 28 and com-bustion and shale cooling zone or vessel 38 arranged below retorting vessel or zone 28.

Oil Shale Retorting

The oil products from retorting are vaporized and carried out with the combustion gas. An important part of the shale oil product leaves in the form of a mist or fog which is formed when the heavy vapors from retorting are cooled as they pass through the shale preheating bed 12.

The gaseous products pass through line 36 and condenser 42 to condense normally liquid hydrocarbons and the condensed mixture is passed to separator 44 to separate gases from liquid. In some cases it may be desirable or necessary to demist the vapors by passing them through an oil scrubber or an electric precipitator. The liquid which comprises shale oil is withdrawn from separator 44 through line 46 and further treated as necessary or desired. The gaseous material which contains gaseous hydrocarbons is withdrawn overhead from separator 44 through line 48 and utilized as a fuel, if desired, or discarded. At least a portion of the gaseous material may be passed through line 52 and into combustion vessel or zone 38 to be burned and to supply additional heat of retorting. As shown, the gaseous material is introduced at the bottom of vessel or zone 38 below stoker bars 54, but, if desired, the gaseous material from line 52 may be introduced into zone 38 above bars 54.

The downward movement of the shale particles in vessels or zones 12, 28 and 38 is controlled by shaker bars or other similar devices 54 arranged in the bottom of each vessel or zone 12, 28 and 38, substantially at the top of the inverted truncated conical outlet of each vessel or zone 12, 28 and 38. The holdup of the shale moving bed in apparatus 10 and in zones or vessels 12, 28 and 38 is controlled by valve 56 mounted in bottom of cylindrical or tubular outlet line 58 extending downward from combustion and shale cooling zone 38. The valve 56 also indirectly controls the rate of introduction of oil shale solids into the top preheating vessel 12 through inlet 16, since the upper level 32 is determined by the angle of repose of the solids.

Preheating vessel 12 has lower tube or cylindrical discharge end 24 which extends into retorting vessel or zone 28 a short distance to determine the level 62 of shale in retorting vessel 28 and to form an annular space 64 around lower tube 24 for receiving retorted gaseous shale products, which may also contain combustion gases. The gaseous products are withdrawn from space 64 and passed through line or pipe 66 into the lower portion of preheating zone 12. Part or all of this gas stream may be withdrawn through line 67 and fed directly to the product recovery system such as separator 44. As shown, the pipe 66 leads from dome-shaped top 26 to the inverted truncated conical portion 22 of preheating vessel 12.

If desired, the outlet from pipe 66 may extend higher or enter preheating vessel 12 above bars 54, in which case multiple pipes 66 are desirable. Although most of the oil products are in the form of vapor or mist and so pass through preheating zone or vessel 12, some of the heavy ends may condense on the solids and be recycled to the retorting vessel to be further cracked or coked.

The retorting vessel 28 is provided with a plurality of vertically arranged internal channels or tubes 72 shown in enlarged detail in Figure 1.3b. There are only two tubes shown, but only one or any desired number may be used. The tubes 72 are shown as being of the same length, but in some cases the tubes 72 may be of different lengths with some being half the length, etc., to give further control over the time-temperature history of the shale particles.

For example, part of the gas may be by-passed through longer tubes, while a smaller portion flows through the shorter tubes to aid in stripping out the oil. The tubes 72 are rigidly mounted in any suitable manner entirely within the retorting vessel 28 to be held in a vertical position parallel to the wall of the retorting vessel 28. The tubes 72 are open-ended and to prevent downward moving shale particles entering the tops of the tubes 72 there are provided deflectors 74 which are inverted V-shaped in vertical cross section and of a slightly larger diameter than the outside diameter of the tube 72. The deflectors 74 are spaced from the upper ends of the tubes to leave a space 76 for gases to pass.

Similarly shaped inverted V-shaped deflectors 78 are provided for the bottom ends of the tubes 72 to prevent entry of shale solids into the tubes. The deflectors 78 are spaced from the ends of the tubes to permit upflowing gaseous material to by-pass the downward moving shale bed for a selected region or portion in the retorting vessel 28. The tubes extend for about 1/10 to 2/3 of the length or height of the retorting vessel 28. With the deflectors in position it is intended to pass only hot gases without solids through the tube or tubes 72. In the preferred form, hot gases, at least in part, are passed from the bottom of the retorting vessel 28 to the top portion of the vessel 28 to by-pass only a portion of the downward moving compact bed in retorting vessel 28.

The bottom portion 82 of retorting vessel 28 is of inverted truncated conical shape and is provided at its lower end with tube or cylinder 84 which extends down through dome-shaped top 86 of shale cooling and burner vessel or zone 38 a short distance to determine the level 88 of the shale particles in burner vessel or zone 38 and to form annular space 92 around tube 84 in the upper part of vessel 38.

Line or pipe 94 connects space 92 in vessel 38 with retorting vessel or zone 28 and is provided to conduct hot combustion gases from zone or vessel 38 to the bottom portion of retorting vessel or zone 28. Air or other oxygen-containing gas is introduced into the lower portion of burner vessel and shale cooling vessel or zone 38 through one or more lines 95 to burn carbonaceous material from the spent shale particles introduced into burner vessel 38 from retorting vessel 28.

Another line or pipe 96 provided with valve 98 communicates with the top space 92 in burner vessel 38 and leads to the bottom portion of preheating vessel or zone 12 for introducing all or a part only of the hot combustion gases from burner vessel 38 into the preheating vessel 12 if necessary or desired. In this way it is possible to pass substantially all of the hot combustion gases from burner vessel 38 directly to vessel 12 and to by-pass vessel 28 which then becomes a soaking vessel. Then it is feasible to draw product vapors off vessel 28 more or less free from flue gases so that recovery of oil is easier.

In operation, cool crushed raw shale of a particle size between 1/4 and 2 inches is introduced into the apparatus from funnel-shaped inlet 16 and passed down as a relatively compact nonfluidized mass through preheating vessel 12 where the shale particles are preheated to a temperature between 500° and 7750°F., preferably 650°F. The shale particles are preheated by countercurrently upflowing hot gases of combustion and retorted shale vapors and gases passing up from retorting vessel 28 and combustion vessel 38.

In passing through preheating vessel 12 the hot retorted products are cooled to a temperature between 200° and 500°F. and some of the high boiling hydrocarbons may condense and be deposited on the shale particles for recycle to the retorting zone 28. The vaporous and mist shale retorted products are withdrawn from the space 34 at the top of preheating zone and passed through condenser 42 and mist separation (not shown), and cooled to a temperature of 100° to 150°F. and the shale oil separated in separator 44 and withdrawn through line 46. The preheated shale particles pass from zone 12 to retorting zone or vessel 28 and are heated to a temperature between 800° and 1200°F. with a preferred temperature of 1000°F. The shale particles are maintained in retorting vessel 28 for a residence time between 1/10 and 2 hours, preferably 1/2 hour.

In the retorting zone the tubes 72 provide channels for a part of the hot gases to by-pass the bed of shale particles so as to decrease the heat exchange between the hot gases and the oil shale particles in the retorting vessel and this allows the oil shale to spend a longer time in the retorting vessel at a retorting temperature of 800° to 1000°F. which is optimum for most shales. The hot gases which are not by-passed contact the shale particles outside the tubes 72 and supply the heat necessary for optimum retorting. In addition, the hot gasses which by-pass the shale bed pass from the lower portion of the bed in retorting vessel 28 and up through the channels or tubes 72 and are introduced into the upper portion of the shale bed in the retorting vessel to supply heat thereto so that the shale particles in the shale bed are more quickly brought up to retorting temperature. The amount of hot gases passing up through tubes 72 is about 20 to 95 volume percent of the total of hot gases passing up through retorting vessel 28.

The spent shale particles leaving the retorting vessel 28 are now largely free of hydrocarbon materials but contain coke or carbonaceous deposits resulting from the decomposition of the kerogen. The spent particles are passed down through tube 84 into the combustion vessel 38. Air introduced through line 95 into the lower portion of the shale bed is heated up and causes burning of the coke deposit to produce hot gases of combustion which are passed up through the shale bed countercurrently and through line 94 into the shale retorting vessel 38. The shale particles are cooled by the air being preheated. Additional heat may be removed from the hot spent shale by injecting or introducing hydrocarbon gas made in the process via line 52. Other gas or fluid, such as flue gas, inert gas, water or steam, or the like, may be introduced through line 52 and below bars 54 to independently control the oxygen being supplied by the air or oxygen-containing gas and also to control the heat capacity of the gases used to supply the heat of retorting the shale in vessels 12, 28 and 38.

The temperature in the combustion vessel 28 is between 1000° and 1600°F., preferably about 1300°F. The spent shale particles are withdrawn via pipe 58 at a temperature of 200° to 700°F. and discarded.

In a commercial design where the retorting vessel is about 17 feet in diameter and has a straight side length (from the bottom of dome-shaped top 26 and the top of inverted truncated conical bottom 82) of about 15 feet, about 25 tubes 72 will be provided. Each tube has an inside diameter of about 12 inches and a length of about 10 feet. The deflectors 74 are spaced from the ends of the tubes by about 6 inches. The oil shale to be used such as Colorado shale contains, for example, about 30 gallons of shale oil per ton of shale, by Fischer assay test. The table on the following page presents pertinent data applicable to the process.

	Broad Range	Preferred Range	Example
Temperature:			
Raw Shale Inlet, ° F	0–500	50–100	70
Preheated Shale, ° F	300–800	550–750	650
Retort, ° F	700–1,300	800–1,200	1,000
Combustion, ° F	1,000–1,800	1,200–1,600	1,300
Time of Retorting, Hours	0.1–10	.5–5	2
Shale Solids Size, Inches	0.10–8	0.25–5.0	1 2
Bed Density of Shale Column	30–110	60–90	75

[1] Average.

In a 2,000 ton unit about 15,000 scf of air per ton of shale are passed up through the vessel 10. The oil shale is ground and screened to a particle size of 0.25 to 4 inches. The combustion gas temperature in the retorting zone is 1300°F. About 90% by volume of the total hot gas is passed through tubes 72 to bypass the moving bed of shale in retorting vessel 28. The temperature of the spent shale is about 300°F. Shale oil recovered is about 250°F. About 25 gallons of oil per ton of shale are obtained and this oil has a gravity of 19° API, an initial boiling point of 415°F. and 70% over at 870°F. The Conradson Carbon number is about 5.2 and the SSU viscosity at 100°F. is about 235.

The daily production of shale oil is about 1,500 b./d. using the tubes 72 in the retorting vessel 28. In a conventional retorting process not using channels or by-pass tubes 72, the shale oil production would be less due to the lower yield of oil caused by inefficient retorting ahead of the combustion zone.

Recycle Gas Bypasses Combustion Zone

J.H. Haddad and J.G. Mitchell; U.S. Patent 3,503,869; March 31, 1970; assigned to Mobil Oil Corporation describe a modified gas combustion shale retorting process where direct contact is minimized between gas combustion products from the combustion zone and both kerogen decomposition products in the retorting zone and recycle gas from the shale cooling zone. Shale having coke on the surface from a retorting zone is passed downward to a combustion zone.

In the combustion zone, the shale is contacted with free-oxygen containing gas to promote combustion of the coke and heat the shale and gas. The combustion gas and shale in the combustion zone are passed concurrently downward through the combustion zone. The shale from the combustion zone is passed over gas disengagement means located within the retort to separate gaseous combustion products from the spent shale prior to contacting recycle gas from the shale cooling zone. The gaseous combustion products are removed from the retort while the separated spent shale is passed downward through a shale cooling zone.

In the shale cooling zone, the spent shale is contacted with upward moving recycle gas whereby heat is transferred from the spent shale to the recycle gas. The recycle gas is removed from the retort prior to entering the combustion zone by gas disengaging means located within the retort. The spent shale is removed from the retort after passing through the shale cooling zone. The heated recycle gas can contain fines and after being removed from the retort is directed to a fines separation zone wherein fines are separated from the heated recycle gas.

The recycle gas from the fines separation zone is directed to the retorting zone located above the combustion zone and is therein passed upward through the downward moving shale. In the retorting zone, kerogen in the raw shale is thermally decomposed to oil vapors. The resultant gasiform material is passed upward through incoming raw shale to transfer heat from the gasiform material to the raw shale. This results in the formation of an oil mist or fog which is removed from the shale preheating zone and directed to an oil separation zone. In the oil separation zone, liquid oil product is separated from gasiform material. A portion of the gasiform material is recycled to the lower portion of the shale cooling zone in a manner described above.

Thus by the process, transfer of gaseous products from the combustion zone to either the retorting zone or the shale cooling zone is minimized. This results in substantial advantages for the overall gas combustion process. By minimizing contact between gaseous combustion products and oil formed by kerogen decomposition in the retorting zone, the chances of burning shale oil product are minimized. In addition, because the large proportion of fines found in a retorting process are formed in the combustion zone, the chances for contacting fines and shale oil product with the attendant undesirable results are minimized. The process also provides substantial advantages by removing the recycle gas from the retort prior to contacting gaseous products from the combustion zone. In this manner, selective burning of coke on the shale is accomplished while minimizing burning of gaseous hydrocarbons.

This results in more uniform coke burning and prevents substantial loss of shale oil vapors in the combustion zone. Accordingly, higher retort shale oil yields are obtained since condensible oil not previously separated will not be consumed as fuel in the combustion zone.

Referring to Figure 1.4, shown on the following page, crushed raw shale particles having a size of from 1/4 to 4 inches mean diameter is introduced into retort 1 through closed conduit 2. The shale particles are directed through a plurality of conduits 3 to the top of a downward moving compact bed of shale particles in preheating and retorting zone 4. In this manner, relatively even particle distribution over the bed surface area is effected. The top of the particle bed in preheating and retorting zone 4 is maintained at a desired distance below the top of the retort 1 to form a plenum chamber 5 which facilitates separation of particles and oil mist.

In preheating and retorting zone 4, the incoming particles are heated by upward moving vapors and reach retorting temperature as the particles move downward. The heat supplying gas is introduced through conduit 6 into header 7 and is introduced into the bed through distributors 8. When retorting temperature is reached in zone 4, the kerogen decomposes to form gas, oil vapors and coke residue. The spent shale having coke on the surface is passed downward through standpipes 9 into combustion zone 10. The standpipes 9 extend from baffle 11 to form a plenum chamber 12 and to provide back pressure means to prevent incoming combustion gas from entering preheating and retorting zone 4. Provision can be made to introduce seal gas into each standpipe 9.

Combustion gas is introduced into plenum chamber 12 through conduit 13. The combustion gas is passed downward from plenum chamber 12 into the combustion zone 10 to effect burning of coke on the shale particles. In combustion zone 10, gaseous material and shale particles are passed concurrently downward to contact a gas-solids disengager comprising a

FIGURE 1.4:   GAS COMBUSTION RETORTING PROCESS

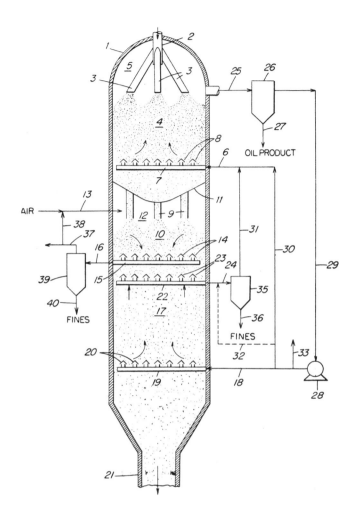

Source: J.H. Haddad and J.G. Mitchell; U.S. Patent 3,503,869; March 31, 1970

plurality of collectors 14 and a header 15.   The gaseous combustion products and spent shale fines are removed from the retort through header 15 and conduit 16.   Due to the burning effected in combustion zone 10, the shale particles become heated.   The heated shale particles pass downward from the combustion zone 10 to shale cooling zone 17 where contact is made with relatively cool recycle gas.   The recycle gas is introduced into the retort 1 through conduit 18, header 19 and distributors 20.   The recycle gas passes upward through the shale cooling zone 17 to contact downward moving shale particles.   In this manner, heat is transferred from the shale particles to the recycle gas.   The cool shale particles are removed from retort 1 through conduit 21 and discarded.   The heated recycle gas is removed from retort 1 by way of gas-solids disengage comprising header 22 and collectors 23 and conduit 24.   Means not shown, are provided in conduit 21 for effecting relatively uniform shale flow through the retort 1.

The oil mist or fog separated from the shale preheating zone 4 is removed from plenum chamber 5 through conduit 25. The oil mist is directed to a separation step 26 wherein liquid oil product is separated from vaporous material. An electrostatic precipitator and/or cyclone can be employed in the separation step 26. Oil product is obtained and recovered through conduit 27. Gaseous material is recovered from separation step 26 and recycled in a manner whereby a portion is directed to the shale cooling zone 17, another portion can be mixed with the gaseous effluent from the shale cooling zone, and the remainder is vented to be employed in other processes.

The gas recycled to the shale cooling zone 17 is pumped by pump 28 through conduits 29 and 18 into header 19. The gas to be mixed with hot recycle gas is pumped through conduits 18, 30 and 6 and mixed with hot recycle gas from conduit 31. Alternately, this cooling gas may pass to conduit 24 through conduit 32. Excess recycle gas is vented through conduit 33. Hot recycle gas is removed from the retort through conduit 24 and directed to a fines separation step 35 where fines carried over with the gas are separated and removed through conduit 36. The hot recycle gas is directed to the preheating and retorting zone 4 through conduits 31 and 6.

Combustion air is introduced into plenum chamber 12 through conduit 13. The air can be mixed with combustion products obtained from the retort and directed through conduits 37 and 38 prior to being introduced into the retort. This is an effective means for diluting the combustion air to control burning in the combustion zone 10 and minimize the development of high localized peak temperatures. The gaseous combustion products are withdrawn from the retort through conduit 16 and directed to a separation zone 39 where carried over fines are separated from the gases and removed through conduit 40. The combustion gas exits from the retort at relatively high temperatures and the heat can be extracted by heat exchange means not shown. The heat from the gaseous combustion products can be converted to steam, for example, which can then be used to drive the compressors which pump recycle gas and combustion air to and from the retorting process.

The amount of free oxygen which is introduced into the combustion zone is regulated so as to maintain the shale temperature in the combustion zone between 900° and 1400°F., preferably between 950° and 1100°F. By operating in this manner, sufficient heat can be transferred to the recycle gas in the shale cooling zone to support kerogen decomposition in the retorting zone without causing excessive shale disintegration in the combustion zone. The amount of free oxygen in the combustion zone can be regulated by diluting combustion air with flue gas to obtain a free oxygen concentration in the resultant mixture usually between 5 and 15 volume percent.

Since carbon burning rate is proportional to oxygen partial pressure, the diluted gas will minimize the attainment of high peak temperatures and carbonate decomposition in the combustion zone while the combustion gas is being diffused into the bed. The amount of recycle gas directed to the shale cooling zone is sufficient to reduce the shale temperature to below 400°F. and preferably below 300°F. By operating in this manner, the hot recycle gas from the fines separation step associated with the shale cooling step can have a temperature as high as 1400°F. It therefore may become desirable to reduce the hot recycle gas temperature prior to introducing it into the retorting zone. Thus, the process provides for mixing the hot gas with a portion of the cold recycle gas prior to introducing gas into the retorting zone. The relative amounts of cold and hot gas mixed is that which will maintain the maximum retorting temperature between 700° and 1100°F., preferably between 850° and 1000°F. In this manner, increased retorting times result which increases oil yield. The oil mist exits from the top of the shale retorting and preheating zone at a temperature below 300°F. and preferably between 100° and 200°F. In the process, the hot recycle gas can be introduced by means of a plurality of inlets at different vertical heights. This permits more effective heating in the retorting zone and permits heat soaking of the shale in the retorting zone. This heat soaking effects increased vaporization of the liquid decomposition products and this provides for increased shale oil yields and flowability of the solids.

J.G. Mitchell and J.H. Haddad; U.S. Patent 3,349,022; October 24, 1967; assigned to Mobil Oil Corporation describes a vertical gas combustion shale retort where a downward moving bed of shale granules is contacted with countercurrently rising gasiform material in a first multichambered open end spent shale cooling zone (recycle gas preheat zone), a combustion zone, a shale retorting zone and a shale preheating zone. The improvement of the above combinations of steps resides particularly in the design and arrangement of the multichambered shale cooling zone to improve heat transfer and provide for more uniform heat exchange throughout the cross section of the retort between recycle gas and spent shale particles before passing the preheated recycle gas through the combustion section. In addition, the improvement resides in passing all gaseous material recovered from the combustion section of the retort to a zone for removal of solid particle fines before passing hot gases upward through the retorting zone of the retort.

Preheat Requirements for Optimum Operation

A process described by E.F. Kondis, F.A. Smith and P.W. Snyder, Jr.; U.S. Patent 3,318,798; May 9, 1967; assigned to Mobil Oil Company involves defining a preferred region of operability of a gas-combustion retort and identifying a correlation of operating conditions which will permit operation in a preferred region of oil shale throughput rate and maximum recovery of desired kerogen decomposition products.

It has been found that the preferred region of operability of a gas combustion retort is confined by (1) a low oil shale flow rate of about 300 lbs./hr.-ft.^{2}; (2) an upper shale flow rate of about 1,000 lbs./hr.-ft.^{2} limit which begins to impose an undesired high pressure drop across the retort thereby requiring usage of expensive compressor equipment to provide adequate gas flow rates; and (3) an upper gas temperature boundary of 1800°F. selected to avoid creating excessive costs in structural and material problems, and (4) an upper shale temperature boundary of 1500°F. selected to avoid excessive thermal cracking and undesirable high carbonate decomposition temperatures.

In addition, it has been found that employing air rates in excess of 7,000 scf/t. of air falls outside a reasonable operating range since above this air rate the pressure drop in a retort of about 12 feet high would be in excess of about 1 atmosphere, the shale outlet temperature would exceed a desired upper limit of 500°F. and peak shale temperatures would exceed 1500°F. leading to excessive thermal cracking and undesired high carbonate decomposition. The method of operation described permits a preferred gas phase burning to the exclusion of substantial coke burning and little, if any, kerogen burning; a better temperature control within the retort; more kerogen can be decomposed above the combustion zone; a high Btu content off-gas may be obtained and recovered from the retort and more rigid spent shale particles will be present, thereby significantly reducing the dust carry over from the retort.

Although it is possible to operate a gas-combustion retort outside the preferred limits defined in Figure 1.5a, it is substantially less desirable for many reasons and generally outside the scope of this process for the reasons herein expressed. That is, if shale rates below 300 lbs./hr.-ft.^{2} are used, large numbers of retorts are required. On the other hand, employing shale rates above 1,000 and as high as up to 2,000 lbs./hr.-ft.^{2} although possible, cause a condition of excessive or large pressure drop in the retort requiring additional compressor equipment and generally undesirable operating conditions leading to inefficient decomposition and recovery of decomposed kerogen.

The process also involves maintaining a temperature profile within the gas-combustion retort for preferred shale throughput rates within the range of above 300 to 1,000 lbs./hr.-ft.^{2} which will permit decomposition and recovery of desired kerogen product in amounts that may be considered substantially optimum without encountering undesired retorting temperature conditions due to insufficient or uncontrolled burning of available combustible materials in the retort.

Accordingly, in the process, a portion of uncondensible shale gas recovered from the retort and separated from desired kerogen decomposition liquid product is recycled to the retort. A substantial portion of the separated and recycled gas is passed to the lower or bottom portion of the retort for flow upward therethrough under conditions to preheat the recycle gas by countercurrent contact with downward moving hot shale particles. The remaining recycled portion of recovered shale gas referred to as dilution gas is employed when combined with air as a heat carrying gaseous material to the combustion section of the retort. That is, the portion of dilution gas and air mixture passed to the combustion section of the retort is preheated either directly or indirectly by combustion, for example, or other suitable means to a desired elevated temperature.

The minimum extent of gas heating effected by the methods described is determined in accordance with the formula relationship provided below, so that upon introduction to the retort the temperature profile of the recycled gaseous material having entered the bottom and passed upward through the retort under heat exchange conditions countercurrent to the hot shale particles will not be reduced any substantial amount at the air inlet of the retort combustion section and will be of a heat carrying capacity and combustible material content to substantially limit undesired burning and undesired temperature profiles within the retort.

Other gaseous materials such as steam or flue gas which are considered relatively inert in the process may be combined with the air and/or dilution gas in desired quantities. In addition, the volume of heat carrying gas comprising air and dilution gas passed to the combustion section may be varied considerably depending upon the method of heating employed and within the range of from 3,000 to 7,000 scf/t. of shale. That is, when employing indirect heat exchange means for heating the combustion supporting gas passed to the retort combustion section, use of air volumes less than 3,500 scf/t. and as low as 3,000 scf/t. is sufficient to provide the oxygen combustion supporting requirements of the retort.

On the other hand, when partial combustion means are employed for directly heating the air either with or without the presence of dilution gas, a greater volume of air is generally required which will be at least about 3,500 scf/t. and more usually at least 4,000 scf/t. to provide the oxygen combustion supporting requirements with the retort.

Accordingly, it is important whether direct or indirect heat exchange means are employed to limit the oxygen available for combustion within the retort to substantial combustion of gaseous material while providing kerogen decomposition heat within the retort within the range of from 300,000 Btu/t. up to 700,000 Btu/t. Therefore, the total heat in the retort is the direct or indirect preheat of the combustion supporting gases referred to as the sensible heat plus the potential heat from consuming the oxygen therein and this combined heat input should be controlled within the range of from 300,000 to 700,000 Btu/t. of shale.

Thus, by heating the gas streams in the manner provided, the amount of air employed may vary over a considerable range of from 2,000 to 7,000 scf/t. of shale so that a higher and desired mix gas temperature is thereby obtained when the gas streams in the retort are combined at substantially the gas inlet of the combustion section. Having a higher gas mix temperature means that the gases have a shorter distance to travel before the oxygen available in the gases is utilized to effect desired limited burning of available combustible materials.

Accordingly, more of the heat of retorting is supplied by sensible heat in the gases rather than by heat of combustion on the surface of the shale particles. Thus, by operating in accordance with the process, significantly more kerogen can be decomposed above the combustion zone and thermal cracking and oxidation of the desired shale oil as it passes out through the surface of the shale particle can be eliminated.

Tables 1 and 2, shown on the following page, show an order of magnitude of the following improvements which may be effected when operating a gas-combustion oil shale retort in accordance with this process.

(1)   A greater portion of the kerogen is decomposed before the shale particles enter the combustion zone.

(2)   Operation at much higher shale rates is possible.

(3)   Higher gas cooling rates are obtained in the mist forming zone which result in a more desirable mist and less refluxing of the shale oil.

(4)   Greater overall heat efficiency, producing lower spent shale temperatures.

(5)   High heat value gas is obtained for recycle to the retort.

Table 1 shows the effect of preheating the air-dilution gas on the performance of the gas-combustion retort for 1 inch particles and Table 2 shows the effect of preheating the air-dilution gas on the performance of the gas-combustion retort for 3 inch particles.

Oil Shale Retorting

TABLE 1

	No Preheat		With Preheat	
Type of Operation				
Range of Shale Rate	Low	High	Low	High
Type of Preheat	None	None	Indirect	Indirect
Operation Conditions:				
Shale Rate, lbs./hr.-ft.²	300	750	300	750
Air Rate, s.c.f./t.	4,000	4,000	3,200	3,200
Air-Dilution Gas Temperature, °F.	133	140	927	1,132
Performance Temperature, °F.:				
Off-Gas	133	(1)	133	137
Spent Shale	285	(1)	248	279
Peak Gas	1,175	(1)	1,335	1,390
Peak Shale	1,140	(1)	1,201	1,246
Decomposition, Percent:				
Kerogen	100	(1)	100	100
Carbonates	9	(1)	14	14
Kerogen Decomposed Above Combustion Zone, Percent	5	(1)	95	84
Products Burned, Percent:				
Coke	17	(1)	8	6
Gas	12	(1)	21	23
Shale Oil	0.5	(1)	0.1	0.1
Gas Cooling Rate in Mist Forming Zone, °F./sec.	1,245	(1)	1,430	2,600
Heating Value of Dry Gas Make, B.t.u./s.c.f.	139	(1)	172	172

¹ Inoperable.
Retort Length=12 Feet
Total Recycle Gas Rate=16,000 s.c.f./ton
Brine=15 lbs./ton
Shale Richness=30 Gal./ton
Dilution Gas-to-Air Ratio=0.4 v./v.

TABLE 2

	No Preheat		With Preheat	
Type of Operation				
Range of Shale Rate	Low	High	Low	High
Type of Preheat	None	None	Direct	Direct
Operating Conditions:				
Shale Rate, lbs./hr.-ft.²	300	750	300	750
Air Rate, s.c.f./t.	4,000	4,000	4,000	4,000
Air-Dilution Gas Temperature, °F.	150	150	1,370	1,800
Performance Temperature, °F.:				
Off-Gas	--------	--------	160	210
Spent Shale	--------	--------	410	500
Peak Gas	--------	--------	1,238	1,340
Peak Shale	--------	--------	1,083	1,134
Decomposition, Percent:				
Kerogen	--------	--------	100	100
Carbonates	(1)	(1)	8	7
Kerogen Decomposed Above Combustion Zone, Percent	(1)	(1)	67	66
Products Burned, Percent:				
Coke	(1)	(1)	4	3
Gas	(1)	(1)	31	32
Shale Oil	(1)	(1)	0.2	0.1
Gas Cooling Rate in Mist Forming Zone, °F./sec.	(1)	(1)	740	1,560
Heating Value of Dry Gas Make, B.t.u./s.c.f.	(1)	(1)	139	139

¹ Inoperable.
Retort Length=16 Feet
Total Recycle Gas Rate=16,000 s.c.f./ton
Brine=90 lbs./ton
Shale Richness=30 gal./ton
Dilution Gas-To-Air Ratio=0.4 v./v.

Accordingly, the gas-combustion retort temperature profile throughout the height for a shale flow rate within the range of from 300 to 1,000 lbs./hr.-ft.^{2} for air flow rates in the range of from 3,000 to 7,000 scf/t. is very carefully controlled and regulated by preheating of the air-dilution gas mixture passed to the combustion section of the gas-combustion retort in an amount which will permit operating with the profile of Figure 1.5 defined by EFG and H and the curves lying within the limits of the area EHJLM.

Within these limits, it has been found that the minimum preheat temperature of the air-dilution gas mixture or preheated gas passed to the combustion section of the retort for air rates in the range of from 3,000 to 7,000 scf/t. may be determined by the following equation:

$$T = 38.82 - 0.11A + 1.87S - 2.59 \times 10^{-4}AS + 1.63 \times 10^{-5}A^2 + 2.09 \times 10^{-4}S^2$$

where T is the temperature in °F., S is the shale flow rate in lbs./hr.-ft.^{2}, and A is the air rate in scf/t. entering the combustion zone.

On the other hand, the maximum preheat temperature employed when operating at shale flow rates in the range of 300 to 1,000 lbs./hr.-ft.^{2} will be a function of the decomposed shale outlet temperature set not to exceed about 500°F., an upper shale temperature limit of 1500°F., and an upper gas temperature of 1800°F.

Referring to Figure 1.5a, shown on the following page, the preferred operating parameters defining the limits within which it is preferred to operate by this method are confined within the envelope defined by the bounds of EFGH. The envelope EFGH is defined on its vertical axis by the air dilution Gas Temperature (°F.) which defines the temperature of the preheated mix gas temperature introduced to the combustion section of the retort when employing shale flow rates within the range of 300 to 1,000 lbs./hr.-ft.^{2} defining the horizontal axis of the envelope. Within the envelope EFGH curves LM, EJ, EK, and EH define the operating conditions for air rates of 3,000, 4,000, 5,000 and 7,000 scf/t. respectively required when operating according to the method herein preferred and defined by the limits of EFGH.

Referring to Figure 1.5b, a diagrammatic arrangement of processing steps is presented which represents one arrangement of steps for practicing the process. In this arrangement, a shale retort 2 is provided having a shale inlet 4 and a shale outlet 6. Recycle gas is introduced to the lower portion of the retort by conduit 8 and withdrawn in part with gasiform products formed in the retort from the upper portion by conduit 10. An inlet conduit 12 discharging into a gas distributor 14 diagrammatically represented as a conical distributor means is provided in the combustion section of the retort for introducing combustion supporting gaseous material under the condition described.

In the operation of the retort, raw crushed shale is introduced by conduit 4 for flow downward through the retort as a dense moving bed of material. The raw crushed shale preferably is of a particle size which will avoid heat diffusion limitations during the particle's time of travel downward through the retort to the combustion section. In this connection, it is preferred that the crushed shale particles be not substantially greater than about 5 inches through at least one plane of the particle and preferably not greater than 3 inches through at least one plane of the particle.

FIGURE 1.5:   PREHEATING OF SHALE IN COMBUSTION PROCESS

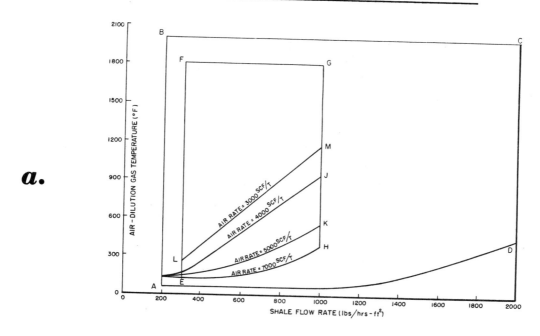

a.

Preheat Requirements for the Optimum Operation of the Gas
Combustion Retort

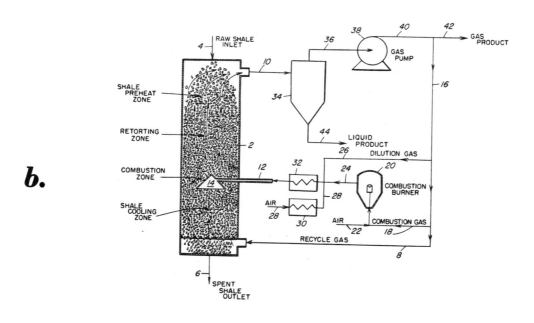

b.

Processing Steps for Gas Combustion Retort Process

Source: E.F. Kondis, F.A. Smith and P.W. Snyder, Jr.; U.S. Patent 3,318,798; May 9, 1967

Oil Shale Retorting

The raw crushed shale granular particles move downward through the retort, first through a shale preheat section and then the retorting section where a major portion and preferably substantially all of the desired kerogen decomposition is accomplished prior to the shale particles moving through the combustion section of the retort. From the combustion section, the shale granules combine to move downward as a relatively dense mass of granular material through the shale cooling section and countercurrent to recycle gas. As indicated above, the shale cooling is effected by directly heating the recycled gas moving upward to the combustion section of the retort. It can be seen therefore, that beneath the combustion section, the shale particles are generally at a higher temperature than the gaseous material passing countercurrent and that above the combustion section the gasiform material is generally at a higher temperature than the shale particles.

Accordingly, operation of a gas-combustion retort is a thermally balanced operation controlled to optimize the temperature profile and efficiency in a manner which will maximize the decomposition of kerogen and recovery of shale oil. To effect and control the thermally balanced operation within the operating ranges contemplated and desired, product gas of the kerogen decomposition is separated and recovered for recycle to the shale retort. A portion of the recycle gas in conduit 16 is passed to the lower portion of the retort by conduit 8. Another portion of the recycle gas is passed to the combustion section of the retort by one of two routes specifically described below. That is, a portion of the recycle gas in conduit 16 may be passed by conduit 18 to a direct fired combustion zone 20 in admixture with air introduced by conduit 22. The minimum proportion of recycle gas to air passed to the burner 20 to achieve the desired preheating of the gaseous material and oxygen content passed to the retort combustion section is determined by the extent of minimum preheat required in accordance with the formula relationship herein provided and discussed. Therefore, for different shale and air rates employed, the extent of preheat will be varied as provided herein to permit a stable and efficient retorting operation. The thus preheated air in combustion zone 20 is thereafter passed by conduit 24 communicating with conduit 12 to the gas distributor 14 in the combustion section of the retort.

In another method of effecting preheating of the gas introduced to the combustion section, a portion of the recycle gas in conduit 16 may be passed by conduit 26 to conduit 24 wherein it is combined with ambient or indirectly preheated air introduced by conduit 28. A heater 30 may be provided for indirectly preheating the air prior to mixing with the recycle gas in conduit 26. The thus formed mixture may be passed directly to conduit 12 and then to the combustion section or additional heat may be added to the gaseous mixture passed to the combustion section by way of an indirect heat exchanger 32. In any of these arrangements, whether used alone or in combination with one another, the air and recycle gas introduced to the retort combustion section is preheated to a desired amount to maintain a temperature profile in the retort above the gas inlet to the combustion section which will preferentially increase the ratio of gas burning to coke burning thereby avoiding undesired peak shale temperatures and maximize decomposition of kerogen to desired product without substantially thermally cracking it.

In addition, by maintaining a temperature profile within the retort as provided, significant reduction in carbonate decomposition is possible since less severe shale temperature peaks are encountered in the retort. Accordingly, a heat balanced operation within relatively narrow limits for any shale rates in excess of 300 lbs./hr.-ft.^{2} may be controlled as desired to assure maximum kerogen decomposition above the combustion section and, therefore, maximum recovery of desired kerogen product.

The decomposed kerogen material in combination with gasiform material introduced and formed within the retort is removed as a fog or mist from the upper portion of the retort by conduit 10 and passed to a separation zone 34 where an initial separation is effected to recover recycle gaseous material from a substantially liquid product. The separated and recovered recycle gas is removed from the upper portion of zone 34 and passed by conduit 36 to gas pump or blower 38. From pump 38 a portion of the recycle gas is passed by conduit 40 to conduit 16 for recycle to the process as hereinbefore discussed. Conduit 42 is provided for removing gas product above that required for recycle to the process.

Control of Fines

T.C. Lyons; U.S. Patent 3,501,394; March 17, 1970; assigned to Mobil Oil Corporation describes a process for retorting fine particulate solids such as shale or Athabasca tar sands containing hydrocarbonaceous material to recover oil. The fine solids are mixed with a hot noncombustion supporting lift gas in a lift pot and the resultant mixture is passed upward through a riser as a dilute phase. Contact time and temperature in the riser are regulated to effect thermal decomposition of the hydrocarbonaceous material to oil vapor which is subsequently recovered. Spent fines can be burned in a separate combustion zone and at least a portion of the hot gas is recycled to the lift pot.

By the process, an effective means is provided for retorting raw fines containing thermally decomposable hydrocarbonaceous material. When retorting raw fines in dilute phase, in accordance with the process, the random movement of fines is greatly reduced so that the major movement of fines is in an upward direction. This permits increased control of fines residence time within the riser reactor so that more uniform residence time in the reactor for individual fine particles is attained. In addition, removal of spent fines from the riser reactor promotes process thermal efficiency in that heat is not expended in maintaining spent fines at reaction temperature.

Referring to Figure 1.6a, shown on the following page, raw fines are directed to lift pot 1 as compact beds through conduit 2. This internal portion of lift pot 1 is structured to provide ease in controlling the amount and velocity of the lift gas entering riser reactor 3. Baffles 4 and 5 are provided so as to permit secondary gas entering conduits 6 to contact a relatively large portion of the compact bed surface area located in the bottom portion of the lift pot 1. Primary lift gas is supplied to the interior of the riser 3 through conduit 7. Conduit 7 has a conical top portion 8 provided with perforations. The primary lift gas contacts the raw fines introduced through conduit 2 to provide a dilute phase within riser 3.

The secondary lift gas stream 6 provides means for controlling the velocity and the amount of lift gas provided to the riser 3. The secondary lift gas stream 6 is provided with means, not shown, for controlling the amount of gas supplied to the riser 3. The secondary lift gas is directed to plenum zones 9 and through openings 10 to contact compact bed of fines in zones 11 and 12. Baffles 5 are held to conduit 7 by ribs 13. The secondary lift gas and primary lift gas are supplied at elevated temperatures to effect the thermal decomposition desired.

FIGURE 1.6: GAS LIFT RETORTING PROCESS

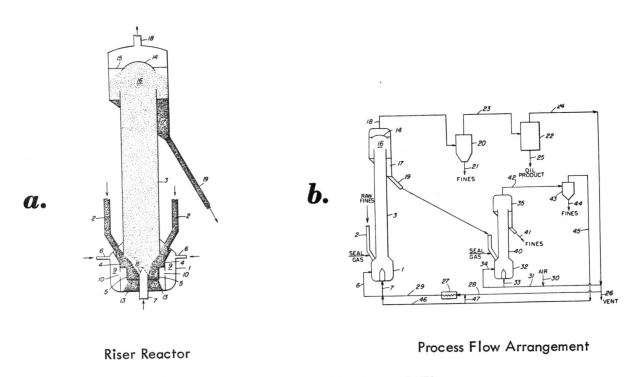

Riser Reactor

Process Flow Arrangement

Source: T.C. Lyons; U.S. Patent 3,501,394; March 17, 1970

The mixture of gas and fines pass upward through the riser 3 as a dilute phase and contact deflector 14 which is held by ribs 15 to the interior walls of the separation zone 16. After contacting the deflector 14, the spent fines from the riser 3 are caused to pass downward to a compact bed of fines 17. The lift gas and the vaporized product pass upward through and out of the separation zone 16 through conduit 18. From the bottom of separator zone 17, the fines are removed through conduit 19. The particular type of deflector employed in the separation zone above the riser is not critical. Any type of deflector which effects adequate separation of vapors from fine particles can be employed.

Referring to Figure 1.6b, raw fines are directed as a compact bed to a lift pot 1 through conduit 2. In lift pot 1, the raw fines are contacted with a secondary gas stream from conduit 7. The fines-gas mixture passes upward through riser reactor 3 as a dilute phase in a manner described previously for Figure 1.6a. In the riser reactor 3, the hydrocarbonaceous portion of the raw fines is thermally decomposed to produce oil vapors. The oil vapors and spent fines exit the riser reactor 3 and contact deflector 14 in the upper portion of separation zone 16. The spent fines are directed downward to a compact bed of spent fines located in chamber 17. The bottom portion of chamber 17 slopes down at an angle greater than the angle of repose of the spent fines. Chamber 17 can be provided with stripping means to remove entrained vapors from spent fines. The vaporous material, including oil vapor and lift gas is removed from separation zone 16 through conduit 18 at a temperature from 700° to 1000°F. and are directed to cyclone 20.

In cyclone 20, vaporous material is separated from any fines carried over from separation zone 16. The fines are removed from cyclone 20 through conduit 21 and are discarded. It is desirable to maintain the vaporous material in cyclone 20 at a high temperature of above 700°F. This is because partial condensation of oil at a lower temperature will result in oil yield loss caused by absorption by the carried over fines. Vapors from cyclone 20 are directed to a condensation step 22 through conduit 23. In condensation step 22, the vapors are cooled to obtain a liquid oil product and a gas overhead.

The condensation step is carried out in a manner to recover the hydrocarbon product boiling in the naphtha boiling range and above. Hydrocarbons boiling below the naphtha boiling range in addition to the lift gas employed in the riser 3 are withdrawn from condensation step 22 through conduit 24. Oil product is withdrawn from condensation step 22 through conduit 25. A portion of the gas from condensation step 22 is vented through conduit 26 while another portion of the gas is employed to support spent fines combustion in a manner described below. The remainder of the gas from condensation step 22 is directed to heater 27 through conduit 28 to be heated to a temperature which supports conversion. The heated gas is directed from heater 27 through conduits 29, 7 and 6 to lift pot 1.

The gas from condensation step 22 which is used to support spent fines combustion is mixed with air from conduit 30. The mixture of air and gas is directed to lift pot 32 through conduits 31, 33 and 34. The lift gas contacts hot spent fines containing unconverted hydrocarbonaceous material and coke in lift pot 32. The spent fines are obtained from chamber 17 and are directed to lift pot 32 through conduit 19. The ratio of combustion air to recycle gas in lift pot 32 is regulated so that the vaporous combustion products from separation zone 35 are oxygen free. That is, the oxygen entering the lift pot 32 is totally consumed in combustion.

In addition, the amount of gas entering lift pot 32 is regulated so that a dilute phase of fines is maintained in riser 40 without an undesirably high pressure drop across the riser 40. The hot spent fines and gas are passed upward as a dilute phase in riser 40 to effect combustion of carbonaceous material in the fines. The fines and vapors are passed upward to separation zone 35 where fines are separated from vapors. The fines are removed from separation zone 35 by being passed downward through conduit 41. The vapors from separation zone 35 are passed overhead through conduit 42 to cyclone 43 wherein carried-over fines are separated from vapor. The fines are removed from cyclone 43 through conduit 44. The hot vapors from cyclone 43 are recycled to lift pot 1 through conduits 45, 46, 7 and 6. A portion of the recycled vapor from cyclone 43 can be directed to heater 27 through conduit 47 to provide additional heat of conversion in riser 3.

Multistage Retort Process

According to a process described by R.B. Needham; U.S. Patent 3,487,001; December 30, 1969; assigned to Phillips Petroleum Company oil-yielding solids in particulate form are introduced into a retorting zone, fuel and oxygen-containing gas are introduced into a combustion region within the retorting zone, a condensible gas is introduced into a diffuse region within the retorting zone, noncondensible combustion gases are removed from the retorting zone, a portion of condensible gas and noncondensible combustion gases mixture is removed from the diffuse region, dust is removed from the gas mixture and the gas mixture is recycled to the diffuse region, hydrocarbons are educed from the solids in a pyrolysis region within the retorting zone, the hydrocarbons are recovered from the retorting zone, and particulate solids are removed from the retorting zone.

Referring to Figure 1.7a, shown on the following page, particulate oil-yielding solids are moved through line 11 and are heated to a desired temperature, e.g., 300°F. in preheater 12. From preheater 12, a compacted bed of solids is introduced through line 13 into the retorting column 14. The compact bed of particulate solids flows into pyrolysis region 15 and educed hydrocarbon products are removed via line 16. A condensible gas, e.g., super-heated steam, is introduced into the upper portion of diffuse region 17 through line 18. Noncondensible combustion gases are removed from the lower portion of diffuse region 17 via line 19. A mixture of steam, fines and small amounts of combustion gases is removed from diffuse region 17 via line 20 to separator 21. After removal of a substantial portion of the fines, the gases are recycled to diffuse region 17 via line 22. Fines are removed from separator 21 through line 23.

In combustion region 24, fuel is introduced via line 25 and oxygen-containing gas, for example air, is introduced via line 26. Upon flowing downward through pyrolysis region 15, diffuse region 17, and combustion region 24, residue solids are removed from retorting column 14 through line 27.

A suitable product mist separation system is illustrated in conjunction with the retorting system in Figure 1.7a. Product mist, removed from pyrolysis region 15 via line 16, flows through heat exchanger 28 to cooling zone 29 wherein steam and a portion of the hydrocarbon vapors are condensed. Water-hydrocarbon product mixture flows through line 30 to separator 31. Hydrocarbon vapors are removed from separator 31 overhead through line 32. If desired, a portion of the hydrocarbon vapors can be transferred via line 25 to combustion region 24 to be used as fuel. Liquid hydrocarbons and water are removed from separator 31 via line 33 to separator 34 wherein a portion of the water is separated from the mixture. Liquid hydrocarbon-water mixture is removed from separator 34 via line 35 and water is removed via line 36. The mixture passes through heat exchanger 28 wherein the water is vaporized. Steam-liquid hydrocarbon mixture is transferred from heat exchanger 28 via line 37 to separator 38. In separator 38 the steam is removed overhead via line 39 and liquid hydrocarbon products are removed via line 40.

Steam flowing through line 39 and water flowing through line 36 are admixed and flow to steam generator 41. Steam is removed from steam generator 41 through line 42 and flows through heat exchanger 43 wherein additional heat is transferred from the combustion gases to the steam. From heat exchanger 43 steam is transferred through line 18 to diffuse region 17.

Combustion gases are removed from diffuse region 17 and flow through line 19 to heat exchanger 43 to warm condensible gases. Combustion gases are removed from heat exchanger 43 through line 44. If desired, a portion of the combustion gases can be recycled through line 45 and admixed in line 25 with the fuel gas flowing to combustion region 24. One advantageous use of excess combustion gas is to cycle the gases through line 46 to preheater 12, thereby supplying a portion of the heat required to preheat the particulate solids.

FIGURE 1.7: RETORTING PROCESS

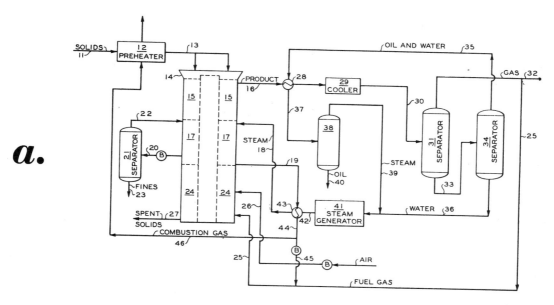

a.

Process Schematic

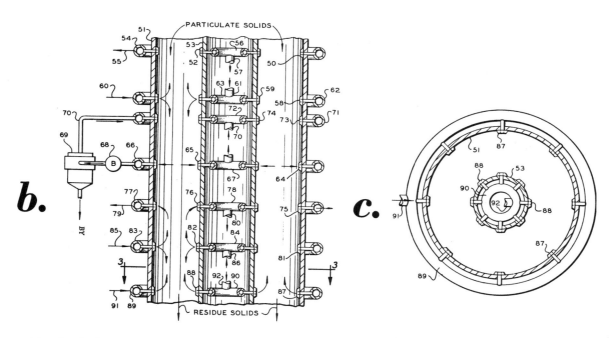

b.

Vertical Cross-Section of Retorting Vessel

c.

Horizontal Cross-Section of Retorting Vessel

Source: R.B. Needham; U.S. Patent 3,487,001; December 30, 1969

In the annular retort of Figure 1.7b, a plurality of ports 50 are positioned in the wall of outer retort shell 51 and a plurality of ports 52 are positioned in the wall of inner wall shell 53 directly across from ports 50. Ports 50 communicate with a manifold 54 and product mist is drawn into manifold 54 through ports 50 and removed via conduit 55. Ports 52 communicate with manifold 56 providing for the removal of product mist through conduit 57. Thus ports 50 and ports 52 define the upper limit of a pyrolysis region within the retorting apparatus.

A plurality of ports 58 in shell wall 51 and a plurality of ports 59 in shell wall 52 are used to introduce a superheated condensible gas into a compact bed of oil-yielding particles. Superheated condensible gas in introduced through conduits 60 and 61 into manifolds 62 and 63 which communicate with the ports. The introduction of steam at this location defines the lower limits of the pyrolysis region and the upper limits of a diffuse region with the retorting vessel.

Removal of fines-gas mixture is effected through a plurality of ports 64 and 65 communicating with manifolds 66 and 67. A blower 68 is used to transfer the mixture to cyclone separator 69. One separator is shown but if desired, a plurality of separators can be used. Conduit 70 communicating with manifolds 71 and 72 recycles the gas through a plurality of ports 73 and 74 to the retorting apparatus. A plurality of ports 75 in shell wall 51 and a plurality of ports 76 in shell wall 53 are utilized to remove noncondensible combustion gases. Combustion gases are drawn through ports 75 and 76 into manifolds 77 and 78 and are removed through conduits 79 and 80 thus defining the lower limit of the diffuse region and the upper limit of a combustion region within the retorting apparatus. Oxygen-containing gas is supplied to the retorting apparatus through ports 81 and 82 in combination with manifolds 83 and 84 and conduits 85 and 86. Fuel is supplied to the retorting apparatus through ports 87 and 88 in combination with manifolds 89 and 90 and conduits 91 and 92.

Figure 1.7c is a plan view taken on line 3—3 in Figure 1.7b and illustrates the port and manifold system. Like numerals in Figures 1.7b and 1.7c denote like elements. A plurality of ports 87 is positioned in outer shell wall 51 and connected into manifold 89. A communicating conduit 91 supplies manifold 89 with fuel to be fed to the retorting apparatus. Fuel is also introduced through a plurality of ports 88 in wall 53 in combination with manifold 90 and conduit 92. Ports have been illustrated as being slightly raised from the shell walls but it is obvious that the ports can be set flush or recessed in the shell walls.

Example: Mahogany Ledge shale from the Green River formation, having an oil content of 28 gallon/ton by Fisher assay, is crushed to obtain particles with a major dimension of 3 inches or less. The crushed shale is screened to remove particles having a major dimension of 1/2 inch or less. The crushed screened shale is preheated to 250°F. Preheated particulate shale is introduced into retorting zone 14 at a rate of 600 tons/hour. Spent solids are removed via line 27 at a rate of 474 tons/hour. 810,000 pounds/hour of superheated steam at 1000°F. under a pressure of 13 psia is introduced into diffuse region 17 through line 18. 13.4M cubic feet/hour of combustion gases are removed via line 19.

Attrition during the downward movement of the compact particulate bed creates fines which, if not removed, cause "gas channeling". 800 pounds/hour of particles having less than 0.05 inch major dimension are removed in separator 21. 10M cubic feet/hour of combustion gases are removed via line 22. Product mist is removed through line 16. Separation results in 188M cubic feet/hour of gas recovered through line 32 and 360 barrels/hour of oil are recovered through line 40. Thus, it can be seen that large quantities of oil shale can be retorted to obtain a high yield of hydrocarbons in the form of a mist from which the hydrocarbons can be easily separated.

Mixtures of Rich and Lean Oil Shale

W.S. Bergen; U.S. Patent 3,574,087; April 6, 1971; assigned to Mobil Oil Corporation has found that by mixing rich oil shale with relatively lean oil shale to obtain an average Fischer assay of between 15 and 36 gallons/ton, that the gas combustion retorting of the mixture can be accomplished without encountering flooding and associated problems within the retort. Further, it has been found that significantly increased yields are obtained from the rich-lean shale mixture, having a Fischer assay within the range from 27 to 36 gallons per ton. Therefore, oil product yields are significantly increased under stable retorting conditions.

Furthermore, considerable savings are realized in reducing mining and material handling costs. Thus, in the method, it is desirable to convert an oil shale mixture having as high an oil content as possible while maintaining at the same time stable retorting conditions so as to maintain and effect a thermally efficient utilization of a gas combustion retorting system. The process provides among other things, a means for retorting relatively lean as well as relatively rich oil shale materials in a manner where the amount of recovered oil is greater than that which would be recovered if separately retorted. The following example illustrates the process.

Example: Gas combustion retorting was carried out on shale of varying richness as shown in the table below. The shale was crushed to a particle size ranging from 3/4 to 1 1/2 inches. The shale particles in runs 6, 7 and 8 were obtained by mixing shale having a Fischer assay of 45 gallons/ton and shale having a Fischer assay of 28 gallons/ton.

Run Number	1	2	3	4	5	6	7	8	9	10
Raw shale Fischer assay, gal./ton	18.8	19.4	19.6	28.8	27.5	36.0	35.4	35.4	38.9	39.8
Shale mass flow, rate lb./hr.-ft.^{2}	491	488	486	486	483	486	489	484	496	492
Air rate, s.c.f./ton shale	4,870	4,890	4,930	4,540	4,580	4,840	4,840	4,920	4,780	4,800
Recycle gas rate, s.c.f./ton shale	13,600	13,500	13,600	13,800	13,400	13,900	13,800	13,800	13,600	13,800
Yield—percent Fischer assay	86.3	83.7	83.1	84.9	89.8	88.6	89.9	91.7	86.5	85.2
Operation	Stable	Stable	Stable	Stable	Stable	Stable	Stable	Stable	[1]	[1]

[1] Unstable retort flooding.

From the table, it can be seen that retorting oil shale having a Fischer assay above 36 gallons/ton results in unstable and undesirable operation. Further, by employing shale mixtures having a Fischer assay in the range from 15 to 36 gallons/ton, it is possible to retort shales under stable operation conditions at high yields in a gas-combustion retort.

Feed Segregation and Shale Oil Recycle

G.E. Irish and R.F. Deering; U.S. Patent 3,133,010; May 12, 1964; assigned to Union Oil Company of California have found that in combustive retorting, when an oil shale feed mixture is separated into a high oil assay portion and a low oil assay portion, the high oil assay portion can be advantageously educted with substantial increased oil recovery (as a percent of Fischer Assay) as compared to an unsegregated feed mixture, and with comparatively little change in solids retorting rate. This finding can be combined in an integrated oil shale retorting process where the raw shale feed from the mine is separated into a high oil assay solids consist, which is fed to a combustion retort, and a low oil assay solids consist, which is fed to a noncombustive hot recycle gas retort. Thus, in this integrated oil shale retorting process, every particle of shale fed to the system is retorted under conditions best suited to obtain the highest possible yield of liquid shale oil in the most efficient manner.

More specifically, in processing a subdivided solids charge which varies in oil assay value, the solids charge is divided into two fractions which differ substantially in average oil assay value. The fraction having the higher oil assay is fed to a combustive retort while the fraction having the lower oil assay is fed to a noncombustive retort. Any difference in the oil assay value of the two portions is advantageous, and a preferred solids feed has an assay value no lower than about 15 gallons/ton at one extreme and about 60 gallons/ton at the other.

In a typical commercial oil shale operation, the shale is segregated into a lean fraction having an assay in the range of 20 to 35 gallons/ton, and a rich fraction having an assay in the range of 35 to 50 gallons/ton. A convenient manner of segregating the shale is to separate the rich shale from the lean shale at the mine and to arrange the solids transportation from the mine to the retort to maintain the segregation. Since low oil assay shale has a higher specific gravity than high oil assay shale, separation according to specific gravity can provide the required oil assay segregation. Further, it has been found that run of the mine shale, when crushed, usually provides an inherent segregation by size, in which case the solids fines consistently are leaner in oil assay value than the larger particles. Thus, size segregation by conventional means, i.e., screening, can sometimes provide the desired assay segregation for this process. The preferred combustive retorting of this process utilizes an upflow of shale solids and a downflow of flue gas, e.g., the combustion retort of U.S. Patents 2,501,153, 2,640,014 and 2,640,019.

G.E. Irish; U.S. Patent 3,228,869; January 11, 1966; assigned to Union Oil Company of California describes a hot gas retorting process where at least a portion of the liquid product oil is recycled to the eduction zone of the retort as a component of the hot eduction fluid. The liquid oil recycle stream can be either the liquid oil phase directly from the retort, or it can be a portion of the retort liquid phase which has been passed through a fractionation column. A heavy fraction obtained from the distillation of the retort oil can be recycled to the retort as the liquid oil recycle, or the oil recycle can be a middle-cut fraction from the aforementioned distillation. Also, any combination of the above streams derived from the retort liquid phase can comprise the liquid oil recycle stream to the retort eduction zone.

Although the recycle of any portion of the retort liquid phase is advantageous, it is most desirable to return to the retort eduction zone the heavier fractions of the hydrocarbons educted from the shale. No matter which stream is recycled to the retort, the essence of the process is to recycle a sufficient quantity of oil to effect a significant improvement in the quality of the net liquid oil product, particularly as evidenced by a reaction in the pour-point and viscosity. No significant effect on pour-point reduction is apparent at recycle rates lower than about 5%, and it is usually uneconomical to recycle more than about 50% of the product oil. Therefore, although higher recycle rates can be employed, the preferable form of the process comprises recycle of at least 5% and not more than 50% of the volume of net shale oil product from the retorting process.

Furthermore, it is preferred that the recycled oil fraction have an initial normal (atmospheric pressure) boiling point in excess of 500°F., and preferably an initial over 600°F. Thus, the recycle stream is essentially comprised of at least a substantial portion of the heavy deleterious materials which contribute markedly to high viscosity and high pour-point of shale oils produced by existing retorting processes. These materials, when recycled to the hot recycle gas retort eduction zone are converted to more desirable products which yield an oil of substantially lower viscosity and substantially lower pour-point with essentially no loss in overall yield. It is essential that the recycle oil be returned to the inlet of the retort with the hot eduction gases for maximum quality enhancement.

In related work, R.F. Deering and G.E. Irish; U.S. Patent 3,058,904; October 16, 1962; assigned to Union Oil Company of California describe an integrated oil shale retorting process where solids-upflow combustion retorting is integrated with hot gas eduction in a solids-upflow, fluid-downflow retort in which eduction is effected without combustion by recirculating an externally heated portion of the rich product gas to the retort.

R.F. Deering; U.S. Patent 3,361,644; January 2, 1968; assigned to Union Oil Company of California describes an oil shale retorting process where eduction is accomplished by recycling a preheated portion of the rich product shale gas to a solids-upflow, fluid-downflow retort, and where the eduction fluid is indirectly heated to retorting temperatures and is maintained essentially oxygen-free throughout the process.

Retorting Total Oil Shale

In a process described by B.L. Schuman and H.P. Dengler; U.S. Patent 3,489,672; Jan. 13, 1970; assigned to Esso Research and Engineering Company shale fines are retorted in a mixture with larger fines by slurrying the fines in a liquid vehicle, such as oil or water, and introducing the slurry into the retort at a selected point where the temperature is sufficient to decompose the kerogen in the fines to shale oil but insufficient to crack the shale oil.

Referring to Figure 1.8, shown on the following page, 11 designates a feed line in which raw oil shale, having particle diameters larger than about 1/4 inch and usually within the range from 3/8 to 3 inches in diameter, depending on the crushing procedures used, is introduced into a gas combustion retorting vessel 12. Gas combustion retorting vessel 12 comprises a preheating zone 13, a retorting zone 14, a combustion zone 15, and a cooling zone 16. The raw oil shale flows serially downward through the several zones and the spent shale, which comprises about 75 to 90% of the raw oil shale, is discharged by way of line 17 to a waste pile which may be located some distance from gas retorting vessel 12.

Heat and gases for retorting and preheating the oil shale are provided by introducing into the combustion zone 15 by way of line 18, controlled by valve 19, a sufficient amount of air to cause combustion of carbonaceous material on the descending shale.

FIGURE 1.8: RETORTING PROCESS UTILIZING TOTAL RAW SHALE

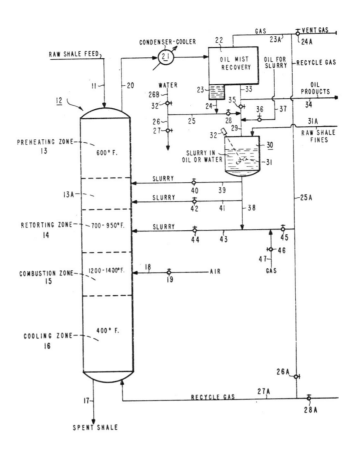

Source: B.L. Schuman and H.P. Dengler; U.S. Patent 3,489,672; January 13, 1970

The amount of air employed may range from 4,000 to 6,000 scf/t. of raw oil shale introduced into the operation, including fines. This combustion operation provides a temperature in the combustion zone which may suitably range from 1000° to 1400°F., but usually within the range of 1200° to 1400°F. The resultant heat and the ascendant flue gases cause retorting and decomposition of the kerogen in the oil shale to shale oil in retorting zone 14. The released shale oil flows upward into preheating zone 13 and the heat preheats the raw oil shale introduced by line 11. Thus, the temperature in the preheating zone may be within the range from 400° to 800°F., usually about 600°F. The temperatures in the retorting zone 14 may be within the range of 600° to 1000°F., usually from 700° to 950°F.

The temperatures in the cooling zone 16 will usually range from 1400° to 200°F., usually about 400°F. As stated, the temperature where the slurry is introduced may be within the range of 500° to 700°F. Pressures in the several zones may range from 0 to 100 psig. Preferably, a pressure within the range from 20 to 60 psig may be used.

As a result of the gas combustion retorting operation in vessel 12, a vaporous product is withdrawn by way of line 20 and passed through a condenser-cooler 21, and then into an oil mist recovery drum 22, provided with a water leg 23, where a separation is made among noncondensable gas, shale oil and water produced in the operation. The noncondensable gases may be discharged by line 23A from the system by opening valve 24A, but preferably a major part of the gas is recycled by line 25A controlled by valve 26A to the gas combustion retorting vessel 12 where the recycle gas serves to cool the spent shale in cooling zone 16. The amount of recycle gas may be within the range from 12,000 to 20,000 scf/t. of raw oil shale introduced into the operation, including fines. If desirable, the recycle gas may be augmented by an extraneously supplied gas through line 27A which connects to line 25A controlled by valve 28A.

The water accumulating in water leg 23 may be discharged by line 24, and then from the system by branch line 25, and line 26 controlled by valve 27. Preferably however, the water in water leg 23 is introduced by opening valve 28 in line 25 into line 29 and, then into a slurry drum 30 into which raw shale fines, having particle diameters less than 1/4 inch, are introduced by line 31A from the oil shale mining and crushing operation. The slurry is formed in slurry drum 30 by means of a mixing device 31, which may be powdered with a suitable power means. The slurry in slurry drum 30 may then be introduced into the gas combustion retorting vessel 12.

It may be desirable to use an extraneous source of water as the liquid vehicle in making up the slurry, and under these instances the water from an extraneous source, which may be fresh water or brine, may be connected to line 26B and introduced by opening valve 32. The slurry may also be made up using a portion of the shale oil. In this instance, shale oil is discharged from oil mist recovery drum 22 by line 33, and a portion thereof withdrawn as product by line 34. A smaller portion is discharged by line 33 controlled by valve 35 into slurry drum 30. Of course, the oil may be from an extraneous source, and when it is desired to use oil produced outside the operation, or from any source, valve 36 in line 37 connecting to the outside source of oil may be opened.

When the liquid vehicle is oil, the slurry will preferably be introduced above the retorting zone 14 into a zone 13A, which may be at a temperature within the range of 500° to 700°F. To this end, the slurry is withdrawn from slurry drum 30 by line 38 and introduced into zone 13A by charge line 39 controlled by valve 40. When the liquid vehicle is water, however, the slurry may be introduced at a point nearer to, or just adjacent to, the retorting zone 13 and to this end, line 41 controlled by valve 42 is provided to allow the slurry comprising water and fine shale particles, to be introduced at least adjacent to the retorting zone 14 and sometimes in the retorting zone 14.

Also, when the liquid vehicle is water, the slurry may be introduced into the retorting zone 14, particularly when a gas is also introduced with the slurry. To this end, line 43, controlled by valve 44, is provided for introduction of the water-raw shale fines slurry directly into the retorting zone 14 with gas which may be recycle gas obtained from line 25A, to which line 43 connects, by opening valve 45.

The process is quite useful in that numerous advantages inure by introduction of raw shale fines into the gas combustion retorting operation as a slurry in a liquid vehicle. Thus, when oil is employed, it has been found that if such oil is introduced above the retorting zone the oil would not be cracked since the oil is evaporated and recovered without loss, thus providing for introduction of fines from which shale oil is recovered. The fines may usually comprise from 10 to 20% by weight of the oil shale which is mined and crushed, which ordinarily would have to be discarded. It is to be understood however, that the fines may comprise a lesser amount of the oil shale and may be within the range of 1 to 20% by weight and may be from 5 to 10% of the raw oil shale. Thus, the fines provide an additional source of oil shale in a very economical fashion, thus providing for recovery of a greater amount of shale oil than previously.

Recovery and Conversion of Shale Oil Mist

In a process described by H.W. Parker; U.S. Patent 3,560,367; February 2, 1971; assigned to Phillips Petroleum Company shale oil mist is recovered by collecting it in a solid subdivided mass, e.g., coke or catalyst, as in a fluidized bed and then converted in a conversion zone. In a specific example, cooled vapors from an oil shale retorting zone are treated to separate liquid oil and an oil mist. The oil mist is adsorbed on a solid, subdivided mass and the mass containing the adsorbed mist is passed to a conversion zone.

FIGURE 1.9:   RECOVERY AND CONVERSION OF SHALE OIL MIST

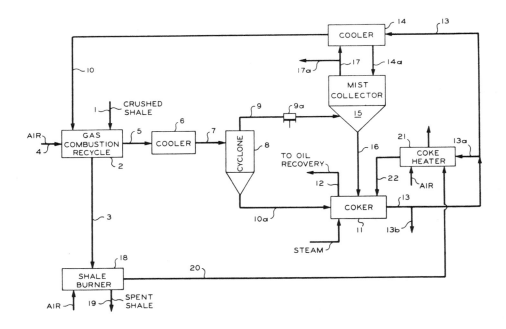

Source: H.W. Parker; U.S. Patent 3,560,367; February 2, 1971

Referring to Figure 1.9, crushed shale is fed at 1 into retort 2 from which spent or retorted shale is removed at 3. To create the heat necessary to pyrolyze or to decompose the kerogen, air is passed by 4 into retort 2. In the retort, the kerogen will begin to decompose at a temperature in the range of 440° to 660°F. A substantial amount, if not substantially all of the oil or oily materials formed from the decomposition of the kerogen will have been removed from the shale at a temperature within the range of 840° to 1020°F. Vaporous products are taken overhead from retort 2 by 5 and passed by coolers 6 and 7 to cyclone mist separator 8. Continuous type crushed shale retort operation is shown. The temperature in this operation can be varied as indicated, but in any event, the cooler 6 is operated to cool the vaporous products to a temperature of 100°F., and accordingly, the interior of the cyclone 8 will be at a temperature of 98°F.

Approximately 3% of the oil will leave the cyclone as a fine mist by 9, the remainder or bottoms liquid are passed by 10A to fluid coker 11 in which the fluid coking operation is conducted according to known manner and conditions. The oil from 10A is mixed with hot coke in 11 and as a result of the coking operations there are produced a stream of oil vapor coking products, taken overhead by 12 to oil recovery, and coke removed at 13 and passed into coke cooler 14, then to fluid bed mist collector 15 by 14A, where oil mist from 9 is adsorbed upon the cook coke. A blower 9A moves the gas through the retorting, mist collecting and coke cooling sections.

The cool coke containing the oil mist is passed by 16 into fluid coker 11. There is contained in the oil mist considerable gas and this shale gas is passed by 17 into counter flow with the coke in cooler 14, cooling the coke while itself is heated and then recycled by 10 to retort 2. Excess shale gas is vented at 17A. Retorted shale is passed by 3 to shale burner 18 from which spent shale is removed at 19. Hot gases from 18 are passed by 20 to coke heater 21 into which coke from fluid coker 11 is passed by 13A. Excess coke is removed at 13B. Hot coke for the coking operation in 11 is passed from 21 by 22. The products from fluid coker 11 are removed by 12 and treated in conventional manner. The following tabulation is of conditions, etc., given by way of specific example of an operation in which 50,000 barrels/day of oil is produced.

Example:

Temperatures	°F.
Retort 2 (maximum)	1200
Pipe 5	125
Pipe 7	100
Cyclone 8	98
Pipe 10	995
Pipe 14A	105
Pipe 17	100
Fluid coker 11	1000
Pipe 20	1200

Pressures	Psia
Retort 2	12
Pipe 5	11.5
Fluid coker 11	14
Fluid bed mist collector	16
Coke cooler	14

Flow Rates

Crushed shale, tons per day	80,000
Recycle gas, pipe 10, cfm	4,400
Gas containing oil mist, pipe 9, cfm	4,400
Vapors from coking operation on liquid basis, pipe 12, barrels per day	50,000

Rotatable Grate

D.A. Vorum; U.S. Patent 3,480,512; November 25, 1969; assigned to Phillips Petroleum Company describes a retorting vessel which has rotatable grates comprising rotatable jacket tubes which can be provided with means for introducing coolants into the annulus of the jacketed tubes.

The retorting vessel is provided with a first rotatable grate means for introducing an oxygen-containing gas into the vessel to support combustion of the hydrocarbons in the oil-bearing solids and a second rotatable grate means for removing the educed hydrocarbons and the products of combustion. In one form of the process, the second rotatable grate comprises a pipe in the form of a tube positioned horizontally across the vessel and spaced beneath the first rotatable grate means. This pipe functions to collect and remove the hydrocarbon educt from within the vessel.

In another example of the process, the second rotatable grate comprises a horizontal pipe in the form a tube positioned across the vessel and spaced below the first rotatable grate and a second pipe in the form of a tube positioned above and spaced from the first rotatable grate. The first and second pipes serve to remove the hydrocarbon educt from above and below the zone of combustion. A third rotatable grate positioned horizontally within and near the bottom of the vessel serves to introduce a coolant into the vessel for the purpose of lowering the temperature of the residue particles. The coolant passes upward in the vessel to the second rotatable grate where it is removed with the hydrocarbon educt. This path of the coolant through the lower portion of the vessel will tend to scrub any remaining hydrocarbon educt from the residue particles, thereby increasing the over-all efficiency of the method.

The third rotatable grate means can also be used to pass steam or air through the descending mass of hot residue particles. Since the residue particles will contain a certain quantity of carbonaceous material, a reaction between the steam and the carbon of the carbonaceous material will produce a combustible gas which will add to the total fuel gas produced. This reaction product will travel upward in the retort to the combustion zone.

The rotatable grates of this process can also be used to supply the combustion air in the so-called Bureau of Mines Gas Combustion Retort. In this environment, the rotatable grates provide an even descent of particles through the retort and a grinding up of the clinkers which form. This prevents channeling of the combustion zone thus providing a more even distribution of heat. When the rotatable grates are provided with cooling means, their life is much longer because they are better able to withstand the heat in the gas combustion retort.

FIGURE 1.10: RETORTING VESSEL CONTAINING ROTATABLE GRATES

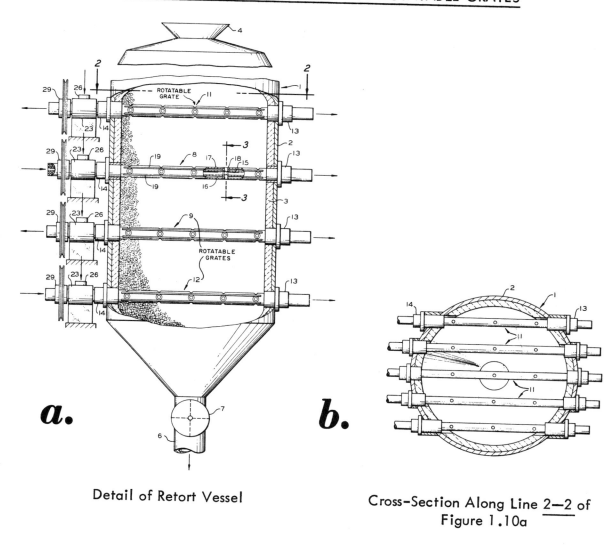

a.

Detail of Retort Vessel

b.

Cross-Section Along Line 2—2 of
Figure 1.10a

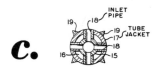

c.

Cross-Section Along Line
3—3 of Figure 1.10a

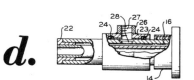

d.

Mounting for
Rotatable Grate

e.

Modified Grate

Source: D.A. Vorum; U.S. Patent 3,480,512; November 25, 1969

Referring to Figure 1.10a, a retorting vessel shown generally by reference numeral 1, comprises a metal shell 2 having a refractory lining 3. The retorting vessel 1 is preferably situated in a generally vertical position with a height-to-diameter ratio of at least 1. It is preferred that the length or height of the retorting vessel be many times its diameter in order to conserve energy requirements for heating the vessel and for removing the product.

A hopper 4 of any suitable construction is attached to the top of the retorting vessel 1 in a manner which will allow a continuous feed of oil-bearing solid particles. The bottom of the retorting vessel 1 terminates in the form of a centrally positioned conduit 6 having suitable valve means 7 such as a star-type valve. It is generally preferred that the upper portion of retorting vessel 1 be of cylindrical shape with the walls diverging outward in a downward direction and that the lower portion be in the shape of a cone which converges into conduit 6. This type of construction reduces the tendency of the particles to bridge within the vessel as they descend. The rate of descent of the oil-bearing solids through the vessel can be controlled by regulating the position of valve 7.

The grates are mounted for rotation within the retorting vessel 1 and comprise a first rotatable grate shown generally at 8; a second rotatable grate including a first pipe 9 situated below the first rotatable grate and a second pipe 11 situated above the first rotatable grate; and a third rotatable grate 12 situated below the second rotatable grate. The first rotatable grate 8, the second rotatable grate including pipes 9 and 11, and the third rotatable grate 12 are each mounted generally horizontal and are carried by the walls of the retorting vessel by means of a plurality of bearing sleeves 13 and 14. The bearing sleeves 13 and 14 serve to allow the rotatable grate means to be rotated.

As illustrated by Figure 1.10b, a plurality of pipes or tubular members 11 are mounted in a substantially common, horizontal plane. This type of construction is generally preferred because it provides more complete and uniform agitation of the descending particles of oil-bearing solids.

As illustrated, each of the rotatable grates in the first, second and third rotatable grate means comprises a tube 15 having a jacket 17 spaced therefrom to form an annulus 16. Fluid conducting means for allowing fluid communication between the interior of tubes 15 and the inside of the retorting vessel comprises a plurality of radial placed tubular-shaped pipes 18. Each of the tubular-shaped pipes 18 is positioned normal to the surface of the tube 15 and the jacket 17 in a manner which will allow fluid to be passed through pipe 18 in a direction normal to the surface of jacket 17. Thus, the pipes 18 in the first and third rotatable grate will serve to allow an oxygen-containing gas and a coolant, respectively, to be introduced into the vessel. The tubular-shaped pipes 18 in the second rotatable grate, including pipes 9 and 11, will serve to collect and transmit the educed hydrocarbons.

In a modification of the process, each of the rotatable grates is provided with a rib 19 extending longitudinally with the jacket 17. The rib 19 can be attached to the jacket by welding or the like. In still another example, each of the rotatable grates is provided with a plurality of spaced spikes 21 attached to the outer surface of the jacket 17. It is generally preferred that the rotatable grates include one of these modifications because the presence of the ribs 19 or the spikes 21 assists in agitating and grinding the particles as they descend through the retorting vessel. This result not only inhibits the formation of clinkers but also exposes more surface area on the particles, thereby promoting the eduction of the hydrocarbons. Each of the rotatable grates in the first, second and third rotatable grate means is provided with a flange 22 at its free end which serves to connect and seal the tube 15 and the sleeve 17. Suitable fluid coupling means 23 connected to each of the sleeves 17 in the first and third rotatable grate means can be used to introduce an oxygen-containing gas and coolant, respectively, into the retorting vessel. A suitable fluid coupling 23 attached to the sleeve 22 in the second rotatable grate can be used for removing the hydrocarbon educt from within the vessel.

Each of the fluid couplers 23 is provided with a pair of O-rings 24 of elastomeric material or the like, which serves to form a seal between the fluid coupler 23 and the exterior surface of shaft 17. Each of the fluid couplers 23 is provided with a flange 26 having an opening 27 in registry with a plurality of circumferentially spaced openings 28 in sleeve 17. This arrangement will allow a coolant such as water to be introduced into the annulus 16 and circulated through the rotatable grates to prevent them from becoming too hot as a result of the retorting operation. The coolant can be allowed to issue from the annulus at the opposite ends of the rotatable grates as indicated by the arrows or another fluid coupler can be attached to the opposite ends of the rotatable grates and the coolant fluid recovered. A pulley 29 attached to each of the rotatable grates through each of the outer sleeves 17 can be connected to a suitable prime mover by means of a belt.

In the process, oil shale in a particle size of about 1/2 to 2 inches can be charged into the retorting vessel 1 by gravity flow from hopper 4. The oil shale particles can be as large as 4 1/2 inches or more if desired. The star valve 7 is stationary at the start of the retorting operation. The hopper 4 is provided with an additional supply of oil-bearing shale particles so that once the rotation of star valve 7 begins, a continued supply of oil shale is available and the descent of the particles will be uninterrupted in the vessel.

The retorting or destructive distillation operation can be initiated by igniting the hydrocarbons present in a horizontal zone extending across the vessel in the vicinity of the rotatable grate 8. This can be accomplished by injecting a mixture of a combustible gas and air through tube 15 and tubular pipes 18 in the rotatable grate 8. This mixture of air and combustible gas can be burned within the vessel for a sufficient length of time to heat the oil-bearing particles to a temperature above their ignition or kindling point. After the hydrocarbons in the oil-bearing solids ignite, the supply of combustible gas can be stopped and the supply of air maintained through the rotatable grate 8 in order to support and continue the combustion.

Other techniques can be employed for initiating combustion. For example, the combustion process can be started by temporarily positioning an air-gas burner within the vessel in the approximate vicinity of the rotatable grate 8. After the combustion process is proceeding with the fuel obtained from the hydrocarbons in the oil-bearing solids, the air-gas burner can be removed from this side of the vessel so as not to interfere with the continuous descent of the particles.

In the destructive distillation of an oil-bearing solid such as oil shale, the rotatable grate 8 is employed for introducing an oxygen-containing gas into the vessel in an amount sufficient to support combustion of the hydrocarbons for the purpose of obtaining heat in an amount sufficient to educe the hydrocarbons from the oil-bearing solids. The second rotatable grate means including pipes 9 and 11 is employed for removing the liquid and vapor hydrocarbon educt and the products of combustion. As previously indicated, the upper pipe 11 of the second rotatable grate can be eliminated if desired. Thus, the second rotatable grate can be pipes 9 and 11 or pipe 9 alone. The third rotatable grate 12 is employed for supplying a cooling medium such as water in a uniform manner to the lower portion of the retorting vessel. The introduction of water in this manner generally is advantageous because the residue material can be more easily handled after it has been cooled. Moreover, when water is used as the cooling medium in this manner, the steam generated when the water contacts the hot residue solids is helpful in forming a seal against product leakage through star valve 7. Since the steam generated is removed from the vessel by means of pipe 9 of the second rotatable grate, it serves to strip or wash the descending residue particles of residual educt as it travels upward through the descending particles. Moreover, as hereinbefore indicated, the steam can react with the carbon in the carbonaceous residue material to produce additional fuel gas.

The heat generated in the combustion zone is sufficient to educe the hydrocarbons from the oil-bearing solids in the form of vapors and liquids. The actual distribution of product between the vapor and liquid states depends at least in part on the temperature level maintained within the combustion zone. The products are forced from the combustion zone and passed upward to pipe 11 and downward to pipe 9 as a result of the oxygen-containing gas issuing from the first rotatable grate 8 as it rotates. The liquid and vapor oil products are collected by the second rotatable grate including pipes 9 and 11 and the tubular pipes 18. These products including the gaseous products of combustion and steam which is rising from the third rotatable grate 12 can be removed from the retorting vessel to a suitable storage area. If desired, a slight vacuum of 100 to 300 mm. of mercury may be placed on the pipes 9 and 11 of the second rotatable grate to facilitate removal of the educed products, the products of combustion, and the steam.

Tunnel Oven with Separate Compartments

A process described by J.D. Bennett; U.S. Patent 3,464,892; September 2, 1969; assigned to Sun Oil Company employs a long tunnel oven containing a suitable flotation liquid which is separated by movable gas-tight partitions into separate compartments, through which barges, carrying the solid material to be treated and floating on the liquid, are moved step-by-step from one compartment to another. Inlet and outlet gas-conveying ducts open into the tops and bottoms of the compartments, the gas flowing from each inlet duct to the outlet duct of the same compartment through the material in the respective barge, the barges having foraminous load carriers which permit this gas flow through the material to take place. The flotation liquid is utilized to seal the bottom of the barge to the bottom duct in each respective compartment.

In each compartment, a separate treatment step is carried out. A typical process comprises the following steps. (1) In the first step (carried out in the first compartment), the fresh raw shale (after being loaded on the barge) is preheated to a temperature below the retorting temperature, by passing through gases at an elevated temperature derived from a burning compartment. (2) In the second step (carried out in the second compartment), the preheated shale is retorted (distilled) to drive off volatilizable constituents (which are collected) by passing through hot lean gases; these hot lean gases comprise noncondensable gases (derived from the volatilizable constituents) which are recycled through the process and are heated by contact with the hot solids in a heat exchange zone. The retorting of the shale causes the same to become spent, which leaves a carbonaceous residue. (3) The third process step comprises the burning of the residue on the spent material, by passing through a hot combustion-supporting gas which has been heated by contact with the hot solids in a cooling zone. From this burning operation are derived the elevated temperature gases which are utilized for heating the raw shale in the preheating zone. (4) The fourth step takes place in a heat exchange zone, where the hot solids derived from the burning compartment give up heat to recycled lean gases passing through this hot material. (5) The fifth and final step utilizes a cooling, where solids at an elevated temperature derived from the heat exchange zone give up heat to a combustion-supporting gas (e.g., fresh air) passing through this solid material. From the cooling compartment, the treated, decoked and relatively cool material is unloaded from the barge and piled on a dump.

The process steps set out in the preceding paragraph actually each comprise two phases, the action described previously taking place during the first phase. In the second phase, the combustion-supporting gas (e.g., air) passed through the burning compartment (or zone) is replaced by steam, thereby generating hydrogen by a water-gas reaction. This steam is developed in the cooling zone. During this hydrogen-generating second phase, the generated hydrogen is led off to a hydrogen collecting system.

Artificially Induced Condensation Nuclei

M.W. Putman; U.S. Patent 2,813,823; November 19, 1957; assigned to the U.S. Secretary of the Interior has found that by providing artifically induced condensation nuclei in the condensing zone, that the size of the fog or mist droplets may be controlled so that none of the droplets are so large that they are disengaged from the gas stream by impingement in passing through the shale bed, nor none so small that they are difficult to recover from the relatively cool gas stream by conventional methods, irrespective of the gas cooling rate in that portion of the shale bed where vapor condensation is initiated. The formation of a fog or mist is accomplished at low degrees of supersaturation only in the presence of a large number of nuclei on which the saturated vapors may condense.

Sodium chloride is particularly useful as the condensation nuclei source in view of its low cost and ready availability. Other salts which have been found to be effective are potassium chloride and calcium chloride. In general, any substance which has an appreciable vapor pressure and is thermally stable at the retort temperature may be employed to supply the artificially induced condensation nuclei.

Artificially induced condensation nuclei may be provided in the retort gas in several ways. In one method sodium chloride crystals are vaporized in the combustion zone of the retort; and in the second method sodium chloride crystals are vaporized outside the retort and injected into the recycle gases. The first method is more convenient but harder to control, while the second method is more difficult to carry out but the results are more reproducible. The process involves continuously passing the oil shale, to which has been added a small amount of sodium chloride in water solution, downward as a bed of broken solids in a substantially vertical column. The solid residue is removed in a cool condition at the bottom of the column while the distillation and combustion products, including a noncondensable gas, are removed from the top of the column. At least a portion of this noncondensable gas, in a cool condition, is recycled to the bottom of the column and passes upward through the downward moving residue, thus cooling the hot residue and itself becoming heated. At this point in the retort the gas stream is raised to a still higher temperature, preferably by passing through a combustion zone in the retort itself. As the gas stream passes on up through the column of shale, it delivers its heat to the cold incoming shale, thus gradually heating it to progressively higher temperatures. The descending shale, consequently, passes successively through a preheating zone, where it meets the still hot vapor-gas mixture rising from the distillation zone, through a distillation zone where it reaches retorting temperature, and through a sublimation zone where it reaches a still higher temperature which is sufficient to cause a portion of the sodium chloride, which has been evaporated to a thin film on the shale particles in the preheating zone above, to sublime.

The sodium chloride vapors so formed, are swept upward by the gas stream, and as the gas stream is cooled by the descending cooler shale, a sodium chloride fume is formed. This fume consists of minute solid sodium chloride particles which are suitable condensation nuclei for the oil vapors to condense upon. In the distillation zone the organic content of the shale undergoes thermal decomposition producing condensable product vapors which are carried upward in the gas stream. The gas-vapor mixture rising from the distillation zone encounters progressively cooler shale as it passes upward through the shale preheating zone, and of course, in this way, itself becomes progressively cooled. Eventually the gas-vapor mixture encounters shale below the initial dew point temperature of the mixture and condensation of the vapor begins. By withdrawing the gas stream from the top of the shale bed at a sufficiently low temperature, viz, between 100° and 200°F. and preferably between 115° and 175°F., substantially the entire vapor content of the gas stream undergoes condensation in the shale bed on the sodium chloride nuclei in the gas stream.

In an alternate form of carrying out the process, sodium chloride is vaporized in a separate burner outside the retort, and the mixture of hot gas and vaporized salt is admitted to the stream of recycled gas entering the bottom of the retort. This may be accomplished by injecting a fine spray of brine into a suitable gas or oil furnace. Another method is to add sodium chloride solution to broken pieces of coke, which are then burned. In this way the salt vapors proceed up the retort and make their way through the combustion zone to the cooler upper part of the retort, where they are condensed as a fine solid fume and form nuclei for subsequent condensation of the shale-oil mist.

The method is applicable to any sort of retorting process where the shale is fed downward by gravity, countercurrent to a stream of retorting gases in which artificially induced condensation nuclei are present, and where the gas stream is withdrawn from the shale bed at a temperature sufficiently low so that substantially all, or the major portion, of the vapor content of the gas stream undergoes condensation before leaving the shale bed.

In related work M.W. Putman; U.S. Patent 2,901,402; August 25, 1959; assigned to the U.S. Secretary of the Interior has found that the oxides of aluminum, tin and titanium are very effective condensation nuclei. The aluminum oxide nuclei may be prepared by vaporizing aluminum chloride, and then introducing the vapors into the recycle gas stream where the aluminum chloride reacts with a portion of the water vapor to form aluminum oxide nuclei.

Oil Shale Retorting

Addition of Coke

In a process described by <u>C.E. Hemminger and R.I. Bergman; U.S. Patent 3,162,583; December 22, 1964; assigned to Esso Research and Engineering Company</u> coal and/or coke is added to the oil shale to be distilled. The coke is preferably coke made by subjecting bottoms from the distillation of shale oil to fluid coking as this coke is generally produced at the shale mines where it has no value other than as fuel and is burned up during retorting to supply part of the heat of distillation or retorting. When using fluid coke and coal in a mixture with oil shale in distilling and retorting, higher yields of oil and better operability are obtained than when using a mixture of coal and shale alone.

Thus, using the underfed type of retort, the efficiency of the retort is increased by adding coal such as bituminous coal, or coal and fluid coke to the shale being fed to the retort. In this type of retort the shale temperature increases from atmospheric to a maximum temperature of 2000° to 2400°F. and then to 100° to 300°F. as it passes down the retort with the result that in the high temperature zone a high degree of carbonate decomposition of the inorganic portion of the shale is produced. With this type of retort a large amount of heat is required and if there is insufficient heat from the spent shale, some of the retorted oil is burned and this is definitely a loss in the process. By feeding coal with the oil shale not only is the liquid hydrocarbon from the coal made available but also the recovery of oil from the shale itself is increased from 75 to 95 to 105% of the Fischer assay of the shale.

Since the heat load in this type of retort is high and practically all of the carbonates are decomposed there is not sufficient residual carbon in the shale to provide the necessary heat for the shale retorting and carbonate decomposition. As a result in the countercurrent flow of air in the retort, air for which there is not sufficient carbon for combustion passes down through the shale bed and consumes a portion of the retorted hydrocarbon product.

By adding coal or coke to the shale feed, the coke from the coal distillation and the added coke are burned and this provides the necessary carbon to burn this excess air and oxygen-free hot gas as it enters the distillation or retorting zone at a lower level in the retort. Consequently there is a substantially complete recovery of oil from the oil shale as well as that from the coal. The fluid coke supplies heat by being burned. The fluid coke will not fuse like coal being distilled and therefore better operability of the retort is obtained. Because of the fusing property of coals, which causes uneven distribution of the air by blocking air passages, the amount of coal is limited to about 25% by weight of the shale. Coke does not have any limitation, but it in itself, gives little or no liquid hydrocarbon. However, more coal can be distilled if coke is added with the shale, the 25% maximum content of coal can be increased to 40% on shale if 30% of coke on shale is added to the feed mixture of the retort. The amount of coal which is added should be at least sufficient to have 1 to 5% carbon in the ash or spent shale leaving the top of the retort. This is the minimum amount of coal and the amount will depend upon the richness of the shale, more coal being used for a 20 gallons per ton than a 40 gallons per ton shale. For a 30 gallons per ton shale 25 weight percent coal is utilized in the coal-shale mixture. If too much coal is added with the mixture, channelling results in the retort due to the coking and fusion of the coke particles. When channelling occurs, there is inefficient contacting of the solids and the gases. The maximum amount of coal to be used is on the order of a 50-50 weight mixture of coal and shale.

Oil Shale Retorting

Retorting and Coking in Single Vessel

F.E. Campion; U.S. Patent 3,112,255; November 26, 1963; assigned to Pan American Petroleum Corporation describes a process for the retorting of hydrocarbon yielding materials such as oil shale under conditions such that the retorting and coking operations are both effected within the same vessel or unit. In such an operation, oil shale and an oxidizing gas such as air, are concurrently introduced into a suitable retort. A zone of combustion is established within the retort at a level determined by the rates of injection of shale and air or oxygen and the temperature of the shale and oxidizing gas. Oil produced from the shale passes through the combustion zone where it is thermally cracked into lower weight molecular hydrocarbons. In this manner the coking process, ordinarily effected in a separate unit, is accomplished in the retort thus eliminating the cost of constructing and operating individual coking units. The oil thus produced is of suitable viscosity for pipeline transmission or, if desired, may be further refined at the retorting site.

Referring to Figure 1.11, shown on the following page, mined shale rock is fed to a grinding unit 2 where it is converted to a particle size sufficiently fine to render the material free flowing. Usually particle sizes of from 1/4 to 1 inch in diameter are satisfactory. The ground shale is taken from a bin 4 by means of endless belt conveyor 6 and added to hopper 8. Retort 10 is first filled with ground shale flowing through line 9, after which the addition of shale is temporarily discontinued. Gas in line 12 and air in line 14 are then mixed and burned in spray type burner 16 to cause the shale to burn. After a burning zone has been established, air heated to 300° to 1000°F., by passage through exchanger 19, is introduced into the top of retort 10 via line 18. The temperature of the air, generally speaking, should be adjusted to the particular case under consideration.

Under some instances it may be desirable, where the oil content of the shale is low, to inject part of the scrubbed gaseous hydrocarbon stream, making up the plant fuel product, back into the retort to provide additional fuel. Also, owing to the inert gas content of this plant fuel product stream, the latter may be injected into the combustion zone as a means for controlling the temperature in said zone.

As the air added to the system through line 18 contacts the burning zone in the lower part of retort 10, the burning front of the zone tends to move upward toward the air source. Flow of gas and air through lines 12 and 14, respectively, is then shut off since the necessary combustion can be sustained and controlled by injection of air through line 18. Introduction of air only at the top of retort 10 is ordinarily continued until the burning zone reaches an intermediate level in the retort, preferably from about one-third to half-way up the column of shale in the retort. When this condition is reached, both shale and air are added concurrently through lines 9 and 18 respectively, to the top of retort 10.

For best operating efficiency the flow of enriched air or oxygen into the retort should be regulated with the flow of shale. The amount of air or oxygen needed in a given case generally does not depend significantly on the quantity of carbonaceous material in the shale. For example, with a retort having a volume of 100 cubic feet and designed to process 100 tons of shale (having an oil content of 30 gallons per ton) per day, air should be added to the top of the retort at the rate of about 18,240 standard cubic feet per hour to maintain steady state conditions.

FIGURE 1.11:   COMBINED RETORTING AND COKING OPERATIONS IN SINGLE VESSEL

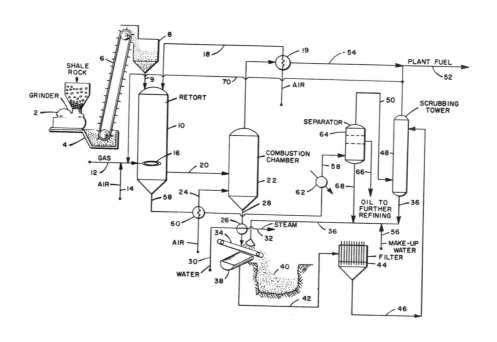

Source: F.E. Campion; U.S. Patent 3,112,255; November 26, 1963

The retort may be operated at atmospheric pressure although higher pressures such as 400 to 500 psi may be employed.

One of the advantages of the process is the fact that it can readily be carried out at relatively low temperatures, i.e., 800° to 1000°F., thus aiding in the prevention of excessive clinker formation in the retort. In some commercial shale retorting processes, temperatures as high as 2000°F. are reached. To avoid shutdown and other difficulties due to sintering and clinkering of the shale, large spiral steel plows are kept moving in the retort bed. The economic advantages in operating without such elaborate auxiliary equipment are apparent.

During the retorting operation, approximately 10 to 12% of the hydrocarbons in the average grade of oil shale is burned to sustain the operation. The remainder of the liquid kerogen decomposition products passes downward through the burned shale bed in retort 10 and is extensively cracked owing to prolonged contact with the hot spent shale as the latter travels toward the base of the retort. It will thus be seen that the level at which the burning zone is to be maintained in the bed will be at least partially dependent upon the degree of cracking desired and the nature of the hydrocarbon fractions liberated from the oil shale. Selection of a proper level for the burning zone in the shale bed for any given set of circumstances can be readily determined by simple experimentation.

The spent shale is withdrawn through line 20 and transferred to combustion chamber 22. The shale at this stage of the process contains an appreciable amount of coke representing substantial quantities of heat as well as fuel gas which can be secured from controlled burning of the coke. Accordingly, in carrying out the combustion of the coke and other combustible components present on the retorted shale, an important factor is the temperature at which the shale tends to sinter or form clinkers in combustion chamber 22. The amount of coke adhering to the retorted shale will, of course, vary. However, in the process, the coke residue on the shale ash should not ordinarily exceed 10% and for the most part would generally be in the neighborhood of 5%.

In general, clinker formation will be avoided as long as the temperature is held below 1200° to 1300°F. Air at 400° to 600°F. is introduced into combustion chamber 22 via line 24, preferably at a rate such that coke and other carbonaceous material present is only partially burned resulting in gaseous products rich in carbon monoxide. Temperatures required to produce gaseous products rich in carbon monoxide are in the range normally used in the well-known methods for making producer gas, i.e., 850° to 1350°F. With some oil shales, clinkering does not occur until temperatures of 1500° to 1600°F. are reached. In case of shale of this type, temperatures as high as 1300° to 1400°F. may be used in the partial combustion step.

Further economies in the process can be realized by generation of steam in heat exchanger 26 through absorption of heat from spent shale withdrawn through line 28. The steam resulting from the conversion of water in line 30 is transferred through line 32 and may be used for the generation of plant power. The cooled spent shale or ash is transferred to a vibrating screen 34 and leached by water flowing through line 36. This operation removes the major portion of the alkaline components present in the ash resulting in an aqueous alkaline solution and a suspension of fine particles passing through screen 34 into an open tank 38. The bulk of the ash discharged from line 28 on to screen 34, is dumped into a suitable disposal pit 40. From tank 38 the aqueous alkaline mixture is taken through line 42 and the solid material removed in filter 44. The filtrate is then transferred through line 46 and used to scrub uncondensed product gases fed to the bottom of tower 48 through line 50. Scrubbed gas is taken off through line 52, combined if desired, with other gases from combustion chamber 22, contained in line 54 and used for plant fuel.

For example, a portion of the scrubbed gas may be taken off through line 70 and combined with the fuel-air mixture in line 12 used to feed the burning zone in retort 10. The scrubbing water from tower 48 is removed via line 36, filtered if necessary and then used as leaching water to remove alkali from spent shale as previously described. Make-up water is added to the system through line 56 as needed.

Cracked retort oil of substantially reduced viscosity is removed from retort 10 via line 53 and heat exchanged in exchanger 60 with cold air in line 24. This product stream is further cooled in condenser 62 before it is sent to separator 64. Oil is taken off through line 66 and sent to further processing while the lower water layer is run off through line 68 and combined with the scrubbings in line 36.

Externally Heated Flue Gas for Temperature Control

In a process described by K.L. Berry; U.S. Patent 3,464,913; September 2, 1969; assigned to Pan American Petroleum Corporation a portion of the heat for retorting oil shale is supplied by injecting externally generated hot flue gas at 800° to 1200°F.; the remainder of the retorting heat is supplied by combustion in the spent shale bed. The purpose is to minimize overheating the shale, which causes carbonate decomposition and excessive cracking. In the proposed method, a portion of the shale is retorted before heat from the combustion zone reaches it.

The process is illustrated by reference to Figure 1.12, shown on the following page, in which a vertical retort 2 is filled with crushed raw oil shale continuously introduced through hopper 4. The process is initiated by first introducing a hot gaseous stream at a temperature from 800° to 1100°F. into the retort via distributor 5 under conditions such that the major portion of the kerogen and/or hydrocarbons is removed from the shale particles, leaving primarily a carbon residue thereon. This hot gaseous stream may, if desired, be derived by burning a portion of the fuel gas recovered from the retorting operation, as will be explained in greater detail below. The spent shale containing this residue is then passed into the combustion zone adjacent spray burner 6 where combustion of said residue in a deficiency of oxygen is accomplished by the introduction of air into the system via line 8. The heat thus generated in large part passes up the bed and assists in the liberation of additional valuable products from the partially retorted crushed raw shale that has passed on downwardly from distributor 5.

Alternately, the retorting process may be initiated by supplying an air-gas mixture to operate burner 6 via lines 8 and 10 respectively, and igniting the mixture to effect combustion of the oil shale in the vicinity of burner 6. Once combustion is established, valve 12 is closed and the burning operation is sustained by the continued introduction of air through line 8. Retorting in the upper portion of the bed may then proceed as described above.

After the process has lined out, burner 6 is likewise preferably operated at a temperature in a range of from 800° to 1100°F. At this temperature level, the retorting step is substantially completed with only a portion of the residual carbon on the shale approaching burner 6 generally being consumed. Thus, after the initial retorting step occurring in the vicinity of distributor 5, the carbon residue on the shale amounts to about 3%. At burner 6 from about 5 to 25% of the residual carbon is burned by combustion with air introduced through line 8. Some of the heat is also generated by combustion in the zone of the cooled recycled gas introduced into the retort at distributor 34. At all times, however, a deficiency of air is maintained in the system so that the temperature both at burner 6 and distributor 5 does not appreciably exceed 1100°F.

Shale oil vapors rise through the descending bed of shale particles, preheating the latter, and at the same time lowering the temperature of the rising vapors and combustion products. At the top of retort 2 shale oil mist and products of combustion are removed by means of line 14. This product stream is sent through separator 16 where the liquid portion is withdrawn through line 18 and sent to further refining while the uncondensed fraction is taken through line 20 to in-line burner 28. A portion of this gaseous stream is diverted through line 22 and the rest taken from the system via line 24. The gaseous fraction in line 22 contains light hydrocarbons, hydrogen, carbon monoxide, and products of combustion and is mixed with air from line 26 after which the resulting mixture is fed to in-line burner 28. Sufficient air is present in the mixture to form a stream of combustion products in line 30, having a temperature of from 800° to 1100°F.

FIGURE 1.12: RETORT PROCESS EMPLOYING HOT FLUE GAS

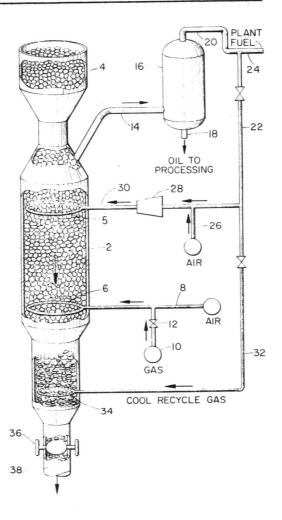

Source: K.L. Berry; U.S. Patent 3,464,913; September 2, 1969

These hot gases then flow into the bed of raw shale via suitably shaped distributor 5 which is preferably spaced from about 2 to 5 feet above burner 6. At this level in the downward moving bed, the oil shale particles are heated to a temperature within the last mentioned range, resulting in the release of a substantial portion of the volatile carbon compounds from the particles. At these temperatures, however, essentially none of the carbonates or other inorganic materials present decompose. Cool fuel gas is returned to the system via line 32 and distributor 34 to take up heat from spent shale being removed from the retort through valve 36 and outlet 38.

Once the supply of fuel gas is generated as explained above, the amount of air supplied to the system through line 8 can be reduced to the volume just necessary to maintain the temperature at burner 6 in the range of 800° to 1100°F. The fuel required to produce temperatures in this range is derived partly from residual carbon on the spent shale and partly from the recycled flue gas from distributor 34. Ordinarily it is considered that about 20,000 scf of gas, i.e., fuel gas plus air, is required to retort 1 ton of oil shale. Under retorting conditions the shale moves through the retort at a rate of from 3 to 10 feet per hour. This volume of introduced gas may be somewhat less than 20,000 scf/t. because the heat in the combustion products resulting from burning of the residual carbon on the spent shale supplies an appreciable amount of heat to the downcoming raw shale. An additional heat source is the spent solids coming in contact with cool fuel gas introduced via line 32.

In a typical case, the 20,000 scf of gas and air may be proportioned as follows: 1,000 scf of fuel gas in line 22 and 1,000 scf of air through line 26, 1,000 scf of air via line 8, and 17,000 scf of fuel gas through line 32. In carrying out the process from 1,500 to 2,500 scf of air per ton of shale processed is used in order to maintain the temperature within the above range. In most cases, and as indicated above, the total volume of air employed is divided evenly between the supply going to line 30 and that introduced into the system via line 8. This constitutes a substantial savings in air pumping costs over previous methods which require from 5,000 to 6,000 scf per ton of shale.

Hydrogen Produced as By-Product

P.H. Gifford II; U.S. Patent 3,577,338; May 4, 1971 describes a process for retorting oil shale and simultaneously producing hydrogen as a by-product with high yields of both oil and hydrogen. The process comprises continuously passing oil shale through a combustion zone in a retort while continuously introducing steam and oxygen into the combustion zone, removing spent shale below the combustion zone and recovering oil and hydrogen from the retort off gas from the combustion zone. Hydrogen is produced by the reaction of carbon-containing material with steam.

Example 1: A reactor was filled with about 1.6 pounds of raw shale analyzing about 30 gallons of oil per ton of rock (Fischer Assay). Superheated steam at a temperature of 1000°F. was fed into the reactor at a rate of 1 scf/m. (standard cubic feet per minute) to preheat the shale; this was also the temperature and rate during the run. After preheating, oxygen was introduced at a rate of 0.105 scf/m. until oxygen breakthrough occurred. The reactor was then allowed to cool, then was opened, and the spent shale inspected.

During the run the off gas was tested every 5 to 10 minutes for the presence of hydrogen. Hydrogen appeared in every run immediately upon the introduction of oxygen. The off gas burned with a violent, almost invisible, blue flame; as opposed to a yellow-orange smoky flame which was obtained during the preheat or from off gases from the prior art processes. The recovery of oil from the shale was from 80 to 90% FA (Fischer Assay), that is, 80 to 90% of the oil present in the shale was recovered.

The examination of the spent shale revealed that it was very light in appearance; this is directly opposite from what was found in conventional oil shale processes in which the spent shale is almost black. It was evident that a carbon consuming reaction, after completely removing all external carbon, had penetrated by diffusion deep into the particles. The spent shale was completely retorted, and there was no evidence of sintering. It was apparent that hydrogen had been produced in significant amounts by the reaction of carbon with the steam which was introduced. As all of the carbon on the outside of the particles and most of the carbon inside the particles had been consumed and since there was no sintering of the particles, it was apparent that clinkering could not have occurred. There was no binder left to cohere the particles together to form the necessary bridge. The carbonate decomposition seemed to be about the same as experienced in the prior art process of Gas Combustion. This was determined by a comparison of the structural strength of the spent shale produced by either process.

Example 2: The purpose of this run was to determine the effectiveness of the process on rich shale. With all prior art processes it is difficult to process oil shale having a Fischer Assay above 30 gallons per ton, and none of them can process shale of a Fischer Assay above 40 gallons per ton.

About 1.6 pounds of raw shale having a Fischer Assay of about 50 gallons per ton of rock was introduced into the reactor. Steam and oxygen were introduced into the reactor in accordance with the procedure used in Example 1. The oxygen was fed until oxygen breakthrough occurred; the reactor was allowed to cool, and when opened, the spent shale was observed again to be very light in color. The shale was completely retorted; there was no evidence of sintering, and all of the carbon had been chemically removed; in other words, the spent shale was very flowable. The tests for hydrogen indicated that about twice as much of this gas was produced as in Example 1, and it had a high purity. The recovery of oil from the shale was approximately 80 to 90% FA.

Examination of the spent shale showed that all of the carbon, external and internal, had been reacted, and there was no evidence of sintering of the particles even though, in this example, the reactor reached a higher temperature than normal. Most of the spent shale particles were friable as would be expected with rich spent shale because of the lower percentage of carbonates present in rich shale. Again, since all of the external and internal carbon on the particles had been completely reacted, and there was no evidence of sintering, it would be impossible for them to cohere, to bridge across large sections, and ultimately to clinker.

Inerting Gas Used in Place of Hydrogen

In a process described by J.R. Hopper, E.L. Wilson, Jr., and N.P. Peet; U.S. Patent 3,573,194; March 30, 1971; assigned to Esso Research and Engineering Company shale oil of improved quality is recovered from oil shale retorted in a plural stage retorting system at an elevated temperature in the presence of an inert gas under an elevated pressure. The pressure on the retorting zone is maintained by injection of an inert gas which is preferably nitrogen, but may be a mixture of inert gases containing nitrogen and carbon dioxide. Such mixtures may be obtained by burning of residual carbonaceous material remaining on the oil shale after retorting and provide heat for the retorting operation.

The pressure on the retorting zone is suitably in excess of 250 psig and may be within the range of 250 to 2,500 psig. Below 250 psig the effect of pressure with an inert gas is not significant. Above 2,500 psig pressure, the added benefits accruing to higher pressures than 2,500 are marginal and are offset by the added operating problems and costs required. Therefore, the range of 250 to 2,500 psig is considered to be necessary and important in the process. The pressure in the other zones of the retorting system may be substantially below that of the retorting zone and allows use of less expensive equipment. It is not necessary to use high pressure except in the retorting zone because pressure has no effect except in the retorting zone. Pressures in the other zones may range from 0 to 100 psig.

Example: In order to illustrate the process, comparative runs were made where crushed oil shale having particle diameters within the range from 3/8 to 3 inches and an average Fischer Assay value of 34.4 gallon per ton was retorted under the same conditions except in one instance H₂ pressure was used and the other instance N₂ pressure was employed. Runs at 750 and 33 psig were conducted, the results and conditions of which are shown below.

	Run Number J R H			
	8	9	10	11
Retort gas	H_2	N_2	H_2	N_2
Retort pressure, p.s.i.g.	750	750	33	33
Shale lot number	8	8	10	10
Oil inspections:				
Gravity, ° API at 60° F.	38.9	36.5	26.2	26.1
Viscosity, cs. at 100° F.	1.70	1.73	12.06	10.34
Pour point, ° F.	20	20	85	85
Nitrogen, wt. percent	1.40	1.46	1.68	1.60
Hydrogen, wt. percent	12.33	12.17	11.96	11.84
Carbon, wt. percent	81.46	84.75	83.83	82.10

As can be seen from these data, gravity, viscosity and pour point are very similar at the same pressure but significantly different as pressure is changed from 33 to 750 psig. Thus, the type of gas had no measurable effect on product quality but an increase in pressure gives a much improved product; i.e., lower density, lower viscosity, lower pour point.

Controlled Retort Atmosphere

A.K. Reyburn and R.T. Ellington, Jr.; U.S. Patent 3,617,467; November 2, 1971; assigned to Atlantic Richfield Company have found that the composition of the atmosphere surrounding the oil shale particles at the time of pyrolysis has a definite effect on the oil yield obtained from the retorting pyrolysis. The atmosphere corresponding to combustion within the bed with air, or air partially denuded of oxygen, as frequently used in gas combustion retorting, gives the lowest yields. For example, oil shale was retorted in the laboratory in a 4 inch diameter batch fluidized bed at 915°F. A fluidizing gas was used containing 5% oxygen, as might be used in a typical conventional, gas combustion retort, and the oil yield was 85 to 88 weight percent Fischer Assay oil. Natural gas in the same equipment and at the same temperature gave a higher yield of 102 weight percent Fischer Assay oil. A mixture of 90 volume percent natural gas and 10 volume percent carbon dioxide gave the highest of all, 107 weight percent of Fischer Assay oil.

Example 1: A batch-type oil shale retorting process was undertaken utilizing natural gas atmosphere that contained various percentages of carbon dioxide. The retorting temperature, pressure and residence time were approximately constant. The results are given below and are depicted graphically in Figure 1.13a.

TABLE 1

Vol. percent CO₂ (balance natural gas)	Retort temperature (° F.)	Residue time (min.)	Oil yield (wt. percent F.A.)
0	915	16	102.12
10.52	920	16	107.41
25.00	915	16	99.30
49.92	915	16	89.72
100	905	16	85.27

This data shows that the maximum oil yield is obtained at 10% carbon dioxide, balance natural gas with yields greater than that obtainable with natural gas alone being obtained when using up to 20 volume percent carbon dioxide diluent.

Example 2:   A retorting process and retorting environment were used where the bed composition was kept essentially constant throughout the run with a variety of residence times utilized, none of which were sufficient for complete retorting of all the feed. Regardless of the retorting temperature, retorting pressure and residence time employed for a specific series of runs, the effect of increasing yields by adding carbon dioxide to a natural gas fluidizing gas as the process retort fluidizing gas is exhibited. The data are given in Table 2 below, and are depicted graphically in Figure 1.13b.

TABLE 2

Fluidizing gas composition	Retort temperature (°F.)	Average residence time (min.)	Oil yield (wt. percent F.A.)
Natural gas	940	15.44	96.09
Do	940	9.12	88.67
Do	960	15.44	99.28
Do	960	9.12	91.42
90% N.G., 10% CO_2	940	15.44	97.87
90% N.G., 10% CO_2	940	9.12	90.52
90% N.G., 10% CO_2	960	15.44	106.32
90% N.G., 10% CO_2	960	9.12	100.38

The data of the examples thus shows that the use of a natural gas atmosphere and natural gas containing up to 20 volume percent carbon dioxide either in batch or continuous processes and under varying conditions greatly improves oil yields.

FIGURE 1.13:   CONTROLLED ATMOSPHERE RETORT PROCESS

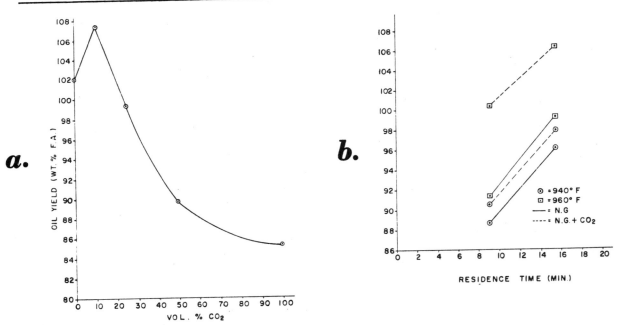

a.

Yield Versus Retort Atmosphere

b.

Yield Versus Residence Time

Source: A.K. Reyburn and R.T. Ellington, Jr.; U.S. Patent 3,617,467; November 2, 1971

Oil Shale Retorting

Catalytic Oxidation

K.L. Berry; U.S. Patent 3,487,004; December 30, 1969; assigned to Pan American Petroleum Corporation describes a retort for the recovery of oil from oil shale, in which hot gases for the retorting are prepared by controlled oxidation of recycled product gases. The oxidation is confined to burners within the retort by the placing of an oxidation catalyst within the burners and the limiting of air introduced into the burners. Retorting temperature is thus maintained between 800° and 1300°F.

Since the heat requirements are reduced, air requirements are less and there is a resulting decrease in nitrogen and carbon dioxide in product gases. Methane and ethane and lower molecular weight oil vapors production are also less due to the lower temperatures. Decomposition of inorganic carbonates is essentially eliminated by operating at temperatures below 1300°F. Consequently, carbon dioxide production is further reduced. In addition, the heat of decomposition of inorganic carbonates need not be added, so even less air is required. The over-all result is that organic materials are present in much higher concentrations in product gases leaving the retort. These higher concentrations, in turn, facilitate recovery of a larger percentage of the kerogen decomposition products as a liquid product. A smaller percentage of kerogen decomposition products appears in the vent gas from the separator.

Heat Recovery

A process described by L.P. Evans; U.S. Patent 2,885,338; May 5, 1969; assigned to Socony Mobil Oil Company, Inc. is concerned with an improved apparatus and process where a hydrocarbonaceous solid is retorted economically and efficiently, with a substantially complete recovery of heat and with internal fractionation of the liquid and gaseous products.

Referring to Figure 1.14a, the basic apparatus of this process is provided. In general, the apparatus comprises an elongated cylindrical vessel 2, provided with a seal leg 3, a conical shaped internal cover disposed at the lower extremity of the seal leg 3 and having a plurality of orifices 10 therein. In the upper, or condensing and heat exchange zone of the reactor proper, there is provided a trap tray 4 disposed around the inner wall of the reactor. The trap tray 4 is provided with a pipe 7 to permit draw-off of liquid products. The design of the trap tray 4 provides an annular opening for constricted passage 35. In the lower region of reactor 2, there is provided a gas distributing device 23 and a series of baffle plates 26 and 27 having orifices 28 and 29. Below the baffles there is an air inlet 30 and a draw-off tube 24.

In operation, raw crushed hydrocarbonaceous material, such as oil shale, is carried to the top of the reactor by means of a suitable lift device 1, e.g., a bucket elevator. The crushed shale thus fed into the top of the reactor gravitates downward in a compact mass through the seal leg 3 and into the main portion of the reactor. Inert gases such as flue gas are introduced into the feed leg via pipe 9 to provide a seal which prevents the escape of gaseous products from the reactor. As the cold shale gravitates through the condensing and heat exchange zone, it is contacted with the hot condensible and noncondensible vaporous products of the process. Upon contact with the hot vaporous products, the cold shale is heated and the condensible products are liquefied and gravitate downward through the bed of shale. Due to the restricted opening 35 a portion of the bed of shale, immediately above the trap tray 4, becomes substantially immobile. The condensed liquid products gradually trickle through the zone of immobile shale and eventually reach the trap tray 4. The non-condensible hot gaseous products of the process are passed through openings 10 into an annular collecting zone 11. These gases are then withdrawn via pipe 13 through pump 12. A portion of the hot gases is sent to a gas recovery plant through pipe 14. The remainder of the hot gases are recycled through pipe 15 into the gas distributing device 23. By means of this operation, the heat requirements of the shale retorting are satisfied.

The shale gravitating downward passes through a combustion zone and then through the openings 28 and 29 in the baffles 26 and 27. Below the baffles, a combustion-supporting gas, such as air or oxygen, is introduced into pipe 30, pressured by means of pump 18. As the combustion-supporting gas passes upward through the baffled region, it is heat exchanged with the hot spent shale so that the gas attains a temperature sufficient to support combustion. Thereafter, the spent shale is withdrawn through conduit 24. In order to provide a more efficient distribution of the raw shale in the upper portion of the reactor, a conically shaped baffle 5 is positioned immediately below the opening of the seal leg 3.

Figure 1.14b represents another form of the apparatus. The raw crushed shale is introduced into the upper portion of the reactor where it is heat exchanged with the noncondensible and condensible vaporous products of the reaction. In this example however, the trap tray 4 is provided with one or more baffles 6 which divide the trap trays into two or more sections. Each section is provided with a separate draw-off tube 7 and 8. By means of this arrangement, a rough fractionation of the liquid product is achieved in the reactor itself. Accordingly, the amount of fractionation required externally is greatly diminished.

Another improvement shown in Figure 1.14b relates to the utilization of the recycled gas via pipe 15. The stream of recycle gas is split into two streams, one stream passes through pipe 22 into gas distributing device 23. The remainder of the recycle gas passes through pipe 16, where it is mixed with a portion of the combustion-supporting gas supplied via pipe 20. The resulting mixture of combustion-supporting gas and recycle gas is then passed through a gas distributing device 21 into the bed of shale. As was described above, the remainder of the combustion-supporting gas is passed into the lower portion of the reactor via pipe 30. The remaining operations involved are substantially the same as those described in conjunction with the discussion of Figure 1.14a.

The oxygen-containing gases absorbed heat from the spent shale as they passed through. The temperature of the gaseous mixture is thus raised to the ignition point at which the oxygen reacts with the combustibles present in the system, such as the combustible components of the gaseous mixture and the coke contained in the spent shale. The combustion thus initiated generates the required amount of heat to maintain the entire process in thermal balance. This is an important feature of the process which serves to minimize heat loss. Since the heat recovery from the incoming and outgoing process is substantially complete, only a small amount of net combustion heat must be supplied to make up heat loss and heat reaction. The temperature required to achieve combustion is ordinarily within the range between 1000° and 1500°F. Accordingly, in order to utilize more effectively the heat evolving from the combustion zone, it is preferred to split the recycle gas stream into two or more streams as was illustrated in Figure 1.14b.

Generally, the amount of recycle gas conducted to the retorting zone is between 1 and 3 unit weights per unit weight of shale charge. The temperature of the gas issuing from the combustion zone is adjusted by means of the flow of residual cold recycle gas lead to the pipe 22 and gas distributor 23. Contact between the residual recycle gas and the gas from the combustion zone takes place in the mixing zone of the reaction vessel. The resulting gaseous mixture rises to the retorting zone.

In general, the temperature of the gas entering the retorting zone varies between 800° and 1000°F. The temperatures in excess of the foregoing range are usually to be avoided in the retorting zone, because excessively high temperatures promote undesired secondary distillation and/or cracking of the shale oil released in the retorting zone. In a typical operation, the volume and temperature of the gas conducted to the retorting zone varies between 120 and 160 pounds of gas per 100 pounds of shale charge at a temperature of 1000°F.

FIGURE 1.14:   FLUIDIZED BED RETORT PROCESS

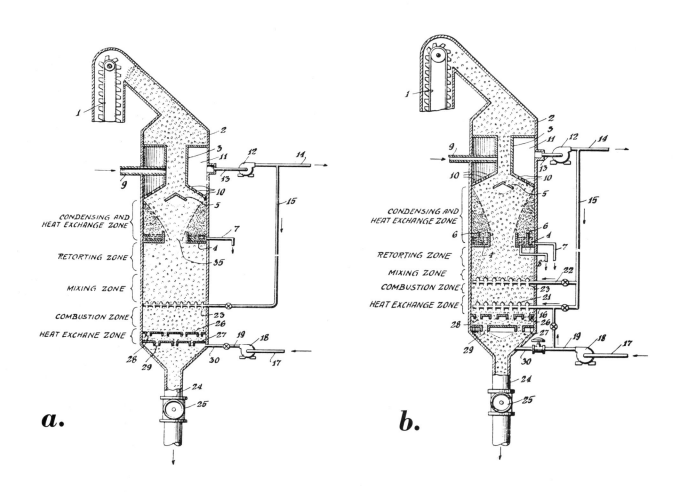

Source: L.P. Evans; U.S. Patent 2,885,338; May 5, 1969

A number of other processes are described which involve increasing the efficiency of the retorting process. For example, J.C. Todd; U.S. Patent 3,617,466; November 2, 1971; assigned to Atlantic Richfield Company describes a method for obtaining oil from oil shale by the gas combustion retort process. The offgas from the retort containing oil, fuel and other combustion products is treated first to remove the oil and second, to burn the fuel components. The resulting gas is recycled into the retort to pass countercurrently to the shale travel. Temperatures in the combustion zone of the retort are moderated and clinker formation is eliminated. The heat from the fuel burning can be used as a power source.

A.L. Saxton; U.S. Patent 3,526,586; September 1, 1970 describes the use of a single vessel oil shale retorting system which comprises a preheating zone, a retorting zone, a combustion zone, and a cooling zone. The crushed oil shale is introduced into the preheating zone and flows serially through the zones and is subjected to preheating, retorting, combustion and cooling conditions as it flows through the zones. During the flow of the oil shale through the zones and subjecting of the oil shale to the several conditions, the zones are maintained under superatmospheric pressure within the range of 5 to 100 psig and thereafter the spent shale is discharged from the cooling zone whereby increased capacity of the system is obtained.

J.H.V. Finney; U.S. Patent 3,006,816; October 31, 1961; assigned to Union Oil Company of California describes a retort which includes essentially three zones, that is, a combustion zone, a distillation or retort zone, and a preheating zone for combustion air which also cools the ash from the combustion zone. The retort includes the desirable feature of having an upward flow of shale and downward flow of gas and oil in the retort zone, but in the burning and ash cooling zone there is the desirable downward flow of shale and ash and an upward flow of air.

The retort includes a lower combustion zone, and an upper retort zone subject to the gases of combustion from the lower combustion zone to perform the pyrolysis and the distillation of shale oil. The retort includes a simplified design where the interior walls of the retort may be made of fire brick in those parts which are subjected to high heat, and which may be constructed so that the depth of the beds of shale in the previous parts are not controlled by the size of the device but may be determined by the optimum operation of the retort.

The simplified design provides means for distributing the weight of contained shale so that it is easily supported, and so that there is no substantial increase of friction of the shale on the supporting walls of the vessel or an increase of size of the retort.

In a process described by D.W. Peacock; U.S. Patent 3,476,650; November 4, 1969; assigned to Phillips Petroleum Company oil shale is combusted under a partial pressure of oxygen of 15 to 105 psia at 500° to 700°F. thereby producing a valuable metallurgical coke suitable for smelting iron, a heavy hydrocarbon fraction and a gaseous fraction.

A process described by R.W. Whiteacre 3rd; U.S. Patent 3,546,092; December 8, 1970; assigned to Koppers Company, Inc. comprises treating shale oil ore particles that have been retorted in a first stage to recover residual energy, by comminuting the particles while hot; collecting the comminuted particles in a receptacle; flowing a gaseous fluid through the comminuted particles; and removing the residual energy in the form of product gas and oil from the receptacle. Thereafter, the product gas and oil flow through a separator to remove ore fines, and the product gas and oil may be conducted into a product removal conduit, or burned at a fuel distributor in order to retort the ore particles in the first stage.

In a process described by L.D. Friedman and L.P. Gaucher; U.S. Patent 3,051,644; August 28, 1962 and by L.D. Friedman; U.S. Patent 3,074,877; January 22, 1963; both assigned to Texaco Inc. oil shale particles are subjected to treatment with steam at a pressure in the range of 1,000 to 3,000 psig and a temperature in the range of 700° to 900°F., for a period of time within the range of 20 minutes to 6 hours. In a preferred operation, shale particles are mixed with sufficient water to form a pumpable mixture and the mixture passed under pressure through an elongated heating zone of restricted cross-sectional area in which the water is vaporized, entraining the shale particles in steam, and the mixture is discharged into a soaking zone of large volume where the oil shale is subjected to the stripping and heating action of steam for the required period and from which recovered oil from the oil shale is withdrawn in vapor form admixed with the steam. Oil yields of more than 100% in comparison with the standard Fischer assay, are obtained from commercial grade oil shales. The quality of the recovered oil is comparable with that obtained by other methods of retorting.

K.I. Jagel, Jr., D. Liederman and L.J. Skowronek; U.S. Patent 3,562,143; February 9, 1971; assigned to Mobil Oil Corporation have found that the operation of a countercurrent retort for oil shale can be improved by reducing the refluxing and percolation in the bed. Localized liquid accumulations in the bed form carbonaceous agglomerates which wedge in the air distribution assembly and burn in this hot oxidizing environment to form clinkers that interfere with retort operability. Removal of these liquid accumulations from the shale bed reduces the formation of carbonaceous agglomerates and vitreous clinkers.

Localized liquid accumulations in the bed may be initiated by pieces of rich oil shale or by locally high concentrations of fine shale in the shale bed. These fines are more heavily wet with oil by the impaction of mist or by the surface condensation of oil than are large shale pieces.

As liquid is vaporized and cracked from these local accumulations, a tarry, carbonaceous residue is left behind which binds pieces of shale and dust together to form cohesive masses. This occurs at a temperature of about 700°F. The cohesive masses of shale, dust, and tarry binder are converted to dry hard agglomerates at temperatures between 800° and 1200°F.

In this process, flooding is caused to occur in a controlled fashion at a section of the retort where liquid can be disengaged. This reduces the likelihood of uncontrolled localized liquid accumulations and thus breaks the chain leading to clinkering and retort inoperability. Complete details of the liquid disengaging system are provided.

C.R. Garbett; U.S. Patent 3,634,225; January 11, 1972; assigned to Shell Oil Company describes a process for retorting oil-bearing shale including passing shale through a preheating zone and a retorting zone. Preheated shale is introduced into the retorting zone where it is contacted countercurrently with a hot gas stream which releases an oil vapor product at high temperature from the shale. The oil vapor product is rapidly quenched by heat exchange with water and the resultant heated water is passed to a steam generating plant where a fuel fired furnace is employed to produce high temperature steam. The steam is employed to generate electric power and in expanding steam through power recovery means, it is cooled enough to be useful to quench the oil vapor product. The exhaust gas from the fuel fired furnace is passed to the preheating zone to preheat the shale.

HOT CERAMIC BALLS

Heat Transfer Balls and Controlled Cracking

T.D. Nevens; U.S. Patent 3,034,979; May 15, 1962; assigned to The Oil Shale Corp. describes a process which comprises the steps of pyrolyzing oil shale to produce effluent oil vapors and gases, cooling the effluent to a predetermined temperature to condense the heavier fractions but not the lighter fractions, thermally cracking the heavier fractions within a certain predetermined range of temperature, and condensing the uncracked lighter fractions as well as the cracked heavier fractions to produce a composite oil product. The composite oil product has a pour point and viscosity comparable to, or slightly less than, that of shale oil produced after pyrolysis and cracking of all the effluent oil vapors and gases from the pyrolysis, but the loss of oil is substantially less than in conventional processes for a given pour point.

Referring to Figure 1.15a, a solid material, such as oil shale and generally spherical solid heat-carrying bodies enter the pyrolysis zone or rotatable drum 10 via lines 12 and 14, respectively. The oil shale usually enters the drum 10 at a low temperature, e.g., 50°F., although, in some cases, it is desirable to preheat the oil shale to a temperature of 300°F. to as high as 600°F. The heat-carrying bodies or balls are made of a hard-heat-resistant material such as alumina, or other ceramic material, or steel and preferably have a diameter somewhat larger than the average mesh size of the incoming fresh or preheated oil shale. For example, the ball diameter usually lies within a range of 1/2 to 1 inch, whereas the average oil shale mesh size ranges between 1/4 to 1/2 inch.

The heat-carrying bodies or balls preferably enter the drum 10 at a temperature lying within the range of 1000° to 1400°F., and are preferably intermixed in parallel flow, with the oil shale. Counterflow of balls and oil shale is also employed, although parallel flow is preferred. The ratio of the balls to oil shale generally ranges between 1:1 and 3:1 depending upon the nature of the oil shale being processed, the type of heat-carrying bodies being employed, and the rate of heat transfer sought. It should be noted that while other modes of heating and pyrolyzing the oil shale can be employed, e.g., fluidized bed processes employing heated gases, the preferred method and means for pyrolyzation (and also for cracking) utilizes the generally spherical solid heat-carrying bodies, above described.

Upon mixing of the balls with oil shale in the rotating drum 10, pyrolysis of the oil shale occurs and the effluent oil vapors and gases leave the drum 10 and enter conduit 16 passing through chamber 17 as indicated by the arrow 18. The effluent oil vapors and gases have a temperature preferably lying between 750° to 950°F. The effluent oil vapors and gases are passed into a fractionator or partial condenser 20 and cooled to a temperature lying preferably between 500° and 800°F. That fraction of the oil vapors and gases which remains a vapor at 500° to 800°F., e.g., gas, gas oil, kerosene and gasoline, is, of course, not condensed, and is passed into condenser 22 via lines 24 and 26. The condensed heavier fraction, which comprises approximately 10 to 50% of the collectible oil product passes along conduits 24 and 28 and then into a reservoir or tank 29 which serves as a gas seal. The heavier fraction is then fed into the thermal cracker 30 via standpipe 32, and is cracked.

FIGURE 1.15:   PROCESS FOR THE PRODUCTION OF LOW TEMPERATURE PUMPABLE OIL FROM OIL SHALE

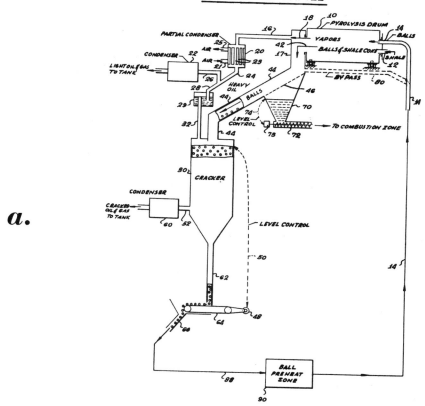

a.

Details of Pyrolysis and Refining Process

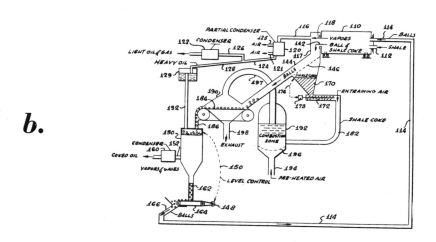

b.

Modified Process Incorporating a High Temperature Cracking Step   (continued)

FIGURE 1.15: (continued)

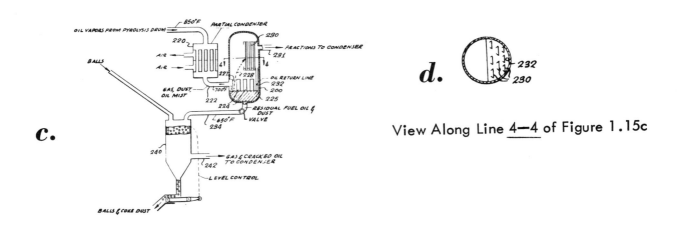

c.

d.

View Along Line 4—4 of Figure 1.15c

Use of Dust Removal Equipment

Source: T.D. Nevens; U.S. Patent 3,034,979; May 15, 1962

Because the reduction in temperature of the effluent oil vapors and gases entering the partial condenser 20 is approximately only 50° to 450°F. the coolant for the condenser is usually ambient air, rather than water, which is extremely scarce in areas where the majority of the oil shale deposits are found. The air enters the condenser 20, via line 21, passes through condenser 20 around a series of tubes 23 in the condenser and exits via line 25.

After pyrolysis, the carbonaceous residue passes, together with the balls, into the chamber 17, as indicated by the arrow 42. The carbonaceous residue passes downwardly into the inclined passageway 44, and is separated from the larger balls by passing through the openings in the inclined screen 46. In this connection, the carbonaceous residue is considerably reduced in size over the initial oil shale mesh size due to the grinding and crushing action of the hard balls on the oil shale in the pyrolysis drum 10. Separation of carbonaceous residue from the balls is thus readily effected by the screening means 46.

The balls, after being separated from the carbonaceous residue, pass downwardly along the passageway 44 and enter the thermal cracker 30, the ball temperature, after the pyrolysis, lying preferably between 900° and 1100°F. The hot balls within the cracker 30 are maintained at a constant level by suitable conventional level control means (shown schematically by the numeral 48 and dotted line 50).

The heavier liquid oil fractions enter the cracker 30 from pipe 32 and pass through suitable distribution means, e.g., a sprayer in the cracker. The heavier oil fraction contacts the hot downwardly moving balls for a predetermined period of time, preferably ranging between one second to two minutes, and a cracking of the heavier oil fractions results. The balls and oils can contact each other in coflow, as shown, or in counterflow, or crossflow, if desired. The liquid oil fractions contain some dust upon entering the cracker 30, the dust being initially carried with the pyrolyzed oil vapors and gases to the partial condenser 20. Because the balls have deposited thereon a certain amount of coke on their surface, the exact amount depending on the conditions under which the cracker is operated, dust adheres to the balls and is carried out with the balls. The dust is removed either during the ball reheating phase of the process, to be described, or is removed during pyrolysis of fresh oil shale in the pyrolysis drum 10.

The cracked oil vapors and gases leave the cracker 30 via the line 52 at a temperature of approximately 825° to 1100°F. and are sent to a conventional condenser 60 and cooled to a temperature of approximately 100°F., usually by means of water. The uncracked noncondensed oil and vapors, entering condenser 22 are also cooled by water to a temperature of approximately 100°F. The oil condensed in both condensers is then fed to a common tank or reservoir to form a composite oil product for transportation by pipeline to market or to further refining steps.

The composite oil product formed by following the above process is advantageous in that, for Colorado oil shale, its pour point generally lies in the neighborhood of 30° to 60°F.; and what is also extremely important, the loss of oil in the process typically amounts to approximately only 5 to 15% computed on the basis of a 100% oil recovery. In prior processes, where cracking of all effluent oil vapors and gases, i.e., both light and heavy ends, occurs, for a given pour point of the resulting shale oil, the loss of oil in the form of noncondensables and coke increases appreciably.

After the balls have passed through the cracker 30, they are returned to the pyrolysis drum 10 for the pyrolysis of additional solid material after being reheated to a temperature of between 1000° and 1400°F. The preferable method of providing heat for the reheating of the balls is to combust the carbonaceous residue remaining after pyrolysis, and to then transfer the requisite amount of heat from the products of combustion of the carbonaceous residue to the balls. Thus, the balls pass from the cracker 30, via an outlet conduit 62, and endless conveyor belt 64, and conduit 66 and 88 to a ball heating zone 90 (shown schematically in Figure 1.15a for heating. As mentioned, the balls have coke deposited on the surface, and this coke is combusted to furnish additional heat for the heating of the balls.

The carbonaceous residue, separated from the balls by screen 46, falls into chamber 70. The level in chamber 70 is controlled by level control means 73 and 74. The carbonaceous residue is then conveyed, by conveyor 72, and other means to an appropriate combustion zone, such as a fluidized combustion zone. The hot products of combustion (which may be both solid entrained particulate products and gaseous products) then impart a substantial portion of their heat to the balls in the ball heating zone 90. The reheated balls, at a temperature of 1000° to 1400°F., then enter conduit 14 and are sent to the pyrolysis drum 10 for pyrolysis of additional solid material. A specific method and apparatus for reheating the balls by means of shale coke is shown in Figure 1.15b and is preferably employed also in conjunction with the process of Figure 1.15a.

Mention has previously been made of the fact that the solid material entering the pyrolysis drum may either be cold, e.g., 50°F. or preheated. If preheated solid material is to be introduced into drum 10, a preferred mode of preheating involves mixing fresh oil shale with hotter balls in either parallel or counterflow, as is described in U.S. Patent 3,008,894.

The hot balls employed for the solid material preheating step are preferably those taken directly from the outlet conduit 66 of the cracker 30. After the solid material preheating, the balls are sent to the ball heating step, just described.

Attention is drawn to the fact that condensation of part of the effluent oil vapors and gases from the pyrolysis zone 10 takes place prior to the cracking of the heavier fraction. While it is possible to first condense all of the effluent oil vapors and gases, and then partially fractionate prior to the cracking of the heavier oil fraction, it will be understood that such a process necessitates an extra condensation step, which in turn, would require additional equipment as well as the use of valuable water. A specific example of the process with reference to Figure 1.15a is set forth below.

1 ton of 25 gal./ton of Colorado oil shale of approximately a 1/4" mesh size enters the drum 10, via line 12, along with 2 tons of 5/8" aluminum oxide-containing ceramic balls, the balls entering the drum 10 via line 14. The oil shale has an average inlet temperature of 50°F. and the balls have an average inlet temperature of 1300°F.

192 lbs. of oil vapors and 30 lbs. of gases are produced during the pyrolysis, the oil vapors and gases passing via chamber 17, and conduit 16 to a partial condenser 20. The partial condenser 20 cools the oil vapors and gases to 600°F., 60 lbs. of oil being condensed and sent to the cracker 30.

These heavier condensed fractions are sent to the cracker 30. They, there, contact balls that have come directly from the pyrolysis drum 10 via line 44, which have a temperature of approximately 1050°F. The period of cracking is approximately 30 seconds, the cracked oil vapors and gases being cooled to 100°F. and being condensed in condenser 60.

The lighter fractions pass from the partial condenser 20 into the condenser 22 and are cooled to approximately 100°F. and condensed. Both the condensed lighter fractions and condensed heavier fractions, when combined total 172 lbs., only 20 lbs. or 10% of the maximum oil recovery being lost as noncondensable gases and coke. The pour point of the composite product is 40°F.

Comparing these results with a process where all conditions are equivalent to that just described except that all the vapors are cracked, the pour point was 50°F. and the loss of oil was 40 lbs. or 20% of the total oil collectible. The balls from the cracker 30 (at 1000°F.) were then reheated to a temperature of 1300°F. by directly contacting them with the hot products of combustion of the shale coke. The balls are then sent to the pyrolysis drum to contact fresh incoming oil shale.

The average inlet temperature of the balls entering the cracking zone 30, in the Figure 1.15a lies between 900° and 1100°F. It is sometimes desirable to increase the average inlet ball temperature to the cracker 30 so that a high cracking rate is maintained. To this end, a predetermined portion of balls sent from the ball heating zone 90 is bypassed around the pyrolysis drum 10 and enters the lower temperatured ball stream in conduit 44, as is indicated by the conduit 80, shown in dotted line. These bypassed balls may have a temperature as high as 1400°F. upon entering the cracking zone, and can appreciably raise the average inlet temperature of the balls.

The amount of total ball temperature increase that is brought about by the use of the bypass feature is optimally approximately 100° to 150°F. Thus, the temperature range of the balls entering the cracking zone 30 of Figure 1.15a can vary from a low of about 900°F. to a high of about 1250°F. It will be noted that the total ball to shale ratio will increase in proportion to the amount of balls passing through the bypass conduit 80.

If a thermal cracking of the heavier fractions at still higher temperatures than previously described with reference to Figure 1.15a (with or without ball bypass) is desired, such a cracking step can be accomplished by referring to Figure 1.15b. The previously described advantages of the Figure 1.15a processes with regard to lower pour point and minimal loss of oil are also present in the high temperature cracking process to be described. A preferred method and means of reheating the balls is also shown in Figure 1.15b.

In the process of Figure 1.15b, the balls leave the pyrolysis drum 110 and are reheated prior to the cracking step, rather than after the cracking step, as in Figure 1.15a. Inasmuch as the Figure 1.15a and Figure 1.15b examples are quite similar, similar pieces of equipment and conduits, etc., are designated by 100 plus the numeral designation given it in Figure 1.15a. Thus, the cracker in Figure 1.15a is designated 30 and in Figure 1.15b the cracker is designated 130.

The balls leaving the pyrolysis drum 110, after giving up some of their heat therein, have a temperature usually ranging between 900° and 1100°F. Instead of being sent to the cracker 130 at this temperature, the balls first pass through a ball heating zone 190 and are there reheated, in a manner to be specifically described, to a temperature lying between 1200° and 1500°F. These hot balls are then conveyed by a moving gate 184 from the heating zone 190 to the cracker 130 via line 186, where the high temperature cracking takes place.

It will be noted that the inlet ball temperature in the cracking zone 30 in the Figure 1.15a ranges between 900° and 1250°F. depending upon whether ball bypass is employed or not. Since in the Figure 1.15b, the ball inlet temperature to the cracking zone 190 ranges from 1200° to 1500°F., the variation in ball inlet temperature ranges between 900° and 1500°F.

A specific means of providing heat for reheating the balls is also shown in Figure 1.15b. For example, shale coke, the residue produced during pyrolysis of such solid materials as oil shale, is sent from conveyor 172, along line 182, in a stream of entraining air, to a fluidized combustion zone 192. Preheated air enters the zone 192 via line 194, and passes through air distribution plate 196 which imparts to the air passing through a velocity higher than the settling velocity of the shale coke particles to thereby prevent the shale coke particles from settling through openings in the plate.

The shale coke is combusted in the presence of the air, and the hot products of combustion, the gaseous and entrained solids, pass into the ball heating zone 190 via line 197. The hot products of combustion contact the balls in crossflow, and leave the zone 190 via exhaust pipe 198.

Referring especially to Figures 1.15c and 1.15d, the plant of either Figure 1.15a or Figure 1.15b is advantageously modified by the inclusion of a dust removal and demistifying apparatus designated by the numeral 200.

Oil Shale Retorting

The oil vapors and gas from the pyrolysis drum 10 or 110 (e.g., at a temperature of 850°F.), enter the partial condenser 220, which is similar in construction to the partial condenser 20 or 120 of Figures 1.15a and 1.15b respectively. The oil vapors and gases usually carry some dust from the pyrolysis drum. The oil vapors and gases are reduced in temperature (e.g., to 700°F.) in the partial condenser 220 by means of an air coolant, and oil mist, gas and dust pass into the demistifier 200 via line 222.

The oil mist, gas and dust enter passages 224 in the demistifier 200 initially causing some oil and dust collection. The upper ends of the passages 224 are closed, and the oil mist and dust are forced downwardly into a reservoir of oil, designated by the numeral 225. The oil mist and dust thus agglomerate into larger particles and move upwardly, through pipes 227, as indicated schematically by a dotted line 228, and strike a second set of staggered baffles 230 (best seen in Figure 1.15d). This causes the oil mist and dust to be substantially completely "knocked out" of the gas and the lighter fractions proceed to the condenser 22 or 122 via line 231 substantially free of the heavier oils in the form of mist, or any appreciable amount of dust. The residual fuel oil collected from the oil mist returns to the bottom of the demistifier 200 via oil return line 232, and along with the dust, is sent to the cracker 240 (which is similar to cracker 30 or 130) along conduit 234 for cracking.

The dust removed from the oil vapors and gases in the demistifier 200 passes through the cracker 240 with the balls, while the heavier oils fractions are cracked and sent via line 242 to a condenser, such as condenser 60 or 160.

It can thus be seen that the demistifier 200 and ball cracker 240 both act to prevent dust from moving out with the lighter oil fractions, and cracked heavier fractions, respectively. The need for additional dust removal equipment such as cyclones, is thus substantially reduced. It will be seen that the demistifier 200, or similar apparatus, will appreciably add to the efficiency of this process where any substantial amount of oil mist is present in the outlet line 222 from the partial condenser 220.

W.J. Culbertson, Jr.; U.S. Patent 3,008,894; November 14, 1961; assigned to The Oil Shale Corporation describes a similar process in which the combined pyrolyzing and thermal cracking continuous process employs one or more steams of hot heat transfer bodies for the furnishing of substantially all of the heat requirements of the process. It is found that the use of such circulating heat bodies in the combined pyrolyzing and cracking process is the primary reason for the substantial reduction in clogging and overheating of the cracking equipment, due to coke and tar formation, and is the primary reason for the substantial removal of dust from the oil vapors and gases produced in the process.

In related work, T.D. Nevens; U.S. Patent 3,018,243; January 23, 1962; assigned to The Oil Shale Corporation describes a process which comprises the steps of pyrolyzing oil shale to produce effluent oil vapors and gases, cooling the effluent to a predetermined temperature to condense the heavier fractions but not the lighter fractions, thermally cracking the heavier fractions within a certain predetermined period of residence time, by recycling at least a portion of the heavier fractions to the zone where the pyrolysis takes place, either indirectly, i.e., via one of the several material streams entering therein or directly to the zone of pyrolysis itself. The uncracked lighter fractions, as well as the thus cracked heavier fractions, are then condensed to produce a composite oil product which has a pour point and viscosity comparable to, or slightly less than that of shale oil produced after the pyrolysis and cracking of all the effluent oil vapors and gases from the pyrolysis, the loss of oil being substantially less than in conventional processes.

A process described by R.M. Otis; U.S. Patent 3,058,903; October 16, 1962; assigned to The Oil Shale Corporation comprises preheating oil shale by means of hot solid bodies in a first zone, the preheated oil shale then being pyrolyzed by means of hotter solid bodies in a second zone. The effluent oil vapors and gases resulting from pyrolysis are then sent to the first zone, for contact with a mixture of additional fresh oil shale and partially cooled solid bodies, which results in the condensation of heavy ends of the effluent oil vapors and gases on the oil shale. The light ends are not condensed in the preheater and pass therefrom, as vapor, to be condensed at a later time or sent to further processing.

The condensed heavy ends are sent, with the oil shale, to the pyrolysis zone where they are cracked by reheated solid bodies. At the same time, the solid bodies cause pyrolysis of the freshly preheated oil shale, and crushing to render the pyrolysis more efficient.

The pyrolyzed and cracked vapors are then sent to the preheating zone. The heavy ends of the vapors are condensed by the oil shale in the preheating zone, and the lighter oil product, both cracked and noncracked, pass out as vapor. The oil product has a low pour point, and is suitable for pumping at temperatures in the neighborhood of 30° to 60°F.

Inert Ball Heater

T.D. Nevens and W.J. Culbertson, Jr.; U.S. Patent 3,020,227; February 6, 1962; assigned to The Oil Shale Corporation describe a process and apparatus for heating solid bodies, spherical or nonspherical, where the requisite amount of heat transfer to the solid bodies is obtained in a relatively short path length while avoiding the great pressure drop usually encountered in the packed tower type of heater.

The process and apparatus for heating thermospheres, or balls, consists in fluidizing the balls by means of hot combustion gases, the combustion gases preferably containing finely divided solid material. This finely divided material is, generally speaking, combusted residue. For example, in the case of the combustion of shale coke, shale ash comprises the finely divided entrained material.

The gas velocity required for fluidization of the balls is necessarily sufficiently high so that any of the finely divided material will not be retained within the balls. At the same time, the rate of heat transferred to the balls, in their fluidized state, both by the finely divided solids and gases, is considerably greater than is the case in a packed bed, and further, the problem of retention of finely divided solids by the packed bed is completed obviated. In addition, balls are readily removed by such a process without resulting channelling of gases or of balls, as would be liable to occur in packed beds.

Referring to Figure 1.16a, a thermosphere or ball heater 10 is shown, in cross section, having an outer wall 12 made of an insulating material, such as asbestos, and an inner liner 14 composed of a higher heat duty insulating refractory material such as kaolin. The inner and outer walls 12 and 14 are reinforced and unified by a plurality of spaced V-shaped rods 15 which are imbedded in, and tie both of the walls. The rods may be made of stainless steel, or other suitable material. The composite liner is built up of discrete cylindrical sections 21. Each section 21 has an outer supporting metal jacket 19, the ends of the jackets having one or two flanges 23, for abutment with an adjacent jacket. Abutting flanges 23 are bolted or welded.

FIGURE 1.16: APPARATUS FOR HEATING SOLID INERT HEAT-CARRYING BODIES

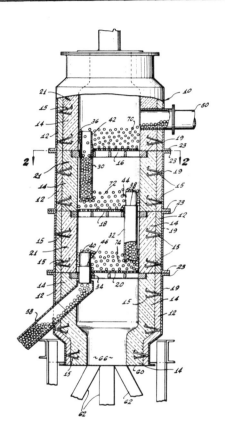

a.

Cross-Sectional View of Heater

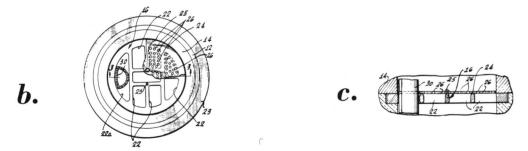

b.   **c.**

View Along Line 2—2 of Figure 1.16a   View Along Line 3—3 of Figure 1.16b

Source: T.D. Nevens and W.J. Culbertson, Jr.; U.S. Patent 3,020,227; Feb. 6, 1962

A plurality of perforated members or grates 16, 18 and 20 are interposed at different levels in the ball heater 10, and are affixed to the composite liner 14 in any suitable manner. The grate members 16, 18 and 20 are made of a highly resistant refractory material such as Meehanite (a highly heat resistant cast iron). Taking grate member 16 as typical, and referring particularly to Figures 1.16b and 1.16c, the grate member is formed with a plurality of openings 22, and a heavy perforated plate 24 is affixed to the upper side of the grate by bolts 25, as shown in Figures 1.16b and 1.16c. The size of openings 26 in the plate 24 is slightly smaller than the diameter of the balls or thermospheres, and it is found that for optimum performance a total open area in the plate of approximately 17% of the ball heater should be employed.

The openings in the grate 16 and plate 24 allow gases and finely divided solids to pass upwardly therethrough while, of course, preventing downward movement of the balls. The upward movement of hot gases and hot finely divided solids enables heat to be transferred to the balls in a manner that will be described.

Three downcomers or downspouts 30, 32 and 34, which may be generally semicylindrical in shape, are mounted to, and pass through, the gate opening 22a of grates 16, 18 and 20, respectively. The tops of the downspouts 30, 32 and 34 are designated by the numerals 36, 38 and 40, respectively, are set a predetermined distance above the upper surface of the grates to which they are mounted. This distance may be varied by means of telescoping downspout extensions, these extensions being designated by numerals 42, 44 and 46. Other modes of downspout adjustment may also be satisfactorily used.

The top of the downspout 30 is mounted below the mouth of the ball inlet pipe 50, and on the opposite side (the left in Figure 1.16a) of the ball heater 10, adjacent the inner wall of the liner 14. The downspout 32 and its extension 44 are mounted so that the extension top 38 lies above the bottom end 52 of downspout 30, and preferably so that it is approximately diametrically opposed to downspout 30. The third downspout 34 and its extension 46 are mounted so that the extension top 40 lies above the bottom end of spout 32. The bottom end of downspout 34 is connected to an outlet pipe 58.

The ball heater 10 is fitted at its bottom end 50 with one or more open skimming tubes 62, through which a gaseous fluidizing medium is passed into the bottom space 66 of the ball heater. In the normal operation of the ball heater 10, thermospheres or balls enter the ball heater via ball feed line 50, and initially form a bed 70 resting on the upper grate 16 and associated perforated plate 24. The top 36 of downspout extension 42 is adjusted so that it is preferably from 3" to 9" above the grate 16, thereby causing the fluidized bed 70 to be 3" to 9" in depth.

Combustion gases, containing entrained solid combusted particles (e.g., shale ash produced in the combustion of shale coke), enter the bottom 66 of the ball heater and proceed upwardly through the heater at a gas velocity sufficiently high to fluidize the upper, intermediate, and lower thermosphere beds 70, 72 and 74, respectively.

It is found that the minimal gas velocity sufficient to fluidize the thermosphere bed is high enough to prevent retention of any of the combusted residue particles passing into the beds and normally, the preferred gas velocity is at or above the minimum fluidization velocity.

As the thermospheres in the bed 70 are fluidized, a random turbulent motion is imparted to them. As the fluidization of the bed 70 proceeds, the balls move across the grate, in random fashion, from their point of inlet to the downcomer 30 and downcomer extension 42, the balls meanwhile being heated by the upwardly moving hot combustion gases. The balls are then discharged, in random fashion, into the downspout extension 42 through downcomer 30 and onto the grate 18, and associated perforated plate 24.

The top of downspout extension 44 preferably lies above grate 18 by about 3" to 9" so that a 3" to 9" bed thickness of thermosphere is built up on grate 18. This bed is fluidized due to the velocity of the upwardly flowing gases, the fluidized bed being designated by the numeral 72. The balls, in fluidized bed 72, due to their random motion, are discharged into the downspout 32, after being further heated by the combustion gases and entrained solids passing upwardly around them.

The top of the downspout extension 46 lies about 3" to 9" above the gate 20 so that the balls discharged from downspout 32 form another fluidized bed 74 of 3" to 9" in thickness. The balls in the bed 74 are further heated by the upwardly moving combustion gases and entrained solids. The balls in the fluidized bed 74 are in random motion, as previously mentioned, and in their random motion, are discharged into downspout extension 46, downspout 34, and then into discharge pipe or passage 58.

It will thus be seen that the path of balls being heated is such that any one ball makes a plurality of passes in a generally transverse direction with respect to the hot upwardly flowing combustion (or other hot) gases and entrained solid particles. Specifically, the balls first pass generally from right to left across grate 16, in random turbulent motion, picking up heat in an extremely efficient manner from the fluidizing gas. They then pass generally from left to right across grate 18, and pass yet a third time, in the same random turbulent fluidized manner, across grate 20, to be discharged, after attaining the desired temperature.

Since higher heat transfer rates obtain between the fluidized balls and hot gases and entrained solids than would exist if the balls were present in the form of a packed bed, a shallower total bed of balls may be employed. In the fluidized bed of balls channelling of either gases or balls is eliminated. Moreover, relatively small equipment may be used because of the high heat transfer rates and the low pressure drop through the ball heater.

A feature of the preferred ball heater 10 is the provision made for discharge of the balls through a downcomer onto a lower grate. The bottom ends of downcomers 30 and 32 lie substantially below the top of the downcomer extension 44 and 46 respectively, so that the bottom ends of downcomers 30 and 32 lie within fluidized thermosphere beds 72 and 74. As the balls are discharged into the downcomers, they cannot fall freely into the fluidized beds.

The stacking of balls, in the downcomers, caused thereby is highly advantageous since, in effect, a gas seal is formed by such ball-stacking or ball-packing. The ball column, so formed, should have a depth sufficient to provide a resistance to gas flow in the downcomer such that the velocity therethrough, for the existing pressure drop across the bed, is less than required for fluidization of the contained balls; so under such circumstances the balls will flow downwardly through the downcomer. The necessary height of this ball column is on the order of 4" to 12" in the ball heater.

Oil Shale Retorting

As fluidization proceeds, and balls pass from a given fluidization bed, e.g., bed 72, into its associated downspout extension, e.g., extension 44, additional balls are discharged from the appropriate downcomer, e.g., downcomer 30, onto the bed to maintain the fluidized bed at a constant level. Since a continuous gas seal is formed in the above described manner, only a small gas flow upwardly through the downcomers is possible and practically no upward flow of balls to an upper level takes place.

Since heat is being removed from the hot gases as they pass upwardly through the ball heater, the gases become progressively lower in temperature and their density decreases. In order to have about the same velocity of gas in each bed of the heater, therefore, the area of the lowest bed 74 is preferably made greater than the area of the middle bed 72, which is, in turn, made greater than the area of the uppermost bed 70. Thus, the degree of fluidization in the three beds is made substantially the same.

It will thus be seen that a ball heater is provided where balls can be heated, in a fluidized state, by means of upwardly moving combustion gases, containing, entrained solids therein. The ball heating is accomplished in a plurality of successive ball passes, the first pass commencing at an upper (cooler) level in the ball heater, and the last pass ending at a lower (hotter) level in the ball heater. The pressure drop through the ball heater is minimized because of the shallow depth of each bed of balls and the fluidized state of the beds, while the balls are enabled to proceed downwardly by means of the gas seal arrangement.

It is also possible, and in some instances it may be preferable, to allow balls that are moved into a downcomer by the just described fluidization process to be then led out of the heating apparatus proper, and then positively fed by screw conveyor means or the like onto the next lower level for a further heating. A preferred use of the ball heater 10 is in connection with the production of oil from oil shale.

H.E. Linden and T.D. Nevens; U.S. Patent 3,164,541; January 5, 1965; assigned to The Oil Shale Corporation describe a process which utilizes an oil for conveying solid bodies from point to point in a process. Thus, balls used in the process for pyrolyzing oil shale are generally quite hot, having a temperature somewhere between 500° to 1050°F., depending upon the point in the process at which the temperature measurement is taken. These hot balls are fed, usually by gravity, into an elevator conduit in which an appropriate oil such as, for example, shale oil, or other high boiling point oil flows upwardly. The oil flows upwardly through this conduit due to the provision of an oil pump therein; as the oil moves upwardly, it carries the solid bodies with it.

After the balls have been conveyed to a desired height, the balls and oil are separated by any suitable means, such as by screening means. The oil may then be recycled to the pipeline through the oil pump, or discharged from the system. If oil obtained from the pyrolysis of the oil shale is used as the transporting hydraulic medium, this oil may be coked to varying degrees.

Heat Supplied by Pyrolysis Products

A process described by C.L. Crawford; U.S. Patent 3,265,608; August 9, 1966; assigned to Technikoil, Inc. provides a method for producing an effluent vapor from a solid carbonaceous material leaving, upon pyrolysis, a spent solid residue. The process comprises the steps of: pyrolyzing the solid material in a pyrolysis zone by solid-to-solid milling contact with hotter heat-carrying bodies to obtain effluent vapor and hot spent solids; recovering the effluent vapor from the pyrolysis zone; separating the hot spent solids from the heat-carrying bodies; transfering the heat-carrying bodies to a pebble heater; heating the heat-carrying bodies in the pebble heater by means of heat derived from the hot spent solids under non-combustion conditions and heat derived by combusting fuel and recirculating the heated heat-carrying bodies to the pyrolysis zone to effect the pyrolysis of fresh solid carbonaceous material.

FIGURE 1.17:   PROCESS EMPLOYING HEATED SOLID BODIES FOR THERMAL TREATMENT OF OIL SHALE

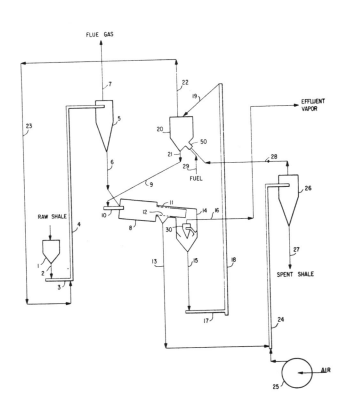

Source: C.L. Crawford; U.S. Patent 3,265,608; August 9, 1966

Referring to Figure 1.17 Colorado oil shale at about 50°F. crushed to an average particle size of about 1/2" in diameter is fed from a bin 1 via line 2 and feeder 3 to a raw shale lift heater 4 where it is contacted and entrained by flue gas having a temperature of about 1100°F. In the raw shale lift heater, the raw shale feed is heated to a temperature of about 300°F. The preheated raw shale is then removed from the gas-solids suspension in a separator 5 and passed to a horizontal rotating pyrolysis drum 8 via line 6. The cooled flue gas from which the heated raw shale has been removed passes from gas solids separation zone 5 through line 7 and is vented to the atmosphere.

Oil Shale Retorting

In pyrolysis zone 8, the preheated raw shale is contacted with hot alumina balls having a temperature of about 1570°F. and entering pyrolysis drum 8 via line 9 and feeder 10. The balls and shale pass concurrently through pyrolysis drum 8 whereby the heat of the balls is imparted to the shale with the production of an effluent vapor and spent shale solids. Effluent vapor and spent solids at about 870°F. and cooled balls at about 900°F. exit from pyrolysis drum 8 through line 11 which is adapted with a screen 12 having openings such that spent solids pass through while the passage of balls is precluded. The effluent vapor and cooled balls are then passed by means of line 11 to a bin 14 where the vapor and balls are allowed to remain in contact for a longer period whereby the removal of dust from the effluent vapor is achieved. Substantially dust free vapor is removed from bin 14 through line 16 and passed to a recovery section. Cooled balls are removed from bin 14 by means of line 15 and passed to a ball elevator 18 via feeder 17. In ball elevator 18 the cooled balls are lifted to the top of a pebble heater 20 into which they are introduced from elevator 18 by means of line 19.

The spent shale solids removed from pyrolysis drum 8 and separated from the cooled balls by means of screen 12 are passed via line 13 to a gas lift line 24. In gas lift line 24 the hot spent shale is contacted and entrained by means of air at about 95°F. introduced into lift line 24 through a blower compressor 25. The entrained spent shale imparts its sensible heat to the air raising the temperature of the solids lifting medium to about 700°F. The air spent solids suspension is then passed through a separator 26 where the entrained solids are removed from the air stream.

The separated solids pass from solid separator 26 through line 27 and are discarded. The heated air from which the spent solids have been removed passes from separator 26 by means of line 28 and is introduced into the bottom of pebble heater 20 via a fuel combustion zone 50 located at the inlet of line 28 to ball heater 20. A gas oil fraction recovered from the effluent vapor produced in the process is introduced by means of line 29 into fuel combustion zone 50 where it is ignited and burned by the preheated air.

The flue gas produced by burning the gas oil fraction and having a temperature of about 3000°F. is then passed upwardly through ball heater 20 to contact and heat balls. Heated balls leave ball heater 20 through line 21 and are recirculated to pyrolysis drum 8 via line 9 and feeder 10 to contact and effect the pyrolysis of additional raw shale. Flue gas having a temperature of about 1100°F. is removed from the top of ball heater 20 by means of line 22 and passed to lift heater 4 where it contacts and preheats a stream of additional raw shale feed.

M.U. Zimmerman, Jr.; U.S. Patent 3,442,789; May 6, 1969; assigned to Technikoil, Inc. describes a process for producing oil from shale in which the shale is pyrolyzed in a rotating mill by rotating and milling with hot solid heat carrying material, e.g., grinding balls, in which the overhead hydrocarbons and residue are recovered and part of the product, e.g., a butanes fraction of the overhead, is heated with hot flue gas and the hot product is returned to the mill to directly heat the pyrolysis zone.

A process described by C.L. Crawford; U.S. Patent 3,167,494; January 26, 1965; assigned to The Oil Shale Corporation is based upon a finding that heat required for pyrolyzing solid carbonaceous materials efficiently and economically can be transferred to the carbonaceous solids from hotter heat-carrying bodies in a vertical pyrolysis zone without the necessity of establishing a completely fluidized solids bed containing the carbonaceous and heat-carrying solids throughout the pyrolysis zone.

In accordance with the process, the carbonaceous solids and heat-carrying bodies are mixed and contacted intimately immediately upon being charged to the top of the pyrolysis zone only by the action of upwardly rising effluent vapor produced in the pyrolysis zone. Thus, the method does not contemplate the utilization of an extraneous gasiform material and/or the formation of a completely fluidized solids bed throughout the pyrolysis zone.

Accordingly, the process provides a method for pyrolyzing carbonaceous solids where an effluent vapor is produced from which the desired components easily and economically can be recovered in smaller and simpler equipment than that required in processes using an extraneous fluidizing gas. In addition, in not requiring that the solids in the pyrolysis zone be completely fluidized, the method suitably is adapted for handling raw carbonaceous solids feed streams containing appreciable amounts of the previously unusable finely divided material thereby enabling increased total product yields to be realized from available raw materials.

Heated Solids for Attrition and Heat Transfer

In a process described by H.F. West; U.S. Patent 3,350,280; October 31, 1967; assigned to The Standard Oil Company externally heated attrition resistant solid bodies such as steel or ceramic balls are used for transferring heat to the oil shale. The process includes the use of a stationary drum retort equipped with an internal rotating screw which contains throughout its length perforated or slotted screw flights together with baffles designed in such a way that the solid bodies or balls are retained on the screw and do not fall through the slots or perforations but the oil shale falls through. The oil shale which is crushed by action of the heated balls upon it is fed into the top of the retort and by gravity falls down through the perforations or slots in the screw in the retort to the bottom where the carbonaceous residue or shale coke is removed and may be burned to supply heat to the external heater which in turn supplies heat to the recycled balls.

The externally heated balls flow by gravity from the heater to the bottom of the retort where the rotating screw picks them up and works them to the top and out of the retort to a point where they flow by gravity back to the external heater where they are reheated and recycled to the bottom of the retort. Proper baffles are present on the screw to retain the balls in their upward movement and to prevent the balls from rolling backwards or toward the bottom of the retort. The screw can be driven by any means such as a variable-speed motor and the degree of heat transfer or contact time between the balls and the oil shale can be varied by adjustment of the speed of rotation of the screw.

Referring to Figure 1.18, the retorting vessel 1 is an inclined stationary drum equipped with a rotatable screw mounted on the shaft 2, the shaft being secured by suitable bearing and seal means at the top and bottom 3 of the retorting vessel. The screw is equipped with openings 4 which are large enough to allow the shale to fall through but small enough to retain the balls and cross baffles 5 which carry the balls in an upwardly direction in the retorting vessel as the screw rotates. The cooled heat carrying solid bodies or balls are continuously removed from the retorting vessel and pass through conduit 6 and are heated in the external heater 7 and the heated balls pass by gravity flow 8 to the bottom of the retorting vessel and enter the retorting vessel at the opening 9. In this particular illustration the rotatable screw is driven by a driving means 10 which may contain a gear system 11 for varying the speed of rotation of the screw and the screw rotates in counterclockwise fashion when in operation.

As the hot balls are removed upwardly in the retorting vessel by action of the rotation of the screw, they come in intimate contact with downwardly moving oil shale 12 which may be externally preheated which enters the upper portion of the retorting vessel at 13 and the shale is ground to a finer particle size and the oil is removed from the ground shale by pyrolytic action of the hot balls. The balls move upwardly by action of the screw and baffles and the crushed shale moves downwardly as it falls through the openings. The gas and oil vapors resulting from the pyrolysis of the oil shale are removed at points 14 and the spent shale or shale coke is removed from near the bottom of the retort 15. The shale coke preferably is used as fuel and is combusted with an oxygen-containing gas such as air or oxygen alone in the burner 16 which supplies heat to the external heater 7 and the flue gas from the burner escapes at 17.

FIGURE 1.18: PROCESS EMPLOYING HEATED SOLIDS FOR ATTRITION AND HEAT TRANSFER

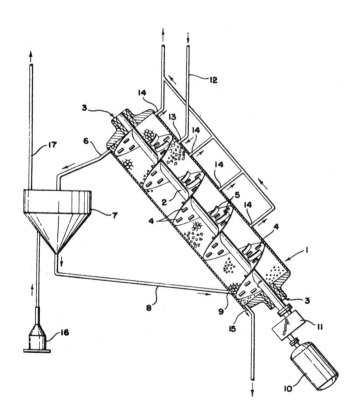

Source: H.F. West; U.S. Patent 3,350,280; October 31, 1967

The solid bodies which serve as heat carriers are usually attrition resistant bodies in the form of balls, pebbles or shot of suitable size and specific gravity. The solid heat carrier may be composed of inexpensive metals such as iron, steel, aluminum, high melting lead alloys, and the like as well as refractory materials and particularly ceramic materials which have relatively large heat capacities and are not subject to oxidation or reduction. The particle sizes of the solid heat carriers usually vary from 50 mesh to about 1" in diameter.

Just prior to the time it enters the distillation apparatus the oil shale may be preheated to a temperature in the range of from 400° to 600°F. Above approximately 600°F. pyrolysis of the shale commences. In the pyrolysis of oil shale, for instance, a temperature of from 750° to 1800°F. and more preferably 800° to 1200°F. may be employed within the reaction zone. The pressure is not critical and may be atmospheric or a few pounds above atmospheric, in other words, sufficient to overcome pressure drops in the system.

Control of Entrained Solids

C.L. Crawford; U.S. Patent 3,252,886; May 24, 1966 describes a method for treating effluent vapor derived by contacting solid carbonaceous materials with heat-carrying bodies where an effluent vapor is provided which is characterized by a relatively low entrained-solids content.

In the pyrolysis process the raw solid carbonaceous material initially is crushed by any suitable method to be of a suitable particle size. Preferably the raw carbonaceous material is reduced in particle size to be of such an average diameter that it is of a smaller value than that of the heat-carrying bodies employed, so that separation of the spent material produced in the pyrolysis and the heat-carrying bodies readily can be accomplished. Usually the average particle size of the raw carbonaceous solid feed stream is in the range of from 3/8" to 3/4" and preferably is about 1/2". The crushed raw carbonaceous material at ambient temperatures then may be passed directly to the pyrolysis zone, although it is preferred that the raw solids feed stream be preheated.

Preheating of the crushed material suitably may be carried out either indirectly or directly with heat from any source available. One preferred method for preheating the crushed carbonaceous feed stream utilizes the residual sensible heat of flue gases previously employed in the process to supply heat to the heat-body heating zone. In such cases the technique preferred for utilization is to effect the desired heat transfer between the crushed raw material and the hot flue gases by entraining the carbonaceous solids in a gas lift line with the flue gas stream. The preheated raw material is then separated from the entraining gas in a gas-solids separation zone and passed to the pyrolysis zone.

The cool or preheated carbonaceous material is then passed into a pyrolysis zone which suitably may be in any form for carrying out the pyrolysis of carbonaceous solids such as a fluidized bed, a horizontal or slightly inclined rotating drum or a vertical stacked solids bed where it is contacted in solid-to-solid heat exchange contact with heat-carrying bodies having sufficient available heat to effect the pyrolysis of the carbonaceous material and produce effluent vapor and hot spent solid residues. Preferably the pyrolysis zone is in the form of a rotating drum where solid-to-solid milling contact between the heat bodies and carbonaceous solids is achieved.

Oil Shale Retorting

The available heat of the heat-carrying bodies is such that essentially complete pyrolysis of the carbonaceous solids is effected with a maximum yield of hydrocarbon values being thereby achieved. For example, when oil shale is subjected to pyrolytic treatment, the heat supplied by the heat-carrying bodies to the oil shale is such as to raise the temperature of the shale in the range of from 750° to 950°F., preferably from 800° to 900°F. Temperatures in the pyrolysis zone greater than about 950°F. usually are avoided due to the fact that some slight cracking of valuable hydrocarbon product may occur under such conditions.

Although countercurrent flow of solids through the pyrolysis zone may be employed, it is preferred to use a rotating drum as the zone where pyrolysis is effected, the carbonaceous materials and heat bodies are passed through the pyrolysis drum in concurrent fashion. By the utilization of concurrent flow in lieu of countercurrent flow, the power requirements for moving the solids through the system are greatly reduced and the chance of coking occurring at the heat-body inlet end of the pyrolysis drum is essentially eliminated.

The actual temperature and amount of the heat bodies introduced into the pyrolysis zone in a particular embodiment of this method, will depend upon, inter alia, the type of carbonaceous material being treated, the degree of pyrolysis desired, the inlet temperature of the carbonaceous feed, and the heat transfer characteristics of the heat-carrying bodies. Where oil shale is treated and alumina balls are utilized as the heat-carrying bodies, the ratio of heat-carrying bodies to raw shale feed to the pyrolysis zone preferably is in the range of from 0.6:1 to 10:1, preferably from 0.8:1 to 3:1. In such oil shale treatments the alumina balls introduced into the pyrolysis zone usually are at a temperature in the range of from 1200° to 1800°F., preferably from 1350° to 1650°F.

The heat-carrying bodies, cooled by giving up a portion of their heat to the carbonaceous material during pyrolysis, the effluent vapor and spent materials produced in the pyrolysis of the carbonaceous solids are then removed from the pyrolysis zone. The condensible effluent vapor containing fine solid materials and the heat-carrying bodies are then sent to a dust removal treatment where the solids suspended in the vapor are removed preliminary to the vapor being passed to a recovery section.

In the preferred dust removal procedure, the vapor is subjected to at least a two stage treatment to effect the removal of suspended solids. In a first dust removal treatment, the solids-containing vapors are introduced into a first solids removal zone where the still hot heat-carrying bodies recovered from the pyrolysis zone are caused to collect in sufficient volume to form a bed of appreciable depth and are maintained in contact with the heat-carrying bodies from the pyrolysis zone. Part of the solids are removed from the vapor by contact with the heat-carrying bodies.

It is believed that by contact electrification, effected by previous particle-to-particle contact in the process, the dust and heat-carrying bodies become differentially charged, and that a portion of the dust particles entrained in the effluent vapor are attracted to and thereby removed from the vapor by the heat-carrying bodies. The vapor containing a reduced amount of suspended solids, is then passed through a vapor-solids separator, preferably of the cyclone type, constituting a second solids removal zone, where the remainder of the suspended solids in the vapor are substantially completely removed. When according to the preferred embodiment of the process the vapor solids separator is located within the first solids removal zone, heat from the heat-carrying bodies prevents condensation of the high boiling constituents of the effluent vapor. To obtain maximum efficiency in removing entrained solids from the effluent vapor, the second vapor-solids separation zone preferably is located within the first solids removal zone in such a manner that the outlet of the second vapor-solids separation zone is in juxtaposition with the heat-carrying body outlet from the first zone.

If the hot spent solids and cooled heat-carrying bodies produced in the pyrolysis zone have not already been separated inside the pyrolysis zone, as is described in U.S. Patent 2,592,738, separation of the spent materials and heat-carrying bodies recovered from the pyrolysis zone is then carried out by any suitable means such as by a screening operation. Separation of the spent materials and heat-carrying bodies easily can be accomplished when a significant difference in the average particle size between the two solid streams is maintained.

The heat-carrying bodies recovered from the pyrolysis zone and separated from the spent material are passed through the dust removal zone, as above described; then are reheated and recycled to the pyrolysis zone to effect the pyrolysis of additional raw carbonaceous material.

Finely Divided Heat Carrier

A process described by P. Schmalfeld, H. Sommers and H. Janssen; U.S. Patent 3,655,518; April 11, 1972; assigned to Metallgesellschaft AG and Ruhrgas AG, Germany is directed to an apparatus for the dry distillation of bituminous or petroleum-containing materials such as coal, lignite, oil shale or oil sand in a finely granular state. The material to be distilled is heated by means of being thoroughly mechanically mixed with a circulating, finely divided heat carrier which is separated from the distillation vapors along with the solid distillation residue, heated in a pneumatic conveyor, and returned to the distillation apparatus.

The apparatus consists of a vertical pneumatic conveying and heating unit for the particulate heat carrier to the bottom end of which a free-oxygen containing gaseous propellant is fed axially as through a venturi tube and finely granular thermal carrier is introduced from a concentric annular chamber thereabout through slits by means of a flow of a control gas.

A separator at the upper end of the conveyor is divided by a wall extending downward from the top into a separating chamber and a secondary chamber containing the discharge for the propelling gas and products of combustion, and a bottom solids collecting chamber that is common to both.

A distillation chamber is connected at its input end to the heat carrier discharged from the separator. It also receives the raw material or feed that is to be distilled. At its discharge end, one conduit carries away the hot mixture of thermal carrier and fresh solid distillation residue and another conduit carries away the distillate vapors. The distillation chamber has a screw conveyor to force and mix the solids. An intermediate reservoir or hopper is connected at one end to the distillation chamber and at the other end to the annular chamber at the bottom of the conveyor.

A dust gas separator is used to remove fines from the distillation vapors after which they are condensed in a product recovery system in which the vapors are condensed by spraying them with previously separated and cooled condensate.

Another dust separator cleans the products of combustion discharged from the conveyor-separator and the gas is then utilized in heat exchange to heat the incoming propellant gas and/or in a waste heat boiler. The particulate solids removed from the process are cooled, preferably with water, in a solids cooler.

The finely divided solid distillation residue which serves as the heat carrier is carried and simultaneously heated in a vertical pneumatic conveying and heating unit and then is separated from the combustion gases by free fall and inertial ejection in a separating chamber, and delivered to a mechanical mixer in the distillation chamber. In the mixer the thermal carrier, heated to 700°C., for example, is combined with the finely granulated starting material that is to be distilled, e.g., coal, oil shale, oil sand or the like, and blended intensely within seconds. A very rapid transfer of heat from the thermal carrier to the finely granulated starting material takes place. This heat quickly brings the starting material to the desired distillation temperature, usually between 450° and 650°C., breaks down the bitumen, and/or drives out in vapor form the oils contained in or developing from the raw material, together with water vapor formed from the moisture and from chemically bound water. The formation of light cracked gases while this is taking place is extremely slight.

The mixture of thermal carrier and fresh distillation residue flows from the distillation chamber into an intermediate reservoir or hopper for the after distillation of the feed material and for the driving of hydrocarbon vapors from the interstices and pores of the solids as by the injection of water vapor returned light distillation gases into the mixture. The solids are then fed back into the bottom part of the pneumatic conveying and heating unit, thereby completing the cycle of the thermal carrier through the heating and distillation steps.

The apparatus permits an effective and simple distillation of finely granulated oil-bearing materials, the condensation of the distillation vapors, and a good recovery of heat from the waste gas from the heating of the thermal carrier. The distillation vapors from the mixer-distilling chamber are processed in a cooling system providing for several stages of contact of the distillate vapors with their own cooled condensate, while the cooling of gases from the heater-conveyor is performed in an air preheater and/or a waste-heat boiler.

IN SITU PROCESSES

Laser Beam Heating

In a process described by M.R. Yant; U.S. Patent 3,652,447; March 28, 1972 the bottom layers of a large body of oil shale are heated by pulsed laser beams. The heated shale when contacted by air drawn into an enclosure, causes eduction of gaseous hydrocarbons that rise upwardly through the shale to a gas collection space. The rising gas and air heat the upper layers of the crushed shale in order to retort the entire body of shale.

Liquid products gravitate downwardly to the bottom and are drawn off while the gas is drawn upwardly by vacuum pressure pulses synchronized to occur between the pulsations of the laser beams. Because of the synchronized vacuum pressure pulses, voids are intermittently produced in the body of crushed shale to maintain its transmissivity with respect to the laser beams which would otherwise decrease as the shale is retorted under the heat produced.

The heat generated by the laser beams is also distributed throughout to cause retorting of all portions of the crushed shale body.

Figure 1.19a illustrates the apparatus of the process generally referred to by reference numeral 10 designed to carry out the oil shale recovery process. The apparatus includes a relatively large, elongated enclosure generally referred to by reference numeral 12 which has a base or foundation 14 on which sidewall sections 16 are mounted to form wall assemblies on opposite longitudinal sides of the foundation. The sidewall sections are interconnected by a roof portion 18. The roof portion as well as the sidewall sections 16 are made of a suitable, opaque material such as steel plate. The sidewall assemblies formed by the sidewall sections 16 are interconnected at the opposite ends by radiation transmissive, end wall portions which are made of a material such as glass including an entry end wall portion 20 at one longitudinal end and an exit wall portion 22 at the opposite longitudinal end as shown in Figure 1.19c.

FIGURE 1.19:   LASER HEATING PROCESS

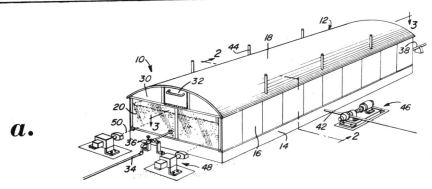

a.

Overview of Housing and Process Equipment

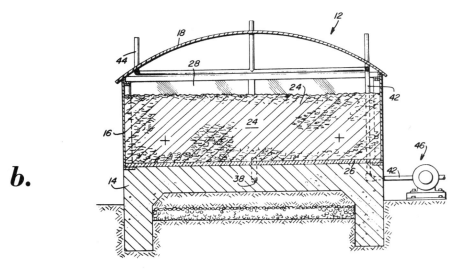

b.

Sectional View Along Line 2—2 of Figure 1.19a

(continued)

FIGURE 1.19: (continued)

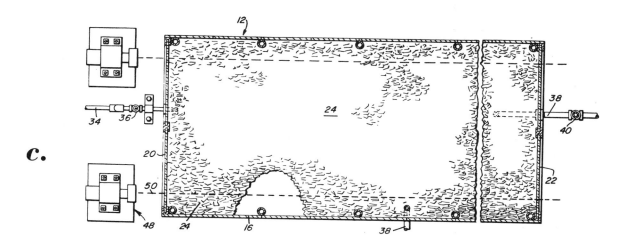

c.

View Along Line 3—3 of Figure 1.19a

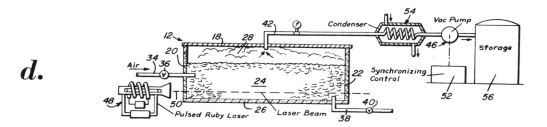

d.

Sectional View of Apparatus

Source: M.R. Yant; U.S. Patent 3,652,447; March 28, 1972

The enclosure 12 is filled up to a predetermined height with a large body of hydrocarbonaceous solids such as crushed oil shale 24 as more clearly seen in Figures 1.19b and 1.19c supported on top of the foundation 14 by a fire clay floor 26. A gas collection space 28 is formed above the body of crushed oil shale. As shown in Figure 1.19a, the roof portion 18 at the ends, is supported on opaque end wall sections 30 above the glass wall portions 20 and 22, the end wall sections having openings mounting hinged access doors 32 through which the oil shale is loaded into the enclosure.

Combustion supporting fluid such as air is supplied to the body of oil shale from any suitable source through an air intake conduit 34 which mounts a control valve 36 to regulate the quantity of air drawn in. Liquid hydrocarbon products or shale oils are withdrawn from the body of crushed solids 24 through a conduit 38 which extends upwardly through the floor 26 into the enclosure. A cutoff valve 40 is mounted in the conduit 38 in order to control the outflow of the liquid.

A suction conduit 42 is interconnected with a plurality of exhaust pipes 44 that extend upwardly from the roof portion. Thus, gaseous products within the gas collection space 28 at various locations above the body of solids 24 are withdrawn from the enclosure through the conduit 42 to which a vacuum pump assembly 46 is connected.

As shown in Figures 1.19a and 1.19c, a pair of laser beam generators 48 are mounted externally of the enclosure 12 adjacent one longitudinal end. The laser beam generators are of the pulsed ruby type arranged to direct a pair of pulsed laser beams 50 through the bottom layer of the body of solids 24. The beams thus enter the enclosure through one end wall portion 20 in horizontally spaced relation to each other, exiting from the other horizontally spaced end wall portion 22. The beams while passing through the body of solids generate the requisite amount of heat for retorting purposes.

Referring to Figure 1.19d, it will be observed that each of the laser beams 50 is emitted from a conventional type of pulsed ruby laser generator 48. In order to obtain efficient and thorough retorting of the entire body of solids, the operation of the vacuum pump 46 is controlled by the synchronizing control 52 so as to time the negative pressure pulses applied to the gas collection space 28 between the pulsations of the laser beams 50 being pulsed at a predetermined rate. In this manner, the transmissivity of the body of solids 24 with respect to the laser beams are maintained as the gaseous products rise upwardly into the space 28 and the liquid products are drawn off through the conduit 38. The negative pressure pulses also draw in a regulated quantity of air through conduit 34 necessary to support the retorting process. Also, the gaseous products may be conducted through a condenser 54 as shown in Figure 1.19d and then delivered by the vacuum pump 46 to a storage container 56.

By way of example, the capacity of the retort enclosure 12 when the body of solids is filled to the top of the plate glass wall portions 20 and 22 will be 480 cubic feet leaving the gas collection space 28 which will be filled with gas from the pyrolytic action of the laser beams. The gas is drawn to the condenser 54 by a vacuum pump of 3 horsepower capacity with a 30 to 35 cfm rating. The negative pressure pulses of the vacuum pump will be synchronized in continuous out-of-phase relation to the pulsations of the laser beams of 5 pulses per minute. A commercially available ruby laser generator of known construction and operation may be utilized. The glass end walls portions 20 and 22 will not only transmit the laser beams but will also permit visual inspection of the interior of the enclosure.

Nuclear Detonation

A process described by P.J. Closmann; U.S. Patent 3,578,080; May 11, 1971; assigned to Shell Oil Company involves exploding a relatively high energy explosive device within an oil shale formation thereby forming a chimney of rubble within the formation having fractures extending from the chimney through the formation. A plurality of spaced wells are extended into the formation radially outwardly from the chimney and adjacent to at least some of the fractures. Fluid flow paths are formed from the wells through the fractures into the chimney and fluid is circulated through these fluid flow paths and into the chimney at rates creating a pressure drop from the wells to the chimney. Oil shale-reactive properties are imparted to the circulating fluid whereby the fluid reacts with the oil shale moving solid components into void spaces formed within the chimney increasing the permeability of the oil shale formation relative to the permeability of the chimney in regions surrounding the chimney.

Oil Shale Retorting

Figure 1.20a shows subterranean oil shale formation 11 having having a primary explosive device 12 located within the formation 11. Primary explosive device 12 is preferably surrounded by a plurality of explosive devices 13. Devices 13 may be of lesser energy than device 12, if desired. However, optimum results may be obtained by the formation of substantially equal-size chimneys as will be discussed further hereinbelow.

The device 12 can be either nuclear or nonnuclear; if a nuclear device is detonated in the subterranean oil shale formation 11, a strong shock wave from the nuclear device begins to move radially outwardly, vaporizing, melting, crushing, cracking and displacing the oil shale formation 11. After the shock wave has passed, the high pressure vaporized material expands, and a generally spherical cavity (i.e., the central cavity 14 in Figure 1.20b) is formed which continues to grow until the internal pressure is balanced by the lithostatic pressure.

The cavity 14 persists for a variable time depending on the composition of the oil shale formation 11 and then collapses to form a chimney 15 (Figure 1.20c). Collapse progresses upwardly until the volume initially in the cavity is distributed between the fragments of the oil shale formation 11. The size of the cylindrical rubble zone (i.e., the chimney 15) formed by the collapse of the cavity 14 can be estimated from the depth and explosive yield of the nuclear device and properties of the earth formations.

A zone of permeability 17 within the fragmented oil shale formation is formed surrounding the chimney 15 as can be seen in Figure 1.20c. The permeability of this zone 17 may be preferably increased by surrounding the primary explosive device which formed the central cavity with a plurality of devices 13. For example, in Figure 1.20a, a primary nuclear explosive device 12 is surrounded by explosive devices 13, equally spaced from each other and radially spaced from the primary explosive device 12.

These devices 13 are preferably on substantially the same horizontal plane as the primary nuclear device and 500 to 1,000 feet from the nearest part of the outer wall of the central cavity 14 produced by the explosion of the high energy nuclear device 12. The devices 13 preferably have an energy yield substantially equal to that of the primary high energy nuclear device 12 and can be either nuclear or nonnuclear.

The explosive devices 13 form cavities 18 (Figure 1.20b) when detonated, surrounded by fractured zones 19 as can be seen in Figure 1.20b. The devices 13 may be preset with detonating means adjusted to explode upon arrival of the main shock wave from the explosion of the primary explosive device 12. Alternatively, the devices 13 may be suitably delayed to explode after passage of the main shock wave. Of course, another characteristic of the explosion of the primary explosive device 12 can be utilized to detonate the devices 13, as, for example, changes in temperature or pressure as a result of the explosion of the primary explosive device.

Because of this time delay, either detonating the devices 13 upon arrival of the main shock wave or after the main shock wave has passed but before the central cavity 14 becomes filled with rubble due to the chimney collapse from above, the filled with rubble due to the chimney collapse from above, the shock waves from the secondary explosions (that is, the explosions of the devices 13) will cause spalling into the central cavity.

FIGURE 1.20: HIGH ENERGY EXPLOSIVE DEVICE USED IN SUBTERRANEAN OIL SHALE FORMATION

a.

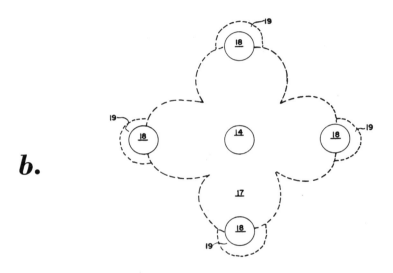

b.

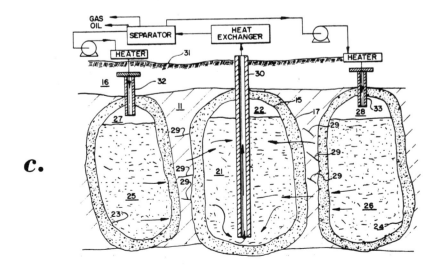

c.

(continued)

FIGURE 1.20: (continued)

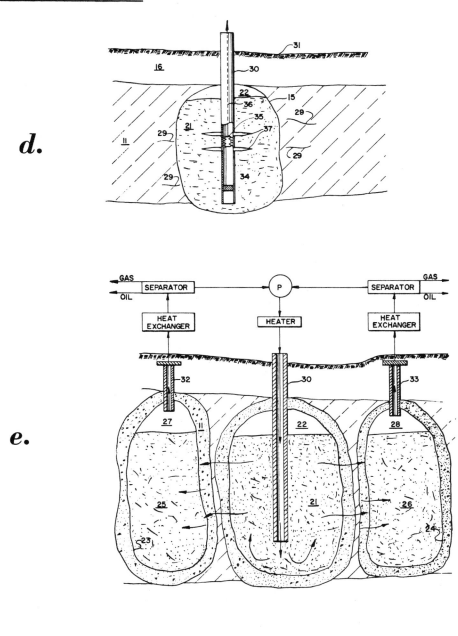

(a) Oil Shale Formation Prior to Detonation
(b) Oil Shale Formation After Detonation
(c)(d) Cross-Sectional Views of Process
(e) Cross-Sectional View of Modified Process

Source: P.J. Closmann; U.S. Patent 3,578,080; May 11, 1971

The movement of rock towards the central cavity 14 due to the satellite explosions will enhance the permeability in the regions between these explosions and the central cavity 14,

by allowing development of a greater void space in this region. This void space, indicated as a zone of increased permeability 17 in the drawings, has a high and uniform permeability in the fragmented oil shale formation 11.

Thus, chimney 15 includes a lower rubble zone 21 and an upper void space 22. Similar chimneys formed by the detonation of the devices 13 also include lower rubble zones and upper void spaces. For example, as illustrated in Figure 1.20c, two such chimneys 23 and 24, formed, for example, by devices such as explosive devices 13, form lower rubble zones 25 and 26 and upper void spaces 27 and 28, respectively.

A plurality of fractures 29 are formed between the satellite chimneys and the central chimney 15 as illustrated in Figure 1.20c. Fractures 29 are generally substantially horizontally extensive through formation 11; however fractures 9 may also be substantially vertically extensive. A more detailed discussion of the formation of chimneys 15, 23 and 24 appears in U.S. Patent 3,448,801.

Alternatively to forming chimneys 23 and 24 as indicated hereinabove, after chimney 15 is formed, fluid flow paths through fractures 29 may be formed by hydraulically or explosively fracturing wells 32 and 33 by fracturing procedures such as those known in the art, so that the latter fractures communicate with fractures 29.

Referring to Figure 1.20c a producing well borehole 30 is extended from the earth surface 31 into communication with the lower portion of chimney 15. A plurality of outlying injecting well boreholes, such as well boreholes 32 and 33, shown in Figure 1.20c, are extended from earth surface 31 into communication with the upper portion of chimneys 23 and 24, respectively. Well boreholes 30, 32 and 33 are preferably cased. The vertical intervals, that is, the chimneys or rubbled or fractured regions into which the outlying wells are opened are preferably located at substantially the same depth as the chimney 15.

Fluid flow paths are then formed from the outlying well boreholes 32 and 33 to chimney 15 through the fractures extending out from chimneys 25 and 26 into communication with interconnecting fractures 29. These flow paths are preferably enlarged by circulating acidizing fluids from well boreholes 32 and 33 through fractures 29 and into chimney 15.

Another method of forming or enlarging such fluid flow paths from the outlying wells to the central chimney 15 is to fracture the oil shale formation by flowing an electrical current between electrodes that contact the oil shale. A more detailed description of this process for fracturing an oil shale is given in an article by Melton and Cross, Journal of Petroleum Technology, Jan., 1968, pp. 37-41. The electrical energy may be applied prior to or during the initial circulation of fluid from the outlying wells to central chimney 15.

In operation, fluid is injected into the satellite chimneys 23 and 24 through well boreholes 32 and 33, through fractures 29 and into the rubble zone 21 of chimney 15 as indicated by the arrows in Figure 1.20c. Fluids are then produced from central chimney 15 through producing well borehole 30.

A preferred method for producing shale oil from the oil shale formation 11 of Figure 1.20c is to inject a combustion supporting gas, such as air or oxygen, into the satellite well boreholes after the hydrocarbons in the formation have been raised to ignition temperature. This may be accomplished by various means known in the art, such as by lowering suitable heaters down well boreholes 32 and 33. A combustion zone is thus formed which gradually moves through the intervening rock between chimneys 23, 24 and 15 by means of fractures 29 into central chimney 15.

As this rock is heated, it expands, releasing gas and other products and effectively provides additional flow paths for the injected fluid. At the same time, as the rock nearest the satellite chimneys expands, it expands or moves towards the central rubble chimney 15 thus tending to relieve some of the thermal stress generated by the hot fluids. This method makes the porosity distribution of oil shale formation 11 more uniform by developing some porosity adjacent the outside of chimneys 23 and 24 where the rock is first heated and by exerting pressure due to thermal expansion on the central rubble zone (i.e., chimney 15) thus tending to reduce the porosity of central chimney 15.

As an alternative to air or oxygen, the injected fluid may be a heated gas, liquid, or steam. If steam is used, thermal expansion of the rock takes place. After the rock is heated, combustion may again be carried out. The displaced fluids are produced from the bottom of the central chimney 15 to which they drain and out of production well borehole 30. As it becomes desirable to treat more of the upper regions of the rock, the production well borehole 30 may be shut off at the bottom and perforated at progressively higher places within the central chimney. This is illustrated in Figure 1.20d where the lower end of the well borehole 30 is packed off, such as by a wireline-set or a tubing-set packer 34, and a perforating device 35 is lowered into well borehole 30 by means of cable 36. The casing of well borehole 30 is then perforated by device 35 as is well-known in the art thus forming a plurality of perforations 37 which may be progressively moved up well borehole 30 as the central chimney 15 is produced.

Alternatively to injecting a fluid, acid may be injected from the outlying chimneys through fractures 29 and into central chimney 15. The acid flows through fractures 29, leaching out part of the rock and developing some heating. This acid is produced from the central chimney 15. In some cases, fine suspended material (e.g., produced by decomposition of the oil shale during combustion or acidizing) may be carried from the inlets of this flow system (e.g., chimneys 23 and 24 and/or fractures communicating with wells 32 and 33) and deposited near the central chimney 15. This action makes the overall flow path more uniform. This step may be then followed by hot fluid injection or a combustion process.

In both cases, that is, the circulation of a fluid such as a gas or an acid, when the oil shale-reactive properties of a fluid comprise or include a temperature sufficient to pyrolyze kerogen in the oil shale and the fluid is flowing through interconnected fractures between chimneys at a rate providing a pressure gradient along the flow path, pyrolysis-induced fracturing tends to enhance the movement of solids and fluids in the direction of the lowest pressure. Within a nuclear detonation chimney, such as, for example, chimney 15, the permeability increases with increases in height and becomes substantially infinite in the void at the top. Since the fractures that are formed by a nuclear detonation are initiated by a radially expanded bubble centered in the lower portion of the region that becomes a chimney, the density of radially extending fractures is less at depths near the top of the chimney.

Conventional equipment and techniques, such as heaters, pumps, a separator and a heat exchanger, may be used for pressurizing, heating, injecting, producing and separating components of the fluid circulated through the oil shale formation 11. The production of the fluid may be aided by downhole pumping means, not shown, or restricted to the extent necessary to maintain the selected pressure within the oil shale formation 11.

When oil shale pyrolyzing fluid is circulated along a path extending through fractures, from the outlying wells to a nuclear detonation chimney, in the initial stages and at depth near the top of the central chimney, the permeability is the least, the pressure gradient is the highest and the resistance to solid material displacement toward the central chimney is the least.

As fractures are formed by the pyrolysis of the oil shale, they tend to form first in the regions which are contacted by the hottest portion of the fluid, and these regions are located near the outlying wells. The largest fractures tend to form at depths near the top of the central chimney where the resistance to the movement of solid material is the least. In addition, the relatively high permeability within the central chimney tends to decrease as solids move into the central chimney. This results in both the creation of additional permeability in regions surrounding the central chimney and an increase in the permeability in the surrounding regions relative to that within the central chimney. The creation of additional permeability in regions surrounding the central chimney increases the amount of permeable oil shale material that is available for depletion and the increase in permeability in the surrounding regions increases the uniformity of the depletion.

The fluid being circulated through central chimney 15 is preferably injected into all the satellite chimneys or intervals into which outlying wells have been opened and, at least initially, produced from near the bottom of central chimney 15. The fluid circulation may advantageously be initiated by circulating air or relatively cool liquid to sweep out any shale oil released by the nuclear detonation. When oil shale reactive properties imparted to the circulating liquid comprise or include a temperature sufficient to pyrolyze the oil shale, the method of this process provides a unique advantage over processes in which production wells are extended through the chimney, or through the immediately adjacent relatively highly fractured zone, to provide conduits arranged for a downward advance of a combustion front.

In the process, when the advance of a heat front towards the production well borehole 30 subjects the borehole 30 to a high temperature, the production well borehole conduit or conduits, i.e., the well casing or tubing string, may be shortened to terminate in a relatively cool zone near the top of central chimney 15. After an extended and relatively uniform permeability distribution has been obtained by circulating fluid from the outlying wells to central chimney 15, the flow direction may be reversed, with central chimney 15 operating as a very large diameter central injection well as illustrated in Figure 1.20e. Such a flow reversal allows the pyrolysis products to be produced from the tops of the intervals (for example, chimneys 23 and 24) into which the outlying wells are opened. This capability of the process to avoid heat damage to the production well conduits provides material improvement in the economy of the shale oil production process.

A process described by G.O. Grady; U.S. Patent 3,601,193; August 24, 1971; assigned to

<u>Cities Service Oil Co.</u> involves the recovery of shale oil by in situ retorting of underground formations of oil shale. The process involves a method for initiating and supporting in situ retorting of the oil shale in the chimney of fractured and crumbled shale of high permeability formed by the detonation of a nuclear device positioned in a subsurface oil shale formation.

The process permits and facilitates the establishment of a hot zone substantially across the cross-sectional area of the chimney. This is accomplished by injecting the retorting fluid into the chimney space by means of at least one injection well positioned generally horizontally across the chimney. The retorting fluid is injected through perforations in the injection well liner.

The injection of a retorting fluid into the chimney from a multiplicity of points permits the establishment of a hot zone at a temperature sufficient to support retorting across substantially the entire width of the chimney. By injecting retorting fluid through a series of injection wells thus positioned, the establishment of the desired hot zone substantially across and around the entire cross-sectional area of the chimney may be accomplished.

The support and advancement of the hot zone throughout the chimney face can readily be accomplished by continued injection of the initial retorting fluid or a suitable gas into the injection wells and consequently into and around the cross-sectional area of the chimney. The injection wells may be positioned either in the upper or the lower portion of the chimney, with the distilled shale oil being recovered through production wells in accordance with normal techniques.

In order to initiate and support retorting of the shale across and around the chimney formed by the detonation of a nuclear device in a subsurface in an oil shale formation, at least one injection well is positioned so that it extends generally horizontally across the width of the chimney. The injection well liner contains perforations through which the retorting fluid may be injected into the chimney. The retorting fluid is used to establish a hot zone in the chimney at a temperature capable of supporting retorting of the shale. The projection of the retorting fluid through a series or multiplicity of perforations in the generally horizontally extending injection well liner facilitates the establishment of a hot zone substantially across the width of the chimney.

Injection of the retorting fluid through a generally vertically positioned injection well extending into the chimney would, on the other hand, result in the establishment of a more localized hot zone in the vicinity of the injection well outlet. Even with the use of very high injection volumes, the extending of the hot zone substantially across the width of the chimney would be difficult to accomplish. The process, therefore, permits the establishment and support of a hot zone that enhances the retorting of the shale and the recovery of the shale oil from the chimney.

The injection well can be provided by known drilling techniques. The injection well is drilled preferably as a slant well by the so-called slant-hole drilling technique. It is also possible to provide one or more injection well boreholes that extend downward from the earth's surface in a generally vertical direction with radially diverging borehole extensions extending into the chimney and across the chimney in a generally horizontal direction. The so-called directional drilling technique can be employed to provide the deviating borehole extensions. Since directional drilling is also a well established technique that has been employed in conventional operations, further details of the manner in which the drilling is accomplished are not included herein.

In order to provide means for injecting the retorting fluid generally across the width of the chimney, perforated liner extensions may be employed in the portion of the injection well passing through the chimney. Alternately, plain liner extensions may be employed and perforations may be made after the liner having been placed. Techniques for perforating the liner after it has been positioned in the formation are well-known in the art. For example, pressure may be employed to blow out plugs in the liner or perforations may be made by chemical action.

Injection of the retorting fluid into the chimney space may be accomplished through one or more injection wells. Each well, of course, preferably will have a generally horizontally extending portion in the chimney. While one such injection well provides a series of injection ports across the width of the chimney, it may be desirable to employ two or more of such injection wells in order to more fully cover the cross-sectional area of the chimney. From about two to about six injection wells would normally be sufficient for this purpose although additional injection wells could also be employed.

Coverage across and around the cross-sectional area of the chimney can conveniently be achieved by positioning four injection wells at intervals at about 45° around the circumference of the chimney. By extending each of these wells substantially across the width of the chimney, thus crossing at the center portion of the chimney, a multiplicity of injection ports can be provided around the cross-sectional area of the chimney.

The various injection wells may be positioned across the chimney at various elevations if desired. Generally, however, the injection well or wells will be positioned near the top of the chimney. The injection wells can, however, be positioned near the bottom of the chimney or at some intermediate position in either the upper or lower portion of the chimney. It is also within the scope of the process to inject the retorting fluid sequentially through injection wells positioned at more than one elevation in the chimney in order to facilitate the recovery of shale oil from the chimney space.

Referring to Figure 1.21a, the chimney of fractured and crumbled shale of high permeability is represented by the numeral 1. This chimney is formed by the detonation of a nuclear device generally positioned at the bottom of oil shale formation 2. Access well 3, which is drilled from surface 4 through overburden 5 and into oil shale formation 2 is employed initially in order to place the nuclear device in position for detonation. Tilted drilling rig 6 may be employed for the drilling of production well 7 positioned at the base of chimney 1. This drilling rig may also be employed in the drilling slant injection well 8 that is positioned in the upper portion and near the top of chimney 2. As can be seen from Figure 1.21a, injection well 8 is drilled so that it extends across chimney 2 and is positioned generally horizontally.

Perforations generally represented by the numeral 9 are provided in the portion of injection well 8 extending across the chimney to provide suitable injection ports for the injection of retorting fluid substantially across the width of the chimney.

FIGURE 1.21: IN SITU RETORTING OF SHALE FORMED BY DETONATION OF NUCLEAR DEVICE

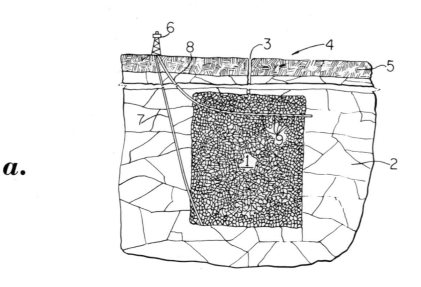

a.

Side View Showing Well and Injection Port

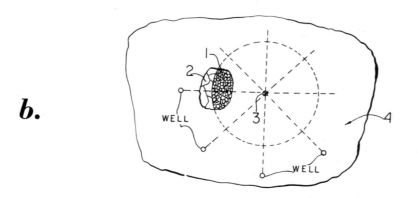

b.

Use of Four Injection Wells Around Oil Shale Chimney

Source: G.O. Grady; U.S. Patent 3,601,193; August 24, 1971

Figure 1.21b illustrates a form of the process in which four injection wells are positioned a radial pattern around chimney 2. The four wells are positioned at 45° intervals around the chimney. Each well extends across the width of the chimney and is provided with perforations on substantially the entire portion crossing the chimney. This arrangement provides for a multiplicity of injection ports substantially around and across the cross-sectional area of the chimney. The injection wells can be positioned in any convenient manner, however, as for example, by passing the injection wells across the chimney in a substantially parallel configuration.

91

The heat generated by the explosion of the nuclear device is insufficient to retort any appreciable portion of the available and recoverable oil in the chimney. The retorting fluid, therefore, is injected into the chimney in order to heat the chimney space to a sufficient temperature to support combustion. The retorting fluid may be any suitable material or combination of materials that will provide the necessary heat to establish retorting conditions in the chimney. The retorting fluid may conveniently comprise a combustion gas formed by burning a combustible-containing gas, such as methane or natural gas, with air or some other oxygen-containing gas.

Carbon Dioxide as Heat Carrier

In a process described by H.E. Gilliland; U.S. Patent 3,480,082; November 25, 1969; assigned to Continental Oil Company oil shale in association with carbonate minerals are heated to a temperature where the hydrocarbon associated with the oil shale is liquefied or gasified by contacting the oil shale with hot carbon dioxide. The oil shale can be contacted in situ or can be mined and contacted in a retort.

When oil shale is associated with carbonate minerals, certain problems are encountered which do not exist with other oil shales. Frequently the carbonate minerals will equal approximately 50% of the mixture of minerals and hydrocarbon material. At temperatures of approximately 1000°F. which are required to retort the shale for recovery of hydrocarbons, the carbonates begin to calcine, e.g., decompose, consuming prodigious quantities of heat which will generally range from 600,000 to 1,000,000 Btu per ton of shale. The cost of supplying this heat can range from 2 to 4 times or more than that required for supplying the minimum heat requirement for heating the shale to retorting temperatures.

The carbonates in the shale are also one of the principal agents for bonding the mineral matrix of the shale. Thus, the strength of the shale is deleteriously affected by carbonate decomposition. This loss of strength leads to particle size degradation and shale "dust" is formed. Particularly in surface retorting, this dust creates numerous operating problems and contributes to atmosphere pollution. To a lesser degree, the dust is also a problem from in situ retorting since the dust is easily carried out through the producing well and also tends to block the flow paths in the subterranean formation.

The decomposition of the carbonate minerals can be substantially reduced if the mineral is heated to calcining temperature in an atmosphere of CO_2. Even at atmospheric pressures $CaCO_3$ decomposition is reduced by a factor between 3 and 4 as compared to the decomposition at calcining temperatures in a nitrogen atmosphere. As the partial pressure of the CO_2 is increased, the amount and rate of decomposition is decreased; therefore, it is preferred to use a pressure of at least 500 psig and generally use a pressure of at least 1,000 psig.

The upper limit on the pressure is limited only by the structural strength of the formation or retorting vessel. Since the retorting temperature is generally around 1000°F., the CO_2 must be heated to some temperature in excess of the 1000°F., the minimum temperature depending upon the formation temperature, the volume of gas per volume of shale to be heated and other heat loss factors which will vary with each given set of conditions. In general, the minimum practical temperature will be about 1250°F. and preferably about 1500°F.

The use of CO_2 as the heat carrier has additional advantages over other inert gases. For example, CO_2 has a relatively high heat capacity and therefore is an efficient heat carrier. The CO_2 is easily liquefied at temperatures below 87.8°F., thus facilitating recovery of the CO_2 for recirculation and handling.

Referring to Figure 1.22, carbon dioxide gas is passed via conduit 1 and well 2 to oil shale formation 3 at a rate of 1,000,000 scfh (standard cubic feet per hour), a temperature of 1500°F. and at a pressure of 1000 psig. The CO_2 heats the shale and vaporizes and/or entrains the hydrocarbons produced by cracking and/or vaporization and liquefaction and is produced from the formation through production well 4 and passed via conduit 5 to heat exchanger 6. The temperature of the stream entering exchanger 6 is 300°F. and has a pressure of 750 psig.

The stream is cooled to about 200°F. and passes via conduit 27 to separator 7 where a first condensate is removed via conduit 8 and passed to product line 9 to be sent to storage, not shown. The gaseous material is then passed to a second heat exchanger 10 via conduit 11 where it is further cooled to about 100°F. and passed via conduit 12 to a second separator 13 where the remaining condensible liquid is separated from the gaseous material and is passed via conduit 14 to conduit 9 and mixed with the liquid from separator 7 to be passed to storage. The mixed product amounts to 1,000 bbl./day oil and 150 bbl./day water.

The water can, of course, be separated from the oil by known decanting or other separating means. The CO_2 and light hydrocarbon gases are then passed at 700 psig to CO_2 liquefaction zone 16 via conduit 15. Makeup CO_2 is added via conduit 17. The CO_2 is liquefied and is separated from the gaseous hydrocarbons. These hydrocarbons amount to 1,400 scf/bbl. of shale oil recovered and have an energy value of about 800 Btu/scf. This fuel is passed via conduit 18 to primary heating zone 26.

FIGURE 1.22:   IN SITU RETORTING PROCESS USING CO_2 AS HEAT CARRIER

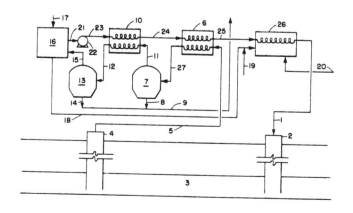

Source: H.E. Gilliland; U.S. Patent 3,480,082; November 25, 1969

Additional fuel is mixed with this recovered fuel via conduit 19. The liquid CO_2 is passed via conduit 21 and pump 22 at 40°F. and 1,200 psig to heat exchanger 10 where it is heated to 140°F. and passed via conduit 24 to heat exchanger 6 where the temperature is raised to 240°F. The CO_2 then passes via conduit 25 to primary heater 26 where it is heated by burning the fuel from conduit 9 with air supplied via conduit 20 to a temperature of 1500°F., the pressure having dropped to 1,000 psig and is then passed via conduit 1 to injection well 2.

Normally, with an oil shale-carbonate deposit, one would expect a net make of CO_2 particularly where the hot gases enter the formation. However, operating according to the method described above, it is necessary to add makeup CO_2 via conduit 17.

Perforated Pipe

J.H. Medlen; U.S. Patent 3,448,794; June 10, 1969 describes a device for extracting oil from oil bearing shale having a four-inch diameter iron or stainless steel pipe perforated with a series of one and one-half inch holes to allow gaseous vapor from the superheated shale to escape down the pipe for cooling and condensation, the cooling pipe consisting of aluminum tubing of 3 to 5 feet in length with coils of copper tubing around it. A cooling agent of water or alcohol may be pumped through the copper tubing. Gaseous oil vapor condenses in the cooling unit into oil at 40° to 50°F. and is collected in a storage tank or oil barrel, as desired. Pumping of gaseous vapors through the perforated tube into the aluminum tube is not necessary, the heavier than air gas being found to flow through the tube by natural gravitational forces.

An advantage of the process is that the device and apparatus is intended to be placed through a drilled hole of a size common to the size of the pipes, into solid shale beds, and may be placed as close together as desired to extract the most oil.

Referring to Figure 1.23a, there is shown a series of perforated pipes 10, 10 having a cap 12, and having a series of vapor holes 14, 14 disposed about the perforated pipe. The perforated pipe may be 4" in diameter and the holes are 1" to 1 1/2" holes. Heating elements 18 connected to electrical conductors 20 provide for the heating and superheating of the shale to produce gaseous vapors which are drawn into the perforated pipe through the vapor holes, and then into a connected solid aluminum pipe 24 around which is provided an iron jacket 26 shown in Figure 1.23a and in part in Figure 1.23b.

Surrounding the cooling pipe 24 is a spirally configured coppper tubing 30 through which a refrigerant gas or liquid is pumped from a pump 36 from a refrigerating means 38 to each of the cooling coils 30, 30 which then returns through a return pipe 40 to the refrigerating means. By means of the cooling effect that is derived and imposed upon the cooling pipes 24, 24, oil is condensed and is then collected in pipe 44 which connects with a barrel or storage tank 46. The storage tank has a vent 48 at the top and an oil outlet valve 50 at the bottom.

In processing the gaseous vapors through the cooling unit, it is found that aluminum tubing of 3 to 5 feet in length disposed within a cooling jacket of iron or stainless steel and filled with insulating material such as glass fibers and in which there is also disposed a spiral of coils of copper tubing around the cooling tube, achieves a maximum result.

FIGURE 1.23: IN SITU OIL EXTRACTION DEVICE

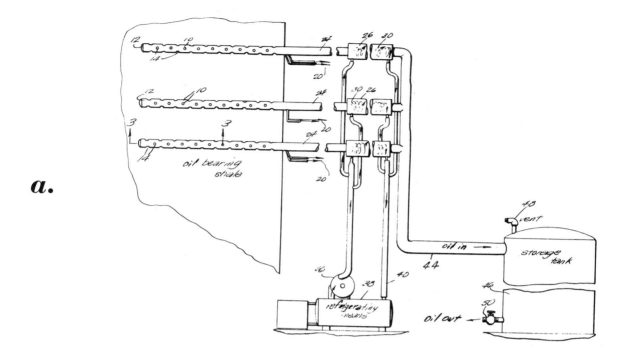

a.

Perforated Pipe Inserted in Oil Bearing Shale

b.

Cross-Sectional View of Cooling Unit

c.

Cross-Sectional View Along Line 3—3 of
Figure 1.23a

Source: J.H. Medlen; U.S. Patent 3,448,794; June 10, 1969

The cooling agent may be water or alcohol that passes from the refrigerator pump 36 to the return pipe 40 into the refrigerating means which may include a storage tank. Gaseous oil vapor condenses into usable oil at 40° to 50°F. Pumping of gaseous vapors through the cooling tube and the perforating tube is not necessary due to at least the reason that heavier-than-air gases will flow through the tube by natural gravitational forces, and condensation of vapors in the cooling tube induce a certain pressure to draw the vapors.

OTHER PROCESSES

Traveling Grate Shale Retorting

J.H. Haddad and J.G. Mitchell; U.S. Patent 3,483,115; December 9, 1969; assigned to Mobil Oil Corporation describe a method of retorting oil shale in a horizontally moving bed where gaseous material flowing transversely through the shale bed, all in a downflow direction through a plurality of gas contacting zones establishes a restricted kerogen decomposition heat front in the top of the bed and drives the decomposition heat front progressively downwardly as the bed moves horizontally through the retorting section. Gaseous material obtained from an intermediate portion of the shale bed, from which oil mist was recovered, is employed to effect partial cooling of gaseous material recovered from a latter portion of the shale bed. This cooled gas is introduced to an initial portion of the shale bed to condense out entrained oil constituents and to preheat the shale.

Figure 1.24 represents in cross section the process where three gas recovery zones are employed and gases from the second and third zones are mixed prior to being directed to the first zone. Particulate shale which has been ground to a target average size of about 0.75" with a maximum particle size of about 4" is introduced into a hopper 1.

The shale is directed from hopper 1 to classifier 3 through conduits 4 and 5. In classifier 3, the shale particles are classified according to size with the larger particles being directed to the bottom of the bed and the fines being directed to the top of the bed. Seal gas is introduced into conduits 4 and 5 to prevent air from entering the shale bed.

FIGURE 1.24:   TRAVELING GRATE SHALE RETORTING

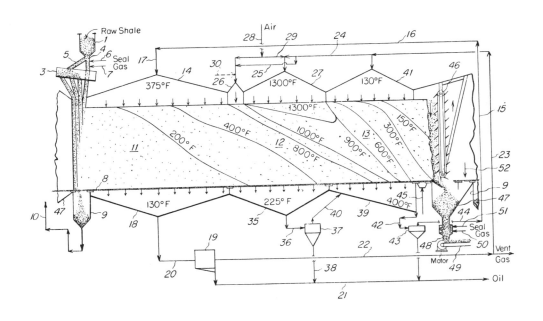

Source: J.H. Haddad and J.G. Mitchell; U.S. Patent 3,483,115; December 9, 1969

In this example, a double seal gas system is employed in conduits 4 and 5. The two seal gas flow rates are controlled so that the differential pressure between the two seal gas inlets 6 and 7 is essentially zero. The shale is introduced at a rate so that a relatively thick bed is formed on a horizontally moving perforated grate 8. The bed thickness on the grate 8 is maintained at about 6 feet.

The small amount of fines which sift through the bed are recovered in hopper 9 and recycled through conduit 10 to the shale inlet hopper 1. The moving grate 8 causes the shale bed thereon to progress sequentially through zones 11, 12 and 13. The uncondensed gas from zones 12 and 13 is recycled to gas plenum 14 on top of the bed in zone 11 through conduits 15, 16 and 17. The uncondensed gas passes downwardly through zone 11 through the grate 8 and into a gas recovery zone 18 located below the grate 8. The gas in gas recovery zone 18 is maintained at a temperature below about 130°F. At this temperature, most of the shale oil is in the form of a condensed mist. The condensate and remaining gas are directed to an oil recovery step 19 through conduit 20. Oil recovery step 19 can be, for example, a cyclone separator or an electrostatic precipitator. Condensed oil obtained from oil recovery step 19 is directed through conduit 21 to storage.

Uncondensed gas from recovery zone 19 is directed through conduits 22, 23, 24 and 25 to the top of the shale bed in zones 12 and 13. The uncondensed gas to zone 12 is first introduced into plenum chambers 26 and 27. Air is introduced to plenum chambers 26 and 27 through conduits 28 and 29. At start up, a fuel can be introduced to plenum chamber 26 through conduit 30 to admix with the air and recycled uncondensed vapor under conditions to cause combustion in plenum 26. After start up it is usually unnecessary to add fuel to maintain combustion in plenum 26. In plenum 27, a portion of the uncondensed gas is burned. The heat from the combustion in these two plenums is absorbed by the shale bed directly underneath these zones. By this heating, a heat wave at kerogen decomposition temperature is initiated on top of the bed in zone 12.

The kerogen decomposition zone is caused to move downwardly and toward the shale outlet in a configuration as shown in Figure 1.24. Representative temperatures of the gas introduced to each zone as well as the bed temperature profile is shown in Figure 1.24. The ratio of gas rate to the shale rate in each zone is adjusted to provide the representative temperature profiles shown. The gas in vapor zone 12 is caused to move downwardly through the entire vertical height of the bed. This gas is recovered in plenum zone 35 at a temperature below about 225°F. At this temperature a major portion of the oil has condensed. The uncondensed and condensed oil and gas are directed through conduit 36 to an oil separator 37 where oil is recovered through conduit 28 and uncondensed vapor and gas are directed to plenum chamber 39 through conduit 40.

In zone 13, recycled gas from oil recovery step 19 is introduced into plenum chamber 41 on top of the bed at a temperature of about 130°F. This gas is caused to move downwardly through the entire vertical height of the shale bed. In so doing, the top portion of the bed is cooled while the bottom portion of the bed is progressively heated until the kerogen decomposition heat wave reaches the grate 8. That portion of the bed lying between this point and the shale outlet in a horizontal direction is cooled through the entire vertical height. The off-gas from zone 13 is recovered in plenum chamber 39 at a temperature, when admixed with the uncondensed vapor from oil recovery step 37, of below about 400°F. At this temperature an additional portion of the higher boiling fraction of the shale oil is condensed. The uncondensed and condensed shale oil and gas is directed from plenum chamber 39 through conduit 42 to oil recovery step 43 where shale oil is recovered. The uncondensed vapor and gas from oil recovery step 43 is directed through conduits 44, 15, 16 and 17 to the top of zone 11 into the plenum chamber 14. The gas in plenum chamber 14 is caused to move through the vertical height of the bed in zone 11 in a manner described above. Blowers are provided in the various gas conduits to ensure gas flow downwardly through the bed. The gas flow rates to plenums 14, 27 and 41 are maintained respectively at about 0.765 ton vapor per tons shale, 0.447 ton vapor per tons shale and 0.483 ton vapor per tons shale.

The grate 8, after progressing through zone 13 is contacted with a small portion of gas introduced through conduit 45 which removes any coke which has formed in the perforations of the grate. This gas moves only through a very small portion of the vertical height and is recovered in plenum chamber 39. The grate 8 is in sections and above hopper 47 the sections are tipped so that the shale thereon can be removed. The shale is broken up by the clinker breaker 46 and thereafter moves by gravity to hopper 47 and directed outwardly from the retort zone through conduit 48 onto a conveyor 49.

Conduit 48 is sealed from the atmosphere by a dual-gas seal system by the introduction of seal gas through conduits 50 and 51 similar to that described above for the inlet seal system. The relative sizes of the gas inlet plenums are approximately proportional to the inlet gas flow rates thereto. To afford relatively complete clearing of the grate 8, it is subjected to a jet of fluid and/or solids through conduit 52. The material entrained on the grate is directed to the hopper.

In the process, the shale bed can be moved in a closed horizontal path as for example in a circular path or in an open horizontal path as for example in a straight line. In any event, the shale bed is continuously moved through a plurality of vapor contact zones. The vapors in each zone are introduced at a pressure sufficient to ensure vapor flow in one direction through the bed vertical height. The gas pressure differential between the top and bottom of the bed to ensure this flow depends upon a number of factors including the average shale particle size, bed thickness, the gas flow rate used, and the temperature conditions of the bed. In the process, the average shale particle size is maintained below about 2" and preferably below about 0.6". The shale bed thickness is maintained below about 15 feet and preferably between 4 and 8 feet.

In operation, the particulate shale can be directed onto the grate through a feeding device which stratifies the shale according to size with larger shale particles being located on the grate and the fines being located on top of the bed. Means can be provided below the bed and preceding the first vapor recovery zone to recycle the small portion of the fines sifting through the bed back to the top of the bed. The stationary gas plenum chambers above and below the moving retort are sealed from the atmosphere as for example by a liquid seal to contain the gases.

The moving grate moves the shale bed serially through the gas contact zones to effect complete kerogen decomposition. The temperature profile of the spent shale upon discharge from the grate may vary from 150°F. at the top of the bed to as high as 600°F. at the bottom of the bed. The spent shale is removed from the grate and directed to spent shale container where the shale is mixed and the temperature of the individual particles allowed to equilibrate by conductive heat transfer to reduce maximum particle temperature below 400°F. maximums. To assist removal of spent shale from the grate, apparatus can be used to break up the shale bed to assist in shale movement to storage. The spent shale container is also sealed from the atmosphere but is open to the retort vapors.

The cool spent shale is removed from the container and disposed of. The moving grate is then directed to the shale inlet portion of the retort where fresh shale is introduced. After spent shale is removed from the grate and prior to introducing fresh shale thereon, any coke and/or particulate shale in the grate perforation is removed therefrom as for example with high velocity jet cleaning or by burning.

The vapors directed to each zone are first directed to inlet plenum chambers adjacent the bed. These inlet plenums operate to separate the vapors so that different conditions of vapor temperature and vapor flow can be maintained in various portions of the bed. In addition, the vapor inlet plenums provide relatively uniform vapor flow through the vertical height of a given portion of the shale bed. Each of the plenums can be subdivided into smaller chambers to provide more efficient vapor flow control. Similarly, the vapor outlet plenums can be subdivided into smaller chambers to improve vapor flow control. Compressors are provided in various vapor lines as needed to maintain the desired pressure gradient through the shale bed.

In a process described by T.E. Ban; U.S. Patent 3,325,395; June 13, 1967; assigned to McDowell-Wellman Engineering Company oil bearing material is first obtained or crushed to a workable particle size not exceeding 18" in diameter. This material is then charged to a traveling grate to form a bed. The traveling grate with its burden passes into a first zone where the burden is exposed to heat reducing or neutral gases at a temperature of from 1000° to 1500°F., by passing the gases through the burden in either updraft or downdraft fashion. This elevates the temperature of the burden to an oil educting temperature of about 800°F., at which point the kerogen breaks down or cracks into an oil vapor which becomes condensed and suspended in the gas stream passing through the bed. This draft or gas is then conducted through a cyclone separator where the oil is separated from the gas. Any suitable means for separating the oil from the gases may be used.

The traveling grate moves to a second zone where the oil depleted gases are recirculated through the spent burden to aid in cooling the burden, and to preheat the gases to oil educting temperature for recycling through a new burden in the first zone. Air may be added to the gas stream as to burn part of the burnable constituents contained in the gas stream, and to elevate the temperature of the gas to from 1000° to 1500°F. The spent burden is removed from the traveling grate.

Agglomeration of Fines in Traveling Grate Process

C.A. Rowland and R.D. Frans; U.S. Patent 3,560,369; February 2, 1971 and U.S. Patent 3,560,368; February 2, 1971; both assigned to Allis-Chalmers Manufacturing Company describe a system for recovering oil from oil bearing shale rock in which the rock is screened to separate fines from larger particles having a dimension of at least about 1/4". The system includes a retorting zone in which heated gases, reducing or neutral, are passed through the larger particles and agglomerates of the fines to heat these particles and agglomerates to oil educting temperature and after which the gases, then containing educted oil, are passed through a zone in which particles and agglomerates are preheated and the gases cooled to condense the oil to small droplets and vapor in the gases. The oil is separated from the gases and into various fractions.

The heaviest fractions of the oil, representing an amount in a range of from 5 to 50% of the total oil educted, are recirculated through the system by using such oil as binder to agglomerate the fines into agglomerates of at least 1/4". These agglomerates may be advantageously utilized by charging them to a traveling grate apparatus with the larger particles to form a bed, with the agglomerates forming an intermediate layer between upper and lower layers of the larger particles. The larger particles will, in a preheating condensing zone, trap and prevent escape from the bed, dust and drops of heavy binder oil (which may escape from agglomates).

With either an upflow or downflow of gas in this preheating condensing zone, heavy binder oil attempting to escape the bed will adhere to and coat particles in the upper or lower layers and dust attempting to escape the bed will adhere to the larger particles coated by the heavy binder oil. Thus, both the heavy binder oil and dust attempting to escape in this preheating condensing zone will be trapped in the bed. In the retorting zone such heavy fraction binder oil retained in the bed will pyrolyze to produce further useful lighter oil, which will leave the bed as vapor, and residual coke which will remain in the bed.

Referring to Figure 1.25a a gas permeable traveling grate assembly 1 defines a loop with an upper strand 2 supported between head and tail shafts 3 and 4 for movement in a generally horizontal path in the direction indicated by arrows. A housing assembly 5 is arranged below and over the upper strand 2 and baffles 6, 7 above strand 2 and baffles 8, 9 below strand 2 divide the interior of the housing assembly 5 into at least three chambers 15, 16 and 17 above strand 2 and windboxes 19, 20 and 21 beneath strand 2 and in vertical alignment with the chambers 15, 16 and 17, respectively.

A feed hopper assembly 22 having three feed chambers 22a, 22b and 22c is provided for feeding, through chamber 22b, agglomerated fines on top of and beneath particles of rock fed through chambers 22a and 22c, to provide a three layer bed of material on strand 2. A combustion chamber 25 is provided remote from strand 2 and housing assembly 5. An oil separator station is indicated at 30, which may be one or more mechanical oil-gas separators, with or without gas coolers as desired. The oil-gas separating operation is also located apart from the strand 2 and housing 5. Separators suitable for the use are known and an example of a patent describing such a device is U.S. Patent 2,386,196.

A gas stream conveying system connects the grate assembly 1, the combustion chamber 25 and the separator 30. The gas stream conveying system includes a blower 40 and a first conduit 41 for delivering gas to windbox 21. A second conduit 42 with a blower 43 is provided for delivering preheated gas to combustion chamber 25. Gas flow communication from the first conduit 41 to the second conduit 42 is by a path established through windbox 21 and material on strand 2 in chamber 17. A gas stream passing from conduit 41 through material on strand 2 to conduit 42 thereby cools the material and is itself preheated before entering combustion chamber 25.

FIGURE 1.25:   RETORT PROCESS EMPLOYING TRAVELING GRATE AND AGGLOMERATION OF FINES

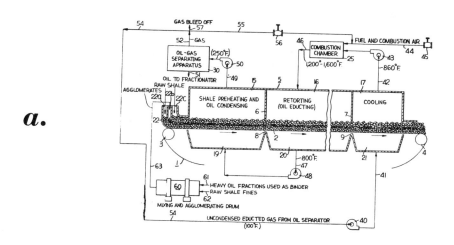

a.

Apparatus Schematic

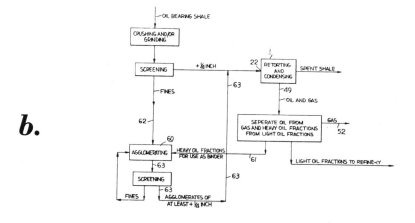

b.

Process Flow Diagram

Source: C.A. Rowland and R.D. Frans; U.S. Patent 3,560,369; February 2, 1971

A third conduit 44 is connected to combustion chamber 25 for delivery of combustion air. Means for controlling the combustion air admitted to chamber 25 is indicated by the valve 45. A fourth conduit 46 is connected to combustion chamber 25 to exit an oxygen free mixture of combustion products and noncondensable combustible gases and deliver such gases to the retorting chamber 16. The gas discharged by conduit 46 to chamber 16 passes downward through material on strand 2 in chamber 16. A fifth conduit 47 is connected to windbox 20 to provide an exit and establish gas flow communication from the fourth conduit 46 through the upper strand 2 of the grate assembly 1 to the fifth conduit 47. A blower 48 is provided in conduit 47 to blow gases from windbox 20 into windbox 19 and up through strand 2 and into chamber 15. A sixth conduit 49 is connected to chamber 15 and to the oil separator 30. A blower 50 is provided in conduit 49 to deliver to the separator 30 liquid oil (mist) and a stream of noncondensable combustible oxygen free gases educted from the shale. The stream of gases passing out of chamber 16 through windbox 20 and conduit 47 is of greater quantity than the quantity of the gas stream passing into chamber 16 from conduit 46. This is true of course because as the heated gas stream passes through the shale, vaporized oil and noncondensable gases are educted from the shale and added to the gas stream.

Liquid oil from the shale separated from noncondensable gases at 30 may be discharged through an exit at 51 and led off to oil refining apparatus. The stream of noncondensable combustible gases from the separator at 30 may be discharged through an exit at 52 to a seventh conduit 54 which is connected to the first described conduit 41. Thus the stream of noncondensable combustible gases educted from the shale supplies the need for an oxygen free nonburning gas stream to cool the shale material in chamber 17 and the need (after being preheated and mixed with combustion air from conduit 44) for a burning stream of gases for heating the shale material in the retorting zone 16. An eighth conduit 55 is connected on one end to separator gas exit 52 to deliver some of the gas from separator 30 to combustion chamber 25 without passing through material on strand 2. Means for controlling this flow is indicated by the valve 56.

Because burning fuel in combustion chamber 25 and heating the shale in retorting chamber 16 generates additional volumes of gases which are continuously added to the system, a bleed off will be necessary and may be provided as at 57.

An agglomerating device, such as the balling drum 60 shown in Figure 1.25a, is fed fines by a conveyor 61 and heavy binder oil through conduit 62. Drum 60 mixes and agglomerates the material and discharges agglomerates to a conveyer 63 for delivery to chamber 22b. The balling drum 60 may be of the type described in U.S. Patent 2,411,873. The heavy binder oil delivered to drum 60 by conduit 62 comprises heavy fractions of the oil discharged from the oil-gas separating apparatus 30 to a fractionator at 51. The fractionator may be a vacuum fractional distillation column operated to divide the oil into two portions, one of light fractions and the other of heavy, i.e., high boiling point, fractions (with the heavy fraction portion being between 5 and 50% of the total volume of oil) as is described in U.S. Patent 3,228,869.

In the best interests of an overall process, the amount of oil recycled through the system as binder oil would be advantageously adjusted within the 5 to 50% range referred to, according to changes in weather. That is, in cold weather more heavy fractions would be desirably removed and recycled to maintain the desired flowability of the lighter oils shipped or pumped to a refinery.

To operate an apparatus such as shown in Figure 1.25a, shale rock is crushed and screened to provide pieces at least about 1/4 inch. These pieces are then charged to feed hopper chambers 22a and 22c. The feed hopper 22 discharges such particles of crushed shale on the upper strand 2 of the grate assembly 1 which is driven to move the grate in the direction shown by arrows. Agglomerates of fines formed in drum 60 are screened, as indicated in Figure 1.25b, to recycle pieces smaller than about 1/4" and the agglomerates that are larger than about 1/4" are charged to feed hopper chamber 22b which discharges this size fraction as a middle layer upon strand 2 thus forming a three layer bed on strand 2. The grate 1 carries the bed of shale through the chambers 15, 16 and 17, which define a downstream material flow sequence comprising a shale preheating and oil condensing zone (in chamber 15); a retorting and oil educting zone (in chamber 16); and, a cooling zone (in chamber 17).

After the shale material has given up oil as a vapor and noncondensable gases while in chamber 16 the residue is moved through the cooling zone in chamber 17 where gas from separator 30 at perhaps 100°F. is blown by blower 40 through the first conduit 41 upwardly through windbox 21, strand 2, and into cooling chamber 17, to cool the material to a temperature for handling by rubber conveyer belts, and preheat the gas to perhaps about 860°F.

The preheated gas passes from chamber 17 into conduit 42. This preheated air is then drawn in by blower 43 and delivered to combustion chamber 25 where controlled amounts of combustion air from conduit 44 and gases from conduit 55 mix to burn a portion of the combustibles therein. Valve 45 controls the air flow through conduit 44 and provides a primary control to cause sufficient combustion of gases from conduit 42 to occur to provide a mixture of unburned noncondensable gases and combustion products, free of oxygen, to exit from combustion chamber 25 through conduit 46 at about 1200° to 1600°F.

Conduit 46 delivers these gases to the retorting chamber 16. Valve 56 provides additional control of the combustion taking place in chamber 25. These gases from conduit 46 pass downwardly through the shale on strand 2 in chamber 16 and heat the shale to at least slightly above oil educting temperature which may be expected to be about 800°F. The gases drawn from windbox 20 at slightly above educting, condensing temperature are blown through conduit 47, windbox 19, and through the shale on strand 2 in chamber 15.

The condensable vaporized oil and noncondensable gases educted from the shale in the retorting chamber 16, along with the hot gases from conduit 46, are passed through the bed of shale in chamber 15 which condenses the oil vapors to a stable mist while preheating raw shale from hopper 22. Oil mist and a stream of noncondensable combustible gases exit from chamber 15 through conduit 49 at about 250°F. and are delivered to the mechanical oil-gas separating station 30. Multistage separating, perhaps including or resulting in further cooling, may provide gases in conduits 54, 41 and 55, 44 at about 100°F.

As indicated by the legend labels in Figure 1.25b, oil bearing shale is delivered to a crushing and/or grinding operation and then to a screening operation that separates pieces which may, for example, be larger than 1/4", from smaller pieces which are referred to as fines. The plus 1/4" particles are delivered to a retorting stage indicated by a box so labeled and additionally labeled with the reference numeral 1 to indicate that this stage may include the entire assembly identified with the numeral 1 in Figure 1.25a. The particles delivered to this stage are discharged into the feed hopper assembly 22, which is also indicated at the box 1.

Fines from the screening operation are indicated in Figure 1.25b to be carried by the conveyor 62 to an agglomerating stage, which may be the balling drum 60 of Figure 1.25a. As shown in Figure 1.25b, agglomerates from drum 60 may be screened with fines being recirculated through the agglomerating stage and the agglomerates at least about 1/4" in size are delivered by the conveyor 63 to the feed hopper assembly 22. Oil (as mist) and gas from the retorting and condensing stage 1, are delivered by the conduit 49 to a gas-oil and light oil-heavy oil separation stage. The gas from this stage passes into conduit 52 for uses indicated in Figure 1.25a. The light oil fractions may be delivered or conveyed as indicated in Figure 1.25b to a refinery, and this may be accomplished by such as pipe lines or tank cars as desired. The heavy oil fractions are conveyed by conduit 61 to agglomerating drum 60 for use therein as a binder additive.

In related work R.W. Weggel and W.A. Blann; U.S. Patent 3,644,193; February 22, 1972; assigned to Allis-Chalmers Manufacturing Company describe a system for recovering oil from oil bearing shale rock in which shale is placed on a traveling grate and transported through a preheating zone; a retorting zone where oil is educted from shale; a combustion zone where the residual carbon in the shale after the oil is removed, is burned; and a cooling zone. A first gas stream, which may be air, is passed through shale that has traveled on the grate at least to where combustion takes place.

This air is thereby heated, and then used to heat a heat transfer media such as alumina balls from which a second and oxygen-free gas stream extracts the heat. The second gas stream, heated indirectly by the first gas stream but not contaminated with combustion gases from the first gas stream, passes through the shale in the retorting zone to educt oil from the shale and then through the shale in the preheating zone where the educted oil is condensed and becomes suspended as a stable mist in the second gas stream from which the oil may be mechanically separated.

Electrothermal Pyrolysis

I.S. Salnikov; U.S. Patent 3,377,266; April 9, 1968 describes an electrothermal method and apparatus for the pyrolysis of oil shale to recover shale oil.

Referring to Figure 1.26a, there is shown a vertical furnace or retort 10 of hollow, elongated cylindrical configuration and which is formed to define in downward succession a preheat zone 12, a distillation zone 13, and a lower heat exchange zone 14. In construction, the retort 10 preferably consists of a pair of heavy walled, upper and lower tubular sections 17 and 18 connected in end-to-end relation by means of abutting flanges 19 interconnected by suitable bolts 20. To form the preheat zone 12, the upper tubular section 17 includes an upwardly convergent wall portion 22 for connection in end-to-end relation with a tubular section 24, of reduced size, again through abutting flanges 25 being interconnected by suitable bolts 26. The top tubular portion 24 also defines the entrance into the preheat zone from the top of the furnace and for this purpose is provided with a central opening 28 for insertion of a generally funnel-shaped hopper 30 in which is disposed an auger 32, the latter being driven by an electric motor 33 through gear drive 34 and drive shaft 35.

In order to separate the tubular section into spaced upper and lower chambers, the lower tubular section 18 has an internal annular shoulder 38 just beneath its point of connection to the upper tubular section 17 which serves to support a downwardly convergent wall portion 40 including a lower tubular portion 42 of reduced size for disposition of a feed screw of auger 43. Here, the wall portion 40 defines the lower terminal end of the distillation zone 13 and, together with the tubular sections 17 and 18 and upper feed screw 32, provides a sealed chamber for passage of shale at a controlled rate of travel through the preheat zone and distillation zone.

FIGURE 1.26: ELECTROTHERMAL PYROLYSIS

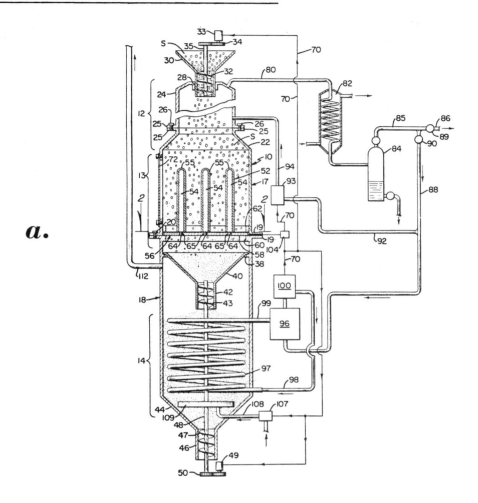

a.

Detail of Apparatus

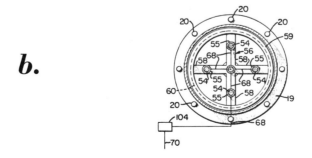

b.

Sectional View Along Line 2—2 of Figure 1.26a

Source: I.S. Salnikov; U.S. Patent 3,377,266; April 9, 1968

Similarly, the lower end of the tubular section 18 has a convergent wall portion 44 extending downwardly into a lower tubular portion 46 for an ejection screw of auger 47, and it will be noted that the augers 43 and 47 are driven through a common drive shaft 48 by electric motor 49 through gear train 50. In general, the various tubular sections and wall portions are heavy-walled and in a conventional manner are surfaced with an inner, refractory lining, not shown, so as to be capable of withstanding the intense heat developed within the furnace during pyrolysis of the shale.

An important feature of the process resides in the construction and arrangement of the heating elements employed in the distillation or pyrolysis zone 13; and in the preferred form of apparatus a nest or series of electrical resistance heating elements 52 are arranged in spaced parallel relation to one another in the zone with each element being disposed on an axis parallel to the path of flow of the shale material through the retort.

Preferably, each heating element is defined by an elongated, cylindrical rod 54 of metallic material having an outer jacket 55 composed of a suitable fire clay or ceramic material whose expansion and contraction characteristics correspond with that of the material defining the rods 54. The heating elements 52 are supported in vertical, spaced relation within the distillation zone by means of an open grid or mounting frame 56 having intersecting cross bars 58 and an outer circular ring 59; and the frame 56 is removably seated in horizontal relation across the distillation zone upon an inwardly projecting annular shoulder 60 at the upper end of the tubular section 18 and is held firmly in place by means of another internal shoulder 62 at the lower extremity of the tubular section 17, the latter engaging the ring 59 on the mounting plate when the tubular sections are secured in connected together relation as illustrated.

Preferably each heating element 52 has a lower threaded end 64 for threaded insertion into a socket 65, there being a plurality of sockets 65 provided at uniformly spaced intervals and in upwardly facing relation on the mounting frame, as best seen from Figure 1.26b, to support the heating elements in desired spaced relation for upward extension through the distillation zone. Moreover, as represented, electrical wire cable network 68 is imbedded within the mounting frame to establish electrical connection from a main power line 70 to each of the sockets 65 and, in turn, to each of the respective heating elements 52.

It will be seen that the entire heating assembly including the heating elements 52 and the mounting frame 56 may be removed from the chamber by removing the top tubular section 17; and a detachable manhole cover 72 is positioned over one open side of the upper tubular section 17 to afford access to the heating assembly so that the heating elements can be individually removed or replaced without disassembling the entire apparatus.

In the process, particles of crushed oil shale S, for example, marlstone crushed to a size of 1/4" to 2" in diameter are conveyed to the hopper 30 at the top of the furnace by suitable means and caused to descend slowly in succession through the preheat zone 12 and distillation zone 13 by rotation of the auger 32. The rate of travel of the shale through the upper sealed chamber is controlled also by the lower auger 43 which as shown is independently driven by the drive shaft 48, and both the augers 32 and 43 are dimensioned to establish sealed relation with the internal wall surfaces of the respective hoppers so as to exclude air from the preheat and distillation zones during pyrolysis of the shale.

It will be noted that the heating elements 52, being aligned in the direction of movement of the shale material through the distillation zone, will establish direct contact with the material throughout a substantial portion of its travel through the chamber so as to bring about most uniform and thorough heating of the shale, and the outer protective jackets 55 will serve to insulate the rods from direct physical contact with the shale while effectively conducting the heat developed in the rods but without impeding the movement of the shale particles through the distillation zone. This arrangement is further advantageous in that the fire clay jackets, once heated to the elevated temperature required for distillation will not experience rapid temperature changes in heating the shale while being maintained at the high temperature level by the resistance heating rods.

Thus, by heating the elements 52 to the elevated temperature level necessary to heat the distillation zone to the temperature of distillation of the shale oil-forming gases, this being on the order of 900° to 1000°F., the shale particles will liberate hydrocarbon gases and vapors which for the most part are the shale oil-forming gases and which can be separately collected and recovered outside the furnace or retort in a well known manner. By excluding air from the distillation zone, the residual or fixed carbon in the shale will pass with the spent shale into the lower heat exchange zone, again at a controlled rate of travel as determined by the speed of rotation of the auger 43.

The vaporous products of distillation formed will rise in countercurrent fashion from the pyrolysis zone through the preheat zone in heat transfer relation to the imcoming shale, then are recovered through gas line 80 for removal through condensor 82 to an accumulator 84 for collection of the condensed shale oil with minor percentages of other condensed hydrocarbon vapors. The noncondensable gases will tend to rise in the accumulator through line 85 either for separate collection through branch line 86 or for recycling through line 88, and the proportionate flow between lines 86 and 88 may be suitably controlled by valves 89 and 90 in the respective lines. Of the recycled gases, a portion is drawn through line 92 and delivered by means of a blower, represented at 93, through line 94 to the preheat zone 12. In this way, the noncondensable gases will mix with the gaseous products of distillation rising from the distillation zone in order to raise the condensation level of the gases formed by pyrolysis and to minimize condensation of the gases when cooled by the incoming shale.

Another portion of the recycled gases may be drawn through recycle line 88 as a source of fuel either in the heat exchange zone 14 or for a steam power plant 96. However, the main source of energy for the power plant 96 is derived from the heat exchange zone, and to this end a circulating coil 97 is directed in helical fashion upwardly through the heat exchange zone having a water inlet 98 and a steam outlet 99 leading to the power plant 96. In this way, water circulated through the coil 97 is increasingly heated as it winds upwardly through the coil in contact with the progressively hotter shale bed moving downwardly through the heat exchange zone, until it is vaporized to form steam for discharge to the power plant.

The steam power plant 96 is most desirably employed to operate a steam turbine or other suitable prime mover for an electric generator 100, thus converting the heat energy from the heat exchange zone to electric energy. The outlet power line 70 leads from the generator 100 to the wire network 68 in the frame 56 for heating the elements 52, and a rheostat 104 is positioned in the line to regulate the supply of current to the heating elements and consequently to establish close control over the temperature level developed in the distillation zone.

Heat transfer to the water circulated through the heat exchange coil is aided by combustion of the fixed or residual carbon in the shale, this being accomplished by directing air from a blower 107 through line 108 and vent 109 to discharge the air upwardly through the downwardly flowing shale bed and promote combustion of the carbon. Thus, the heat of combustion developed from oxidation of the fixed or residual carbon will substantially increase the heat energy available for conversion of the water to steam supplied to the power plant in order to operate the electrical generator and provide a closed regenerative system for oil shale pyrolysis. The gases formed in the heat exchange zone are recovered through outlet line 112 located above the heat exchange zone.

The rate of travel of the spent shale through the lower heat exchange zone is controlled independently of its rate of travel through the upper zones by regulating the speed of rotation of the augers 43 and 47, and will permit direct introduction of the spent shale at an elevated temperature from the distillation zone into the heat exchange zone for most effective use in forming steam to generate electricity. Moreover, electrical power line 70 serves as a power source for the gas blower, air blower and electrical motors for the feed screws so that the entire system is self-contained without resorting to outside power sources.

Hot Spent Shale Ash as Heat Source

R.T. Ellington, Jr.; U.S. Patent 3,597,347; August 3, 1971; assigned to The Oil Shale Corporation describes a process for retorting carbonaceous material, such as oil shale, where the heat of pyrolysis is supplied by mixing hot spent shale ash with raw shale feed. Shale particles lose their strength progressively above about 500°F. so crushing of the feed to minus 1/8" size does not take place until after mixing or retorting. Cold shale feed fines are added to the mixed hot shale ash and larger shale feed before retorting.

One of the processes of interest is the "sandcracking" process. In operation, spent shale ash preheated to about 1200°F. is mixed with cold raw shale feed that has been previously crushed to minus 1/8" size. The spent shale ash thus provides the heat of pyrolysis. After mixing, the shale ash and feed are discharged into a retorting vessel. The size of the vessel and the rate of withdrawal of spent shale ash are in such relationship that the shale feed has adequate time to absorb heat from the shale ash and to be fully retorted before it is discharged from the retort vessel.

Air is introduced into the solid effluent discharged from the retorting vessel and the air-entrained effluent is passed into a lift-tube combustor where the carbon content of the spent shale is burned off to heat the air and the shale ash to the desired temperature. At the top of the lift pipe, part of the entrained shale ash is knocked out and dropped in the retention bin to provide heat for retorting. The remainder is carried off with the hot combustion products, through a waste heat boiler and/or any other heat recovery means and then through a cyclone where the ash is separated from the cooled combustion products and sent to disposal. The gaseous retort products are withdrawn from the top of the retort vessel and transferred to a hot-dust separator where the entrapped waste dust is removed. The thus purified gaseous retort products are then conventionally treated to remove oil and other products.

While this process, as outlined above, offers oil yields of at least 90% Fischer Assay, it also presents problems. The raw oil shale feed must be crushed from a size of 1" or more to the minus 1/8" size to give optimum operation of the lift-tube combustor. Also, there is the possibility that the burned off shale ash will absorb shale oil vapors in the retorting drum and thus carry part of the yield from new shale out to the combustor, thus reducing the yield in the recovery system.

It has been found that these problems may be overcome by mixing shale ash of a temperature of 1000° to 1500°F. preferably 1200° to 1400°F. with cold raw oil shale feed fines and larger feed of a size of minus 1.5" to minus 1" down to 1/8", the larger feed preferably being preheated to 500° to 550°F., transferring the mix to a retort vessel where the atmosphere is maintained noncombustion supporting (an atmosphere of natural gas or processed retort gas containing 10 volume percent CO_2 is preferred), retorting off volatile material at a preferred retort temperature of 800° to 950°F., such as oil, with the heat of pyrolysis supplied by the hot spent shale ash, crushing the shale mixture at temperature above about 500°F. to essentially minus 1/4" size, preferably minus 1/8" size, passing the spent shale through a lift-tube combustor by the addition of air where the carbon content of the spent shale is burned off to heat the air and shale ash to the desired temperatures, and recycling part of the heated spent shale back to the mixer for mixing with raw feed oil shale.

It has been found that oil shale commences to lose crushing strength above about 500°F. and is very friable by the time it reaches retort temperature and is retorted. As a consequence, crushing of the oil shale above about 500°F. is much easier and requires less extensive crushing apparatus to achieve the fineness normally sought in the low temperature crushing. Retorting for the oil can be done with the large pieces nearly as easily as with the finer particles normally used.

However, finer particles are desirable for flow through the lift-tube combustor under the action of air. The crusher can thus be placed in the process anywhere the shale is at a temperature of over 500°F. and before the lift-tube combustor. It may thus be placed at the outlet of the mixer, or, if residence time in the mixer is not sufficient to raise the raw shale temperature to above 500°F. and larger particles in the retort vessel do not affect yield, at the outlet of the retort vessel.

Referring to Figure 1.27, raw shale feed 1 of a size of about minus 1.5" to minus 1" is fed into the raw shale preheater 2 where the feed 1 is preheated to a temperature range of 500° to 550°F. The preheater is heated by heat taken from the ash and flue gas taken from the retort vessel as described below. The preheated raw shale feed 3 is then transferred to a mixer 4, which can be any conventional mixing apparatus such as a screw mixer, where it is mixed with hot shale ash 5 from the retention drum 6, described below, and fine-size, i.e., minus 1/4", raw shale feed 7.

The fine-size raw shale feed 7 is preferably separated from the larger raw shale feed 1 before the latter is preheated. The mixed shales 8 are then transferred to the retorting vessel 9. If the mixed shales 8 are discharged at a temperature of 500°F. or higher, a crusher 10 can be used between the mixer 4 and retort vessel 9 to crush the shale pieces to a size sufficient to be transferred by air to the retention drum 6, i.e., essentially minus 1/4" size, preferably minus 1/8" size. If the discharge temperature at the mixer 4 is not 500°F. or above or if it is desired to omit any further fine-size pieces that may carry away the oil vapor, the crusher may be inserted intermediate the discharge side of the retort vessel 9 and the liftpipe 11, as indicated in the figure at 12. The feed shale is retorted in retort vessel 9 with the heat of pyrolysis supplied by the hot shale ash 5. The retorting is carried out at a temperature range of 500° to 1500°F., preferably 800° to 950°F. The charge of mixed shales 8 is preferably maintained during retorting in a noncombustion supporting atmosphere. The atmosphere may be pure natural gas or a gas of similar composition but optimum results are achieved using an atmosphere of natural gas containing up to 20 volume percent carbon dioxide, preferably 10 volume percent.

Processed and recycled retort gas can also be employed as the atmosphere. This surrounding atmosphere is injected into the retort vessel 9 at inlet 13. Compositional control can be achieved through conventional means such as an on-line chromatograph and gas mixing. The gaseous effluent 14 from the reactor vessel containing the retorted oil is taken off the top of the retort vessel 9 and transferred to a hot dust separator 15 through conventional piping. The dust removed gas 16 is transferred to a conventional product recovery system 17. The dust 18 removed in the separator is disposed of.

FIGURE 1.27:   RETORT PROCESS EMPLOYING HOT SPENT SHALE ASH FOR PYROLYSIS HEAT

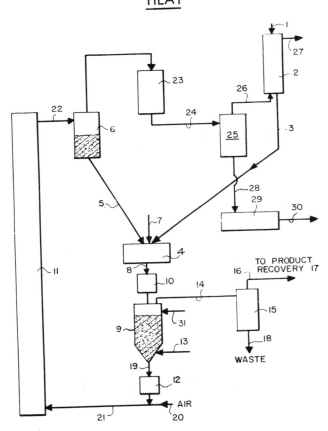

Source: R.T. Ellington, Jr.; U.S. Patent 3,597,347; August 3, 1971

If extra insurance is needed against condensation in transfer piping or hot cyclones used to remove shale ash or shale dust from the retort vapor, extra gas of the same composition as surrounding the particles or recycled processed retort gas and preferably preheated can be fed above the bed in the retort vessel 9 as indicated at 31 to lower the dew point of the vapor stream leaving the retort.

The solid oil-depleted shale mixture 19 is removed from the retort vessel 9, passed through the optional crusher 12, as explained above, and is transferred into the liftpipe combustor 11 by the injection of air 20. As the solid-air mixture 21 passes up the liftpipe combustor 11, the carbon in the oil-depleted shale is burned off, raising the temperature of both the shale and the air. At the top of the liftpipe 11 is a retention drum 6 into which the combusted shale ash is transferred. Part of this hot shale ash 22 is recycled into the mixer 4 as explained above for heat transfer to the raw shale feeds 3 and 7.

The balance of the hot shale at 22 and the flue gas combustion products from lift pipe 11 are transferred into the heat exchanger 23, such as a waste heat boiler. The cooled ash-gas mixture 24 is then further transferred to cyclone 25 where the shale ash and the flue gas are separated. The flue gas 26 is then transferred into raw shale preheater 2 for direct or indirect heat exchange with the large size raw shale feed 1. After this exchange, the flue gas is vented into a stack as generally indicated at 27. The shale ash 28 from cyclone 25 is transferred to shale ash cooler 29 from where it is disposed of as generally indicated at 30. The following example illustrates the process.

Example: Raw shale feed of minus 1.5" size and at a temperature of about 60°F. is fed to a raw shale preheater where it is preheated to a temperature of about 520°F. The preheated raw shale is transferred to a mixing vessel where it is mixed with hot shale ash at a temperature of about 1250°F. After one to three minutes residence time, the mixed shale ash and feed are discharged into a retort vessel maintained under an atmosphere of processed retort gas containing at least 90% CH_4. Shale oil is retorted from the feed with the heat of pyrolysis being supplied by the hot shale ash.

After 3 to 10 minutes residence time, the shale ash and shale coke at equal temperatures of about 875°F. are discharged into a crusher which crushes the mix to essentially minus 1/8" size. The crushed particles at a temperature of about 900°F. are transferred into a lifttube combustor by the injection of air.

The carbon in the shale coke is burned off in the combustor. At the top of the lifttube combustor, the shale ash is transferred to a retention drum at a temperature of about 1250°F. Part of this shale ash is recycled back to the mixing vessel for retorting. Part is transferred to a heat exchanger unit where steam can be generated by heat exchange with the hot shale ash.

The shale ash is then transferred to a cyclone where the shale ash and flue gas are separated. The hot flue gas is then transferred to the raw shale preheater where it preheats the raw shale feed by direct or indirect heat exchange. The shale ash is transferred to a spent shale ash cooler from where it is disposed of. The table on the following page shows the flow rates of materials in the example.

Oil Shale Retorting

Stream

In	Flow Rate (lbs./hr.)
Raw shale feed	916,667
Fluidizing gas	62,861
Combustion air	355,347
Total	1,334,875

Out	
Retort vessel effluent vapors	231,318
Spent shale ash to disposal	690,069
Flue gas	413,488
Total	1,334,875

Internal	
Preheated raw shale	916,667
Raw shale/spent shale ash mixture (retort feed)	2,223,741
Retort vessel effluent solids	2,055,284
Crusher product	2,055,284
Combustion lifttube effluent	2,410,631
Spent shale ash to retort	1,307,074
Flue gas plus spent shale ash	1,103,557
Flue gas to raw shale preheat	413,488
Flue gas to stack	413,488

In related work, C.E. Gessner; U.S. Patent 3,573,197; March 30, 1971; assigned to The Oil Shale Corporation describes a retorting process which utilizes the heat in the spent shale and in the shale oil vapors to heat the raw shale without condensing shale oil vapors on the raw shale and without contaminating the shale oil vapors with other gaseous material such as flue gas.

The process first distills shale oil vapors in a retorting zone from raw shale heated to a retorting temperature. The hot spent shale is then separated from the retorting zone. A circulating stream of a normally gaseous hydrocarbon such as natural gas, propane, butane, or mixtures is passed in direct contact with hot spent shale separated from the retorting zone in indirect heat exchange with the shale oil vapors.

The normally gaseous hydrocarbon is thus heated to a high temperature and the circulating stream of the normally gaseous hydrocarbon thus heated to a high temperature is passed into direct contact with raw shale. The raw shale is thereby preheated and a particulate solid heat transfer medium is also thus heated, particularly the hot spent shale, to a temperature in excess of the retorting temperature. The preheated raw shale and the thus heated particulate solid heat transfer medium are then passed into direct contact in the retorting zone thereby heating the preheated raw shale to a retorting temperature.

Preheating the sized raw shale with a closed circulating system of gas other than air and preferably being natural gas, propane or a propane/butane mixture is superior to those processes which preheat with flue gases where any desirable constituent evolved from the raw shale during preheating is lost with the flue gases. The method is superior to those processes which utilize retort vapor for preheating where desirable constituents in the retort vapor are condensed on the raw shale and carried back to the final heating section. For a specific oil shale, preheating is precisely controlled to a temperature that gives incipient evolution of desirable constituents. Should any desirable constituents be liberated during preheating, they are not lost but are retained in the closed circulating gas system.

The use of propane or a propane/butane mix as the gas for the closed circulating gas system of the process is preferred due to the advantageous thermodynamic properties of propane as compared to gases such as air, flue gas, or retort gas product. For a specific oil shale, the gas circulation horsepower is substantially lower than is required for other processes. The propane or propane/butane mix is economically recoverable from the retort gas product by conventional gas processing methods. Replenishment of the propane to offset seal leakage and to displace those constituents that may be liberated from the shale during preheating is desirable and economical.

Controlled Nuclear Reactor

M.L. Natland; U.S. Patent 3,109,781; November 5, 1963; assigned to Richfield Oil Corporation describes a process which comprises a unitary system for heating and recovering by-products from materials such as oil shales. The apparatus consists of a retort, the upper end of which is in communication with a fractionation unit and a gaseous heating unit, preferably a gas cooled nuclear reactor, the outlet of the heating unit being in communication with the lower portion of the retort and preferably the inlet of the heating unit being in communication with the upper portion of the fractionation unit.

Referring to Figure 1.28a, it can be seen that the system comprises three integrated units designated generally as the gas heating unit 1 here shown as a controlled nuclear reactor, the retort unit 3 and the fractional distillation unit 5. Each of the three units are in intimate intercommunication one with the other in order to provide a closed processing system for the recovery of valuable by-products from the hydrocarboniferous material treated.

The retort unit 3 can comprise an elongated tubular section 7 in which the material to be treated can flow downwardly as by gravity. Upwardly in the section 7 there is provided entrance line 9 for conducting the material to be treated into the retort 3 from a gravity hopper 11 and crusher 13. Disposed at any convenient location in line 9 are provided hydraulic flow regulating gates 15 and 17, the details of which are described in conjunction with Figure 1.28b.

Although it is preferred that two such gates be provided, more can, of course, be used if desired. The elongated tubular section 7 extends upward above the juncture of line 9 and opens into the lower section of the fractionation unit 5. The vertical section 7 can, of course, take other configurations if desired.

Entering the retort 3 at its lowermost end are provided hot gas lines 19 and 21 conducting the noncombustion supporting or oxygen-free gases from the heating source 1 via pump 23 to the retort unit 3. The lines 19 and 21 are disposed so that they rise upward from the point of entry into the retort and they can be provided with screens across their juncture with the retort, all for the purpose of preventing or impeding the crushed material and sediment in the tubular section 7 from flowing into the hot gas lines and causing plugging and clogging thereof. Preferably, lines 19 and 21 will join the retort at an acute angle. It is to be realized, of course, that more or less hot gas lines can be provided depending upon the volume of hot gas necessary to treat the material descending downwardly in the retort.

FIGURE 1.28: RETORT PROCESSING EMPLOYING CONTROLLED NUCLEAR REACTOR

a.

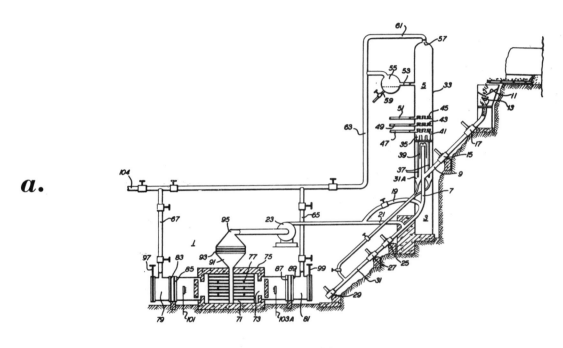

Overview of Process

b.

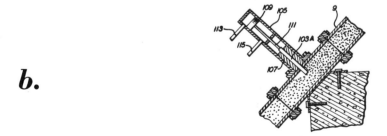

Sectional View of Hydraulic Gate

Source: M.L. Natland; U.S. Patent 3,109,781; November 5, 1963

Beneath the juncture of the hot gas entrance lines 19 and 21 there is provided a second series of hydraulic flow regulating gates 25, 27 and 29 disposed at intervals in the hydrocarboniferous material exit line 31.

The upper end of section 7 communicates with and opens into the lower section of fractional distillation unit 5. Unit 5 can comprise a fractionation tower 33, the lower part of which can be provided with cyclone separators 35 having diplegs 37 for separating any dust and sediments which may be carried upward with the gases out of the retort 3 and into the fractionation unit 5. The diplegs 37 can extend downward and terminate as here shown in the converging material exit line 31A of the retort 3. A bell deflector 39 is provided over the point where the opening from the retort extends into the unit 5 so as to deflect the rising gases downward and assist in the separation of the dust and sediments.

A plurality of liquid vapor condensation plates 41, 43 and 45 are provided in the fractionation tower 33 having liquid-take-off lines 47, 49 and 51 leading therefrom in order to condense and withdraw a liquid fraction boiling at the desired range. Plates 41, 43 and 45 can be of any conventional design such as a bubble cap type and as many levels as necessary or desired can be provided. The heavier gases and vapors are withdrawn from tower 33 as at 53 and sent to condenser 55 where the heavier lower boiling materials are separated and withdrawn as a liquid product and the lighter higher boiling materials are separated and withdrawn as a gaseous product. The lighter gaseous materials in tower 33 are taken off as overhead as at 57.

The liquid products withdrawn from condenser 55 and tower 33 via lines 59 and 47, 49 and 51, respectively, can be conducted to suitable storage facilities or to various processing and refining facilities as desired. The gaseous products collected from condenser 55 and as overhead via line 61 are recycled to the heating unit 1 via lines 63 and branch lines 65 and 67 in order to be reheated and again used in treating the hydrocarboniferous material in the retort 3. The heating unit 1 can be, as intimated previously, any type of heating arrangement desired so long as the gases to be used in treating the hydrocarboniferous material are heated to temperatures in the range of 500° to 1500°F.

In general, it is preferred to use a nuclear reactor of the type described in U.S. Patent 2,836,554. Reactors of this type can be operated at power levels of about 60,000 kilowatts to produce exit cooling gases having temperatures in the range of 500° to 1500°F. and which are sufficiently high for purposes of the process.

It can be seen that the reactor can comprise a reactive core constructed of graphite blocks 71 interlocked together to provide a moderating shield and having channels 73 to accommodate aluminum finned tubes loaded with the reactive uranium slugs. The reactive core is surrounded by a concrete shield 75 the thickness and density of which can be any found necessary to contain the radioactivity produced by the fission reaction.

The rate of fission and hence the temperature produced by the reactor can be controlled by the withdrawal or insertion of boron control rods as shown at 77. Cooling gas is drawn into and through the reactor at either end by means of ducts 79 and 81 having filters 83, 85, 87 and 89 therein for removing impurities and dust particles from the cooling gases which may tend to poison the nuclear fission reaction.

Heated gases are withdrawn from the reactor by means of outlet $\underline{91}$ after which they pass through filter $\underline{93}$. The filtered hot gases are then conducted by way of manifold $\underline{95}$ to compression pump $\underline{23}$, and thence to the retort unit $\underline{3}$ by means of lines $\underline{19}$ and $\underline{21}$ as hereinbefore set forth. Gates $\underline{97}$ and $\underline{99}$ can be placed at each end of ducts $\underline{79}$ and $\underline{81}$ in order to seal the reactor so as to provide a closed gaseous cycle through the entire system and, if necessary, a heat exchanger can be interposed in line $\underline{63}$ to cool the gases prior to return to the nuclear reactor $\underline{1}$.

The system can be operated as follows. A hydrocarboniferous material such as oil shale can be fed into hopper $\underline{11}$ and ground to any desired particle size, preferably less than about 5 mm. by means of crusher $\underline{13}$. Gates $\underline{15}$ and $\underline{17}$ are opened and the crushed shale flows downwardly by gravity into the elongated section $\underline{7}$ of retort $\underline{3}$. The level of shale in section $\underline{7}$ is maintained at about the height of the juncture of line $\underline{9}$ with section $\underline{7}$ or somewhat below. In section $\underline{7}$ the shale is contacted with the hot oxygen-free gases entering the retort $\underline{3}$ by means of lines $\underline{19}$ and $\underline{21}$ and the temperature of the shale is increased to such a point that the petroleum is vaporized.

Since the gases are substantially oxygen-free the hydrocarbon will be vaporized without causing a burning of the solid material and hence the tendency of the solids to fuse and agglomerate will be substantially lessened. The hot gases and the vaporized hydrocarbons rise upward in the tubular section $\underline{7}$ and pass into the fractionation unit $\underline{5}$.

By contacting the shale in this manner it is stripped of its hydrocarbon content as it passes downwardly in section $\underline{7}$ countercurrently through the uprising hot nonoxygen-containing gases and the spent shale passes out of the retort unit via line $\underline{31}$ and hydraulic gates $\underline{25}$, $\underline{27}$ and $\underline{29}$. The flow of shale through the retort is adjusted to the desired rate by regulating the amount of shale introduced and withdrawn by a suitable positioning of the hydraulic gates above and below the retort. These gates as mentioned previously are provided at least in pairs so that the pairs can be reciprocally operated thus allowing for the continuous flow of shale yet at all times maintaining the retort section closed in order to prevent the escape of pressure and heat.

The vapors and hot gases in retort section $\underline{7}$ will rise upwardly, leaving the retort at the upper open end thereof and entering the lower section of fractionation tower $\underline{33}$ where any dust and particles carried upward with the ascending gases and vapors will be removed by the cyclone separators $\underline{35}$ and returned to the spent shale discharge line $\underline{31}$ by the diplegs $\underline{37}$. The gases and vapors will pass upward in the tower $\underline{33}$ and the various constituents will condense at the appropriate temperature level and are removed as a liquid product by lines $\underline{47}$, $\underline{49}$ and $\underline{51}$.

The heavier hydrocarbon gases are removed from the tower at $\underline{53}$ and condensed in condenser $\underline{55}$ with the liquid being directed to appropriate storage or further processing facilities. The lighter gases composed to a large extent of the treating gases initially injected into the retort are removed as overhead via line $\underline{61}$ and, joined by the gases withdrawn from condenser $\underline{55}$ are recycled via line $\underline{63}$ and branch lines $\underline{65}$ and $\underline{67}$ to the heating unit $\underline{1}$ to be reheated and recharged to the retort unit $\underline{3}$ via lines $\underline{19}$ and $\underline{21}$. Pump $\underline{23}$ is operated so as to provide the vacuum necessary to draw the cooling gases through the heating unit and to supply the necessary pressure in the retort unit.

If desirable the hydrocarbon vapors ascending in retort 3 and tower 33 can be further bene-facted by introducing, along with the hot treating gases, a gamma emitting material, the gamma radiation causing a preliminary cracking of some of the heavier hydrocarbons and hence the production of more useful products.

One can provide spray injectors 101 and 103 in the intake ducts 79 and 81 of the reactor unit 1 and a suitable quantity of water can be injected along with the heat exchange gases into and through the nuclear reactor, this water being irradiated and carried to the retort unit 3 as radioactive steam along with the hot treating gases.

The treating gases passing through the reactor 1 and retort 3 can in general be any noncom-bustion supporting or substantially oxygen-free inert or heat stable gas desired. For instance, nitrogen, carbon dioxide, helium, argon, and hydrocarbon gases such as methane and ethane can be utilized as the heat exchange gas if desired and these gases can be continuously re-cycled to the reactor. If necessary, makeup gases can be provided as necessary by means of line 104. It is preferred, however, that the heat exchange and treating gas be a light hydrocarbon such as methane or ethane since limited amounts of this gas will be recoverable from the hydrocarboniferous material treated and then very little if any makeup gas will be necessary. It is, of course, feasible that an excess of such gases will be produced in the treatment and, if necessary, any excess can be taken from the system also through line 104 and conducted to suitable storage facilities.

As mentioned previously the flow regulating means in the entrance line 9 and exit line 31 can take the form of hydraulically operated gates extending through the cross section of the lines. Thus, as shown in Figure 1.28b the flow regulating means can comprise a gate 103A slidably mounted in housing 105 attached to the outer wall of the material flow line 106. The gate 103 can move through sealing gasket 107 disposed inside of housing 105 and it can movably extend vertically into the flow line 106. Housing 105 forms a cylinder in which piston head 109 attached to rod 111 and gate 103A slidably operates and fluid flow lines 113 and 115 are provided respectively above and below the piston 109.

When it is desired to lower the gate and thus block the flow of hydrocarboniferous material fluid can be pressurized into the cylinder through line 113 and the piston and gate 103A will be forced downward thus cutting off the flow. Fluid can be withdrawn from the upper part of the cylinder 105 through line 113 and pressured into the lower part of the cylinder through line 115 in order to raise the piston and the gate 103A so as to continue the flow of material through the line. By reciprocally operating a plurality of such gates both above and below the retort it is obvious that a continuity of flow of the material can be achieved through the retort without at any time permitting either the entrance or exit lines to be open thus avoiding undue losses of pressure and heat in the retort.

Sonic Energy Induced Separations

C.E. Morrell and P.V. Smith, Jr.; U.S. Patent 2,722,498; November 1, 1955; assigned to Esso Research and Engineering Company describe a process which permits the separation of organic chemical constituents from solid inorganic material with which it may be associated. In the process, the pulverized or finely divided inorganic material, containing organic ma-terial to be extracted is subjected to the action of a suitable organic solvent while being submitted to the action of compressional waves. This technique results in the extraction of a substantial portion of the organic material contained in the inorganic material treated.

Compressional waves of the nature required are often termed "acoustic waves," describing a longitudinal wave motion consisting of waves of alternate compression and rarefaction which are propagated through fluid medium. In general, the nature of acoustic waves or compressional waves is described in connection with the frequency of the waves as being within the sonic or the so-called ultrasonic range.

Thus, sonic compressional waves are characterized by frequencies varying from a few cycles per second to about 15,000 or 16,000 cycles per second corresponding to the audible range, while ultrasonic compressional waves have higher frequencies extending up to and including the magnitude of frequencies employed in radio transmission.

The following examples illustrate the process. In all of the experiments reported, the sedimentary material treated was first reduced to a particle size of about 1 micron by the action of a micropulverizer.

Example 1: A shale sample obtained from a point 3,400 ft. above the base of the Green River formation in Duchene County, Utah, was employed in a variety of extraction experiments. In a first series of tests, this shale was subjected to the action of carbon tetrachloride in a Soxhlet extractor. The extraction was conducted over a period of 15 hours employing 50 ml. of carbon tetrachloride and 2 g. of shale. It was found that 5% of organic material was removed by this treatment.

Example 2: The shale employed in Example 1 was subjected to this process employing the same solvent, carbon tetrachloride, as employed in Example 1. A piezoelectric compressional wave generator was employed operating at 1,500 kilocycles on an electrical power input of 0.6 kilowatts. Under these conditions, the compressional wave generator produced compressional waves causing cavitation. In exposing a sample of shale and solvent having the weight relation given in Example 1 to these compressional waves for a period of 5 minutes, and on then filtering the shale from the solvent, it was found that 49.8% of organic material had been extracted.

This same experiment was repeated under the identical conditions except that the frequency of the compressional waves was changed to 700 kilocycles. It was again found that 49.8% of organic material was extracted. This data indicates that extraction of organic material from an inorganic material such as shale is relatively ineffective by utilization of solvent action alone. However, when employing a solvent in the presence of compressional waves of sufficient intensity to provide cavitation, the amount of organic material which can be extracted is remarkably increased.

Example 3: This conclusion is further borne out by a series of tests concerning the extraction of organic material from a sediment obtained from the floor of the Gulf of Mexico off Freeport, Texas. The organic carbon content of this sediment was 0.53% corresponding to 0.69% organic matter. Different solvents were employed to extract this organic material. For comparative purposes, the particular solvent was employed in a Soxhlet extractor for a period of 15 hours and in the presence of compressional waves for a period of 10 minutes.

250 ml. of solvent and 20 g. of sediment were employed when using the Soxhlet extractor, while 100 ml. of solvent and 20 g. of sediment were employed when compressional waves were used. The generator employed was a piezo-electric generator operated at 400 kilocycles on an electrical input of about 600 watts, producing cavitation in each case. The results of these experiments are shown in the following table.

Extraction of Gulf of Mexico Sediment

Solvent	Percent Organic Matter Extracted	
	Soxhlet	Ultrasonic
Benzene	1.2	3.4
Chloroform	1.4	3.5
Carbon disulfide	0.4	2.8
Methyl ethyl ketone	6.8	10.3
n-Butanol	8.2	24.0
Ethyl acetate	2.0	5.4
Nitromethane	12.7	28.9

The data of this table again bears out the material increase in the amount of organic material which can be extracted by employing compressional waves during the extraction. In the case of each solvent employed, with one exception, more than twice the quantity of material could be extracted by employing the technique of the process as compared to treatment in a Soxhlet extractor. This is particularly striking since the time required to secure this result was only 1/90 of the time employed in the Soxhlet extractions.

Recovery of Aluminum

R.A. Van Nordstrand; U.S. Patent 3,516,787; June 23, 1970; assigned to Sinclair Research, Inc. describes a process for separating oil and aluminum values from oil shale containing kerogens, sodium aluminum carbonate hydroxide, quartz and dolomite by retorting the shale at 500° to 1200°F. to separate the oil, leaching the resulting spent shale with an alkaline solution at a temperature of up to 220°F. to dissolve the aluminum values from the shale without substantial precipitation of SiO_2, and recovering the aluminum values as hydrous alumina from the alkaline solution. The following examples illustrate the process.

Example 1: An oil shale from Section 21, Township 1S.98W., Rio Blanco County, Colo., taken over the depth interval 2186' to 2189' was crushed to a 1/8 to 1/4 inch size. In addition to about 30% kerogens, this shale contains about 20% dawsonite [$NaAlCO_3(OH)_2$] with the remainder being primarily quartz (SiO_2) and dolomite ($CaMg(CO_3)_2$). Twenty samples of 80 g. each were separated. Each sample was placed in an oil shale assay retort constructed so that both the oil and water produced from each sample is recovered and measured.

The retort operates with limited access of air, so the pyrolysis of the shale is carried out in the effective absence of oxygen. Pyrolysis of this sample was carried out for 2 hours at 900°F. Each of the 20 portions produced about the same amount of oil, the average being 13.9 cc for the 80 g. sample, corresponding to 41.7 gallons of oil per ton of shale. The weight loss of the shale is estimated at 25%.

Oil Shale Retorting

The retort was opened while the sample was still hot, about 500°F., and the retorted oil shale was then cooled in air. The retorted oil shale was a black, porous, friable substance. A small portion of this retorted sample was crushed and analyzed by x-ray diffraction. The dawsonite was no longer present in its original crystal form and there was no crystalline compound which could be identified by x-ray diffraction as the product of the dawsonite decomposition. The quartz appears to be present in unchanged amount. The dolomite was partially lost. The expected amount of calcite was observed in the retorted shale. The dawsonite was apparently decomposed to a sodium aluminate ($NaAlO_2$).

A portion of the retorted sample was then treated by a leaching operation to obtain alumina. The leaching solution consisted of sodium hydroxide and distilled water, specifically, 50 g. of NaOH per liter of solution. A portion of the retorted shale described above was pulverized, and 5 g. were placed in a 250 ml. Pyrex beaker. Thirty-nine ml. of the leaching solution was added. The mixture was heated to about 180°F. and maintained at this temperature for 15 minutes, with frequent stirring.

The mixture was diluted with water and filtered. The filtrate was acidified with hydrochloric acid and heated (driving off carbon dioxide and hydrogen sulfide). The solution was then made slightly alkaline with ammonium hydroxide to precipitate aluminum hydroxide. The latter was filtered off, ignited to Al_2O_3 and weighed. The five gram sample of retorted oil shale produced 0.2283 g. alumina, or a 4.57% recovery. This value when corrected for the 25% weight loss on retorting gives a value of 3.4% alumina based on the raw shale or 68 lbs. alumina per ton of raw shale.

Example 2: The table below illustrates the oil and alumina yield obtained from a second group of 20 samples from a second oil shale obtained in the vicinity of the first shale and having essentially the same composition. After retorting at 900°F. for 2 hours, the twenty (3-gram) samples were leached according to the procedure described in Example 1 using three-fifths of the amount of leaching solution. The alumina yield from samples obtained at depths of 2,050 to 2,530 ft. average 4.1% alumina based on the retorted shale which is about 3.1% based on raw shale or 62 lbs. alumina per ton of raw shale. The alumina yield is clearly related to the dawsonite content as measured by x-ray diffraction analysis of the individual oil shale samples.

Sample (foot depth)	Oil Produced	Alumina Produced (percent on retorted shale)	Oil Yield (previous assay) (gal./ton)	Dawsonite Content (by x-ray diffraction)
850	Yes	0.11	14	0.00
1,041	Yes	0.17	9	0.00
1,257	Yes	0.59	10	0.00
1,371	Yes	0.06	28	0.00
1,474	Yes	0.03	26	0.00
1,567	Yes	0.00	13	0.00
1,666	Yes	0.00	31	0.00
1,820	Yes	2.07	11	0.27
2,039	Yes	0.23	11	0.03
2,050	Yes	4.94	17	0.61 (cont'd.)

Oil Shale Retorting

Sample (foot depth)	Oil Produced	Alumina Produced (percent on retorted shale)	Oil Yield (previous assay) (gal./ton)	Dawsonite Content (by x-ray diffraction)
2,110	Yes	2.05	24	0.47
2,170	Yes	2.41	11	0.25
2,230	Yes	5.50	41	1.00
2,290	Yes	5.22	25	0.49
2,350	Yes	6.62	55	0.80
2,410	Yes	3.38	33	0.65
2,470	Yes	3.40	48	0.63
2,530	Yes	3.62	33	0.75
2,588	Yes	0.15	9	0.00
2,650	Yes	0.03	45	0.00

Pipeline Transportation and Recovery

In a process described by P.E. Titus; U.S. Patent 3,527,692; September 8, 1970; assigned to Shell Oil Company hydrocarbons are recovered from an oil shale formation by fragmenting oil shale and forming a slurry of the fragmented oil shale which is injected into a pipeline and maintained at a sufficiently high temperature to aid in extracting hydrocarbons from the oil shale and recovering it at the terminal end of the line. The oil shale can be obtained from a subterranean formation by any known means, such as mining, to produce appreciable quantities of large fragments of oil shale.

The fragments of oil shale can be passed to a crusher to reduce the fragments to a size sufficient to be flowed, when mixed with a solvent, within a pipeline. For example, about 15% fines have been produced in crushing Green River shales, this size being sufficient for the operations to be discussed. However, power requirements increase as the size of the oil shale particles decrease; accordingly, for purposes of this process, a preferred particle size distribution should consist of a range of particle sizes from 1/4" to fines passing a 325 mesh sieve.

The crushed oil shale may be preheated if desired. However, preheating is merely a way to conserve the heat energy latent in a shale and to counteract the low rate of heat transfer. It does not increase the oil yield or improve its quality.

Preferably, the mined oil shale fragments are passed into the crushing plant where the fragments are crushed and the crushed oil shale is mixed with a solvent to form an oil shale/solvent slurry. The oil formation may, for example, be located in the Green River Formation of the Piceance Creek Basin of Colorado.

The solvent is preferably crude oil, retorted shale oil, or some appropriate fraction of these. It has been found that oil shale bitumen solubility is favored by the presence of aromatics, both cyclics, such as benzene, and heterocyclics, such as pyridine. Therefore, while any fraction of crude oil containing some aromatics would act as a solvent, those fractions rich in aromatics, either cyclics or heterocyclics, are preferred as the most efficient for extraction. It is also preferable to add small quantities of H_2S, as in the order of about 2.2 mol percent, to the solvent. This has been found to accelerate the rates of extraction of the kerogen in the oil shale into the solvent.

The slurry is then heated and passed into a pipeline where it is transported, to a remote refinery area, as for example, to the west coast or to the Gulf coast refineries. The slurry is periodically heated by means well-known in the art to replace heat lost in transit and to maintain the desired temperature range. The pipeline is preferably insulated to minimize heat loss. The slurry may be removed from the pipeline to effect the heating, if desired.

It has been found that heating a slurry of crushed oil shale and solvent for a relatively long period of time, such as periods of up to 18 to 20 days, and at a temperature of approximately 550° to 600°F., results in the extraction of shale oil having 80% weight of Fischer assay with benzene and 90% weight Fischer assay with benzene-H_2S mixtures. This relatively low temperature process breaks the kerogen within the oil shale down into bitumen, which is then dissolved in the appropriate solvent. Thus, at approximately 550° to 600°F., the insoluble kerogen in the oil shale decomposes to soluble bitumen very similar to conventional crude oils. The material recovered is more like typical refinery crudestocks (i.e., not thermally cracked) with relatively high hydrocarbon content (i.e., relatively low ash, nitrogen, oxygen).

Since the refinery area is generally far enough away from the location of the oil shale formation, as for example, from the oil shale formations in Colorado to west or Gulf coast refineries, efficient utilization is taken of the relatively long processing time required (approximately 18 to 20 days) to decompose the kerogen to bitumen and extract oil therefrom. Thus, the shale oil delivered to the refinery is recovered en route. At the refinery, the extracted shale oil is conventionally processed and the waste material is removed following appropriate heat recovery. The heat put into the slurry may be partially recoverable at the refinery during the distillation process furthering the efficiency of the overall process.

Mining of Deep Thick Oil Shale Deposits

J.M. Whiting; U.S. Patent 3,588,175; June 28, 1971; assigned to Atlantic Richfield Co. describes an oil shale mining method for deep thick deposits which can be referred to as a "cut-and-fill" method or more simply, as "blasthole stoping."

In the process, a mining zone is selected and divided vertically by horizontal haulage levels into a preselected number of production levels. A plurality of subordinate level networks is established above each haulage level to divide each horizontal production level into production blocks of desirable size.

Muck raises are driven to create outlets for broken ore at the bottom of each block. Ore remaining at each subordinate level is removed to form horizontal slots or voids. A vertical raise is driven at the longitudinal center of each block and then a slot or void is slashed for the width of block. Volumes of each block are sequentially blasted from the central vertical slot to form a stope of increasing dimensions. Lastly, the broken ore is drawn and removed via the underlying haulage level. Thin weak pillars are left between adjacent stopes to retain fill and as roof support to temporarily control caving. After suitable bulkheads are constructed, the empty stopes are filled with spent shale and other waste material.

Oil Shale Retorting

Production is carried out at several horizontal levels at the same time with the active stopes vertically staggered from level to level at such an angle as to minimize stress and strain on adjacent support pillars. Backfilling is accomplished as soon as possible so that each stope remains empty a minimum amount of time. As the development proceeds from level to level, the effect is to create an inverted pyramid-shaped mass of consolidating and subsiding fill.

Advantages of the process include the following. It is possible to safely recover 50 to 80% or more of the oil reserves from oil shale deposits; surface subsidence and attendant restoration problems are minimized; breakdown or weakening of strata and overburden adjacent to the mining limits is prevented or minimized; ground pressures and rock deformation at the periphery of the mined out region are minimized; surface waste disposal requirements are minimized; and hazards such as violent air displacement, rock falls, shock and dust, caused by sudden breakdown of many large open stopes are eliminated.

OIL SHALE REFINING PROCESSES

HYDROGENATION

Hydrotorting Using Hydrogen and Water

W.G. Schlinger, D.R. Jesse and J.P. Tassoney; U.S. Patent 3,617,469; November 2, 1971; Texaco Inc. have discovered a continuous process for preparing maximum yields of shale oil of reduced nitrogen and sulfur content from raw shale under relatively reduced pressure. It has been found that raw shale can be readily converted to shale oil and relatively kerogen-free, dry-powdered shale by injecting a slurry of raw oil shale in shale oil with hydrogen (about 5,000 to 20,000 scf of hydrogen per ton of raw shale) and water (about 0.01 to 0.6 tons of water per ton of raw shale) under pressure, and immediately introducing the mixture into an externally fired tubular retort under conditions of turbulent flow.

Within a period of from about 1/4 to 3 minutes at an outlet temperature of 850° to 950°F. and at a pressure in the range of 300 to 1,000 psig and preferably at a critical pressure of 475 to 525 psig, hydrogenation takes place with no addition of a supplementary catalyst. Shale oil is produced having a substantially reduced nitrogen and sulfur content and with increased yields of 116 volume percent of the Fischer Assay. Furthermore, if desired, still greater yields of shale oil may be obtained (in some instances as much as 135% of the Fischer Assay) by submitting solids-free prehydrogenated gaseous effluent from the tubular reaction zone to further hydrogenation in a separate catalytic hydrogenation zone.

Addition of hydrogen to the slurry and the hydrogenation of the pyrolysis products of the kerogen improves the yield of the product shale oil and provides the product with a greater amount of the desirable middle distillate material, while the formation of heavy polymers, unsaturated hydrocarbons and carbonaceous residues which characterize known processes are suppressed. Injecting water into the slurry before the tubular retort was found to have several benefits. The velocity through the tubular retort, the turbulent flow, and the heat transfer coefficient of the mixture in the retort are all increased. Thus, rapid heat transfer is brought about which allows conversion of the kerogen to crude shale oil in the retort coils at residence times of about 1/4 to 3 minutes.

Furthermore, vaporization of the water in the coils tends to disintegrate the shale particles and facilitates atomization of the shale oil. Also, coking of the slurry may be minimized or eliminated at a substantially reduced hydrogen consumption. Other advantages for injecting the water under pressure into the shale-oil slurry just prior to introducing the slurry into the tubular reactor include: (1) greater concentrations of raw shale may be incorporated in pumpable oil-shale slurries, (2) less water is required in this process than when water is added to the shale in the slurry-mixing tank; (3) clogging of the retort tubing is prevented; (4) better control of the amount of water added; and, finally, (5) it was found that water addition reduces the endothermic decomposition of inorganic carbonates in the shale to form CO_2, thereby preventing the undesirable reaction between CO_2 and hydrogen to form H_2O and CO. Thus by water injection, there is a savings of energy in the form of heat used for carbonate decomposition as well as a reduction of hydrogen consumption in the tubular retort.

Referring to Figure 2.1, particles of raw shale in line 1 and heavy shale oil in line 2 are introduced into mixing tank 3 where they are mixed by agitator 4, forming a raw shale-shale oil slurry. This slurry is passed from the bottom of mixing tank 3 through valve 5 and into the suction end of screw pump 6. At a temperature in the range of about 100° to 500°F., the slurry is pumped through line 7 to a conventional gas-liquid contactor 8, which may be in the form of a venturi mixer. Recycle hydrogen from line 9 and makeup hydrogen from the line 10 are mixed in line 11 and injected into the accelerated slurry stream at the throat of the venturi 8. Recycle water in line 12 is similarly injected into the slurry. The pressure of each of the streams in lines 11 and 12 exceeds the system line pressure by about 25 to 200 psi.

The intimate mixture of hydrogen gas, water, raw oil shale particles, and heavy shale oil at a temperature below the vaporization temperature of water leaving contactor 8 is directed through line 13 into externally heated tubular retort 14 situated immediately after contactor 8. Under conditions of high turbulence in tubular retort 14, the mixture is raised within seconds to a temperature in the range of about 700° to 1,100°F. and disintegration and pyrolysis of the raw shale, vaporization of the shale oil and water, and hydrogenation of the kerogen and shale oil all take place simultaneously. No supplementary catalyst need be added to the materials in the tubular retort to promote the reactions.

A hot gaseous effluent stream comprising shale oil vapor, unreacted hydrogen, water vapor, H_2S, NH_3, CO_2, CO and shale dust in the form of a fine dry powder of 200 to 325 mesh, leaves tubular retort 14 through line 15 and is discharged into gas-solids separator 16. Spent shale, substantially free from any hydrocarbonaceous residue, falls to the bottom of chamber 16 and is removed from the system through line 17. To prevent plugging with spent shale and heat loss, the gas-solids separation chamber 16, the overhead transfer lines, line 15 from the tubular reactor, and exposed flanges and pipe joints are insulated to maintain the gaseous stream at a temperature of 850° to 950°F.

Since this example of the process involves the production of shale oil by hytrotorting in tubular retort 14 only, that is, with no subsequent hydrogenation in a catalytic reactor 19, valves 20, 21, and 22 are closed and bypass valve 23 is opened. Hot gaseous effluent from separator 16 comprising shale oil vapor, water vapor, H_2, and minor amounts of NH_3, H_2S, CO_2, CO and CH_4 is then directed to cooler 24 by way of lines 18, 25, 26 and 27. The water and shale oil that are condensed out in cooler 24 pass through line 28 and into gas-liquid separator 29. Unreacted hydrogen and other uncondensed gases are removed from the top of separator 29 and are passed through line 30 into compressor 31. Compressed hydrogen-rich gas from lines 32 and 9 are mixed in line 11 with makeup from line 10. If necessary this hydrogen-rich mixture may be heated to a temperature in the range of 100° to 500°F. before it is introduced into conductor 8 by means of one of the many heat exchangers in the system.

FIGURE 2.1: CONTINUOUS HYDROTORTING OF RAW OIL SHALE

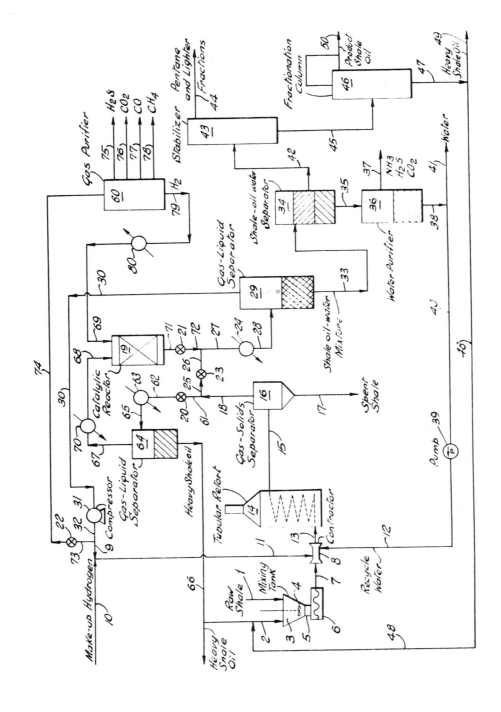

Source: W.G. Schlinger, D.R. Jesse and J.P. Tassoney; U.S. Patent 3,617,469; November 2, 1971

Oil Shale Refining Processes

Shale oil-water mixture is withdrawn from the bottom of gas-liquid separator 29 and is passed through line 33 into shale oil-water separator 34, where the lighter shale oil separates out and floats on a water layer which contains dissolved H_2S, NH_3 and CO_2. The water layer is removed at the bottom of separator 34 through line 35 and is introduced into a standard water purifier 36 where H_2S, NH_3 and CO_2 are removed through line 37 and are directed to a standard NH_3, H_2S, and CO_2 recovery system. Purified water is removed through line 38 and a portion may be recycled to contactor 8 by means of pump 39 through lines 40 and 12, in the manner previously described. Surplus water is dischared from the system through line 41. Since most oil shale deposits are located in arid regions, one significant advantage of the process is that there is not net consumption of water; but in fact, an excess of water may be produced.

The crude shale oil layer in separator 34 is withdrawn through line 42 and is introduced into stabilizer 43 where by fractionation, pentane and lighter hydrocarbon fractions are separated and are passed out the top through line 44. Crude shale oil is withdrawn from the bottom of stabilizer 43 through line 45 and is introduced into fractionation column 46. A portion of the heavy shale oil bottoms from column 46 at a temperature of about 600° to 900°F. is recycled through lines 47, 48 and 2 into mixing tank 3 for making the raw shale-shale oil slurry feed to the process, in the manner previously described. Generally, no heavy shale oil recycle pump is necessary since the system pressure will move the oil to the mix tank. The remainder of the heavy shale oil is removed from the system through line 49. Product shale oil is removed from the system through line 50.

A second example of the process involves two separate hydrogenation steps: first, the raw shale-shale oil slurry is hydrogenated in the noncatalytic tubular retort as described previously; and second, the prehydrogenated shale oil vapors from the first step are hydrogenated in a fixed or fluid bed hydrogenation catalytic reactor 19. Also, a gas purification system is integrated into the system to supply pure hydrogen to the catalytic reactor and to prevent the buildup of gaseous impurities in the recycle hydrogen stream.

Catalytic reactor 19 and gas purifier 60 are introduced into the system by closing bypass valve 23 and opening valves 20, 21 and 22. The hot gaseous stream from gas-solids separator 16 is then passed through lines 18, 61, and 62 into cooler 63 where heavy shale oil and tars condense out and pass with the uncondensed gases into gas-liquid separator 64 by way of line 65.

Separator 64 also serves as a catch pot for all shale dust that may have passed through gas-solids separator16. Heavy shale oil and tar, which are the least valuable portion of the product shale oil may then be removed from the system through line 66 at the bottom of separator 64. This also protects the catalyst in reactor 19 from contamination. However, if desired all or a portion of the material in line 66 may be introduced into mixing tank 3 by way of line 2 for slurrying with the raw shale.

The gaseous stream leaving from the top of gas-liquid separator 64 is passed through lines 67 and 68 and into the catalytic reactor 19 where hydrogenation takes place. This hydrogenation step is facilitated by a hot stream of pure hydrogen which is introduced into reactor 19 by way of line 69. The preferred mol ratio of hydrogen (from line 69) to gaseous feed to the catalytic chamber (from line 68) is within the range of 0.0 to 0.3. Heat exchanger 70 is provided to help maintain the gas stream at the inlet to catalytic reactor 19 at the proper temperature to effect maximum denitrification and desulfurization. If it is desired to operate the catalytic reactor at a higher pressure than the pressure in tubular retort 14, then a pump may be inserted in line 68. The effluent from catalytic reactor 19 is discharged through lines 71, 72, and 27 into cooler 24 where the treated shale oil and water are condensed out. Except for the gas purification unit, the remainder of the system involves shale oil-water separator 34, water purifier 36, stabilizer 43, and fractionation column 46. The operation and function of these units are the same as that which has already been described.

To prevent the buildup of gaseous impurities in the system, a portion of the uncondensed gases from gas-liquid separator 29 comprising unreacted hydrogen and traces of H_2S, CO_2, CO and CH_4 is purified, and the hydrogen is returned to the system. For example, a portion of compressed recycle gas in line 32 is passed through lines 73 and 74 into a standard gas purifier 60 where H_2S, CO_2, CO, and CH_4 are separated from pure H_2 and leave respectively by way of lines 75, 76, 77 and 78 for recovery. A standard gas purifier utilizing refrigeration and chemical absorption may be employed to effect separation of the gases, e.g., U.S. Patent 3,001,373.

Hydrogen leaves gas purifier 60 by way of line 79 and is passed into heater 80 where it is raised to a temperature in the range of 800° to 900°F. before it is introduced through line 69 into catalytic reactor 19, in the manner previously described. If desired, high purity makeup hydrogen from an external source may be introduced into the system by mixing with the H_2 in line 79. The preferred mol ratio of gases recycled in line 73 to gases passed through line 11 is in the range of about 0.1 to 1.0.

Example: Colorado oil shale having a Fischer Assay of 31.2 gallons of shale oil per ton of raw oil shale and 2.9 gallons of H_2O per ton of raw oil shale is crushed to −8 mesh and mixed with heavy shale oil to form a slurry comprising 75.6 weight percent of raw shale.

Immediately after water and hydrogen are injected into the slurry under pressure, the mixture is hydrogenated in a 1 inch SCH 40 pipe x 530 feet long noncatalytic tubular retort.

Operating conditions and results of runs in accordance with the first example of the process as previously described are summarized in the table on the following page, column 1.

In column 2 there is shown a summary of the conditions and results of double hydrogenation, first in the noncatalytic tubular retort and second over a Co-Mo hydrogenation catalyst, as described in the second example of the process.

It appears, for a comparison of columns 1 and 2, that the second method is the preferred procedure because it provides high yields of product shale oil having a higher °API and characterization factor, improved distillation characteristics and considerably less sulfur, nitrogen, and carbon residue.

Further, in comparison with the Fischer Assay, the data for both examples show a substantial increase in product-oil yields; an improvement in API gravity, pour point and yield of distillate; and a reduction in the nitrogen and the sulfur content in the shale oil product.

Oil Shale Refining Processes

Operating Conditions and Results	1	2	Fischer assay
Operating conditions:			
Pressure, p.s.i.g.:			
Tubular retort	500	500	....
Catalyst chamber	N	480	....
Temperature,° F.:			
Tubular retort	925	925	....
Catalyst chamber	N	800	....
Catalyst	N	Co/Mo	....
Retorting period, seconds	19.6	19.6	....
Turbulence level	2,800	2,800	....
Input materials:			
Shale: Raw shale charged, lbs./hr	980	980	....
Hydrogen:			
Feed purity	99.8	99.8	....
Consumption, s.c.f./bbl. oil:			
Total	1,977	2,199	....
In tubular retort	1,977	1,977	....
In catalyst bed	N	222	....
Feed rate to contactor, s.c.f./ton raw shale.	13,800	13,800	....
Make-up rate, s.c.f./ton raw shale	1,709	2,170	....
Temperature at inlet to contactor, ° F.	155	155	....
Pressure at inlet to contactor, p.s.i.g.	625	625	....
Velocity at inlet to tubular retort, ft./sec.	9.00	9.00	....
Water:			
Feed rate to contactor, lbs./ton raw shale.	520	520	....
Temperature at inlet to contactor, ° F.	100	100	....
Pressure at inlet to contactor, p.s.i.g.	625	625	....
Raw oil shale-shale oil slurry: Temperature at inlet to tubular retort,° F	140	140	....
Gaseous effluent from retort: Velocity at inlet to gas-solids separator, ft./sec	33.6	33.6	....
Output materials:			
Product shale oil:			
Gravity,° API	24.0	30.0	24.1
Viscosity, SSU at 122° F	55	41	50
Pour point,° F	60	55	75
Sulfur, wt. percent	0.64	0.24	0.98
Nitrogen, wt. percent	1.49	0.75	1.80
Conradson carbon, wt. percent	4.10	0.10	2.3
Characterization factor	11.5	11.6	11.4
ASTM distillation,° F.:			
IBP	180	165	192
10%	308	283	336
30%	482	450	518
50%	630	590	655
70%	702	675	705
80%	724	701	....
Heavy shale oil (line 49):			
Gravity,° API	15.0	16.0	N
Viscosity, SSU at 122° F	1,000	900	N
Pour point,° F	125	120	N
Sulfur, wt. percent	0.63	0.25	N
Nitrogen, wt. percent	2.00	1.25	N
Conradson carbon, wt. percent	8.10	.30	N
Recovery:			
Product shale oil:			
Gals/ton of raw shale	36.3	38.0	31.2
Percent Fischer assay	116	121	100
Heavy shale oil: Gals/ton of raw shale	None	None	N
Water:			
Gals/ton of raw shale	4.4	4.9	2.9
Percent Fischer assay	152	169	100
Spent shale:			
Lbs./ton of raw shale	1,653	1,653	1,670
Carbonaceous residue, wt. percent	2.98	2.98	5.0
Pentane and lighter fractions, lbs./ton of raw shale	35.2	38.7	N
Removal of spent shale in gas solids separator, wt. percent	100.0	100.0	N

NOTE.—N=Not applicable.

In related work W.C. Schlinger, D.R. Jesse and J.P. Tassoney; U.S. Patent 3,617,470; November 2, 1971; assigned to Texaco Inc. describe a process which combines tubular hydrotorting of a raw shale–shale oil slurry and the centrifugal separation of entrained spent shale from the gaseous effluent stream.

Hydrotorting Using Synthesis Gas and Water Injection

W.G. Schlinger, D.R. Jesse and J.P. Tassoney; U.S. Patent 3,565,784; February 23, 1971; assigned to Texaco Inc. describe a continuous process for recovering shale oil from a slurry of raw oil shale in shale oil. Water and hot unquenched synthesis gas from the reaction zone of a partial oxidation generator are injected into the raw oil shale-shale oil slurry under pressure and the mixture is immediately introduced into a noncatalytic tubular retort maintained at a temperature in the range of 850° to 950°F. and at a pressure in the range of 300 to 1,000 psig, and preferably at 500 psig for maximum yields of shale oil having a minimum nitrogen content. Substantially all of the hydrogen and a large fraction of the heat required in the tubular retort are provided by the synthesis gas.

In the tubular retort under conditions of turbulent flow, the raw shale is completely stripped of kerogen in about 1/4 to 3 minutes (preferably less than a minute), and by simultaneous pyrolysis and hydrogenation the kerogen is converted to a gaseous effluent from which shale oil is separated. Simultaneously, hydrogen is generated in the tubular retort by the exothermic water-gas shift reaction, whereby CO in the synthesis gas reacts with H_2O the spent shale acting as a shift catalyst. Pure hydrogen and the prehydrogenated shale oil are introduced into a catalytic reactor to produce denitrogenated and desulfurized shale oil at yields of about 125% of the Fischer Assay. Feed to the synthesis gas generator comprises a portion of the heavy shale oil and steam produced by the process and in this respect the process is self-sustaining.

Referring to Figure 2.2, particles of raw oil shale in line 1 and heavy shale oil in line 2 are introduced into mixing tank 3 where they are mixed by agitator 4, forming a raw oil shale-shale oil slurry. This slurry is passed from the bottom of mixing tank 3 through valve 5 and into the suction end of screw pump 6. At a temperature in the range of 100° to 500°F., the slurry is pumped through line 7 into a gas-liquid contactor 8, which may be in the form of a venturi mixer.

Unquenched hot synthesis gas from the reaction zone of partial oxidation synthesis gas generator 9 is passed through line 10, into line 11 where it is mixed with recycle hydrogen containing gas from line 12 and then injected into the accelerated slurry stream at the throat of the venturi contactor 8. Recycle water in line 13 is also injected into the slurry at the throat of the venturi mixer. Ordinarily, the pressure of each of the streams in lines 11 and 13 exceeds the system line pressure by about 25 to 200 psig. The synthesis gas may be generated at the desired pressure and thereby eliminate a costly high temperature gas compressor. Moreover, a substantial portion of the heat necessary in the next hydrotorting step may be obtained from the sensible heat in the synthesis gas.

The resulting intimate mixture of synthesis gas, water, raw shale particles, and heavy shale oil (about 12° to 19°API) at a temperature below the vaporization temperature of water is accelerated to a high velocity in contactor 8 and is then directed through line 14 in to tubular retort 15 situated immediately after contactor 8. Although tubular retort 15 may be externally heated, little or no heating is usually necessary because of the heat supplied with the hot synthesis gas and the exothermic shift reaction that takes place.

Under conditions of high tubulence in tubular retort 15, the mixture is raised within a minute to a temperature in the range of about 700° to 1100°F. and disintegration and pyrolysis of the raw shale vaporization of the shale oil and water, and hydrogenation of the kerogen and shale oil all take place simultaneously. No supplementary catalyst need be added to the materials in the tubular retort to promote the reactions.

130

FIGURE 2.2: HYDROTORTING PROCESS EMPLOYING SYNTHESIS GAS

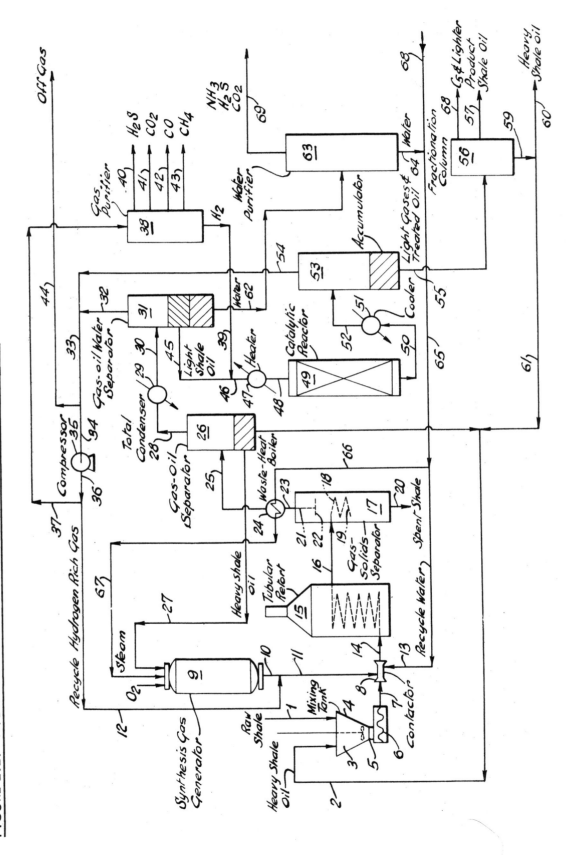

Source: W.G. Schlinger, D.R. Jesse and J.P. Tassoney; U.S. Patent 3,565,784; February 23, 1971

A hot gaseous effluent stream comprising a shale oil fraction, unreacted hydrogen, water vapor, H_2S, NH_3, CO, CO_2, carbon particulate and shale dust in the form of a fine dry powder of about 325 mesh, leaves tubular retort 15 at high velocity through line 16 and is discharged into gas-solids separator 17 where the kinetic energy of the gaseous effluent is employed to effect separation of the spent shale from the rest of the effluent stream.

Separator 17 is a vertical cylindrical shaped chamber with line 16 entering about midpoint and then descending in a spiral of about two loops 18. Thus, whirling motion is imparted to the gaseous effluent as it discharges from the end of the spiral pipe at point 19. By centrifugal force or acceleration, shale dust particles in the gaseous effluent are separated from the remainder of the effluent and move to the walls of the separating chamber. From there, the dry spent shale dust, substantially free from any hydrocarbonaceous residue, falls to the bottom of chamber 17 and is removed through line 20, which leads from the spent shale discharge system. To prevent plugging with spent shale and heat loss, the gas-solids separation chamber 17, the overhead transfer lines, line 16 from the tubular reactor, and exposed flanges and pipe joints are insulated to maintain the gaseous stream at a temperature of about 850° to 950°F.

Spent shale essentially free from carbon and carbonaceous matter is removed from separator 17 without severe loss of hydrogen or pressure drop in the gaseous system by means of a shale removal system. The hot spent shale powder is suitable for use as preheated feedstock in a chemical process, such as making cement.

An exit pipe 21 for removing essentially solids-free gas from separator 17 depends axially from the upper end of separator 17, and terminates above loop 18. A T fitting 22 with two ports open in a direction perpendicular to the axis of the separating chamber is joined to the end of exit pipe 21 inside of the chamber.

Hot gaseous effluent is withdrawn through line 23 at the top of gas-solids separator 17 and is introduced into waste heat boiler 24 which is used to produce steam which is fed to synthesis gas generator 9. The hot gaseous effluent is cooled in waste heat boiler 24 to condense only the heavy shale oil fractions and tar. The uncondensed portion of gaseous effluent and the heavy shale oil liquid and tar are passed through line 25 into gas-oil separator 26. A protion of heavy shale oil and tar is withdrawn through line 27 at the bottom of gas-oil separator 26 and introduced as feed to synthesis gas generator 9.

The remainder of the heavy shale oil from the bottom of separator 26 may be recycled to the slurry mixing tank 3 by way of line 2. Generally, no heavy shale oil recycle pump is necessary since the system pressure will move the oil to mixing tank 3. Hot gaseous effluent is withdrawn from the top of separator 26 through line 28 and passed into total condenser 29 where water is condensed out along with the remainder of the shale oil vapors in the gaseous stream. Uncondensed gases comprising H_2, H_2S, NH_3, CO_2, and CH_4 along with water and light shale oil are passed through line 30 into gas-oil-water separator 31 where the light shale oil separates and floats on the water layer containing dissolved NH_3, CO_2, and H_2S.

Unreacted H_2 and substantially all of the CO and CH_4 leave the system through line 32 at the top of separator 31 and are directed through lines 32, 33, and 34 by means of compressor 35 and into lines 36, 37 and gas purifier 38 where pure hydrogen is separated from the other gases. Pure H_2 leaves gas purifier 38 through line 39 while H_2S, CO_2, CO, and CH_4 leave by way of lines 40, 41, 42 and 43 respectively. About 0.3 mol of gas are recycled through line 37 to the gas purifier 38 per mol of hydrogen containing gas passed through line 12. Standard gas purifier 38 utilizes refrigeration and chemical absorption to effect separation of the gases, such as described in U.S. Patent 3,001,373. A bleed stream of off gas may be taken periodically through line 44 to prevent the buildup in the system of gaseous impurities.

Light shale oil is withdrawn from separator 31 by way of line 45 and is mixed in line 46 with hydrogen from line 39 at a ratio of about 1,000 to 7,000 mols of H_2 per mol of light shale oil. The mixture is then raised to a temperature in the range of about 700° to 900°F. by means of heater 47, and at a pressure in the range of 300 to 2,200 psig, the feed mixture is then introduced through line 48 into a fixed bed catalytic reactor 49 containing cobalt molybdate hydrogenation catalyst. The catalytic reactor 49 may be operated at a higher pressure than tubular retort 15. For example, by inserting a pump in line 45, catalytic reactor 49 may be operated at a pressure of 2,200 psig while tubular retort 15 is simultaneously being operated at a preferred pressure of 500 psig and thereby obtain maximum yields of shale oil having a minimum nitrogen content.

The effluent stream from catalytic reactor 49 comprising essentially hydrorefined light shale oil and unreacted H_2 is passed through line 50 into cooler 51 where the treated oil is condensed as a liquid which flows with the uncondensed gases through line 52 into accumulator 53. Unreacted H_2 and some carbon oxides, H_2S and CH_4 are withdrawn through line 54 at the top of accumulator 53, mixed in line 33 with the gases leaving gas-oil-water separator 31 through line 32, and purified in gas purifier 38. Treated oil and light gases leave accumulator 53 through line 55 and are fractionated in a fractionation column 56 to produce product shale oil, C_5 and lighter fractions, and heavy shale oil which leave column 56 through lines 57, 58 and 59 respectively. A portion of the heavy shale oil is discharged from the system through line 60 and the remainder is recycled to mix tank 3 by way of lines 61 and 62.

Water is withdrawn from the bottom of gas-oil-water separator 31 through line 62 and is introduced into a standard water purifier 63. Pure water is withdrawn from the bottom of purifier 63 through line 64. A portion of the purified water in line 64 is recycled to contactor 8 by ways of lines 65, and 13, as previously described. A second portion of the purified water in line 64 is passed through lines 65 and 66, into waste heat boiler 24 where it is converted into steam by heat exchange with the effluent gaseous stream leaving gas-solids separator 17 through 23. The steam from waste heat boiler 24 is passed through line 67 into synthesis gas generator 9. The remainder of the pure water in line 64 is directed to other areas of the system through line 65 for use in the process. Makeup water, if required, may be supplied through line 68. NH_3, H_2S and CO_2 are removed from the system through line 69 at the top of water purifier 63 and recovered. The following examples illustrate the process.

Example 1: Colorado oil shale having a Fischer Assay of 31.2 gallons of shale oil per ton of raw oil shale and 2.9 gallons of H_2O per ton of raw oil shale is crushed to -8 mesh and mixed with heavy shale oil to form a raw oil shale slurry. In a venturi mixer, hydrogen gas and water under a pressure of 625 psig are injected into the slurry. The slurry mixture at a velocity of 9.0 ft./sec. and a temperature of 140°F. is immediately introduced into a non-catalytic tubular reactor consisting of a 1 inch SCH 40 pipe x 530 feet long, in accordance with the process as previously described and as shown in the drawing.

Operating conditions and results are summarized below. The results clearly show that compared with the Fischer Assay, greater amounts of shale oil and water are produced by this process. Further, the shale oil has improved characteristics and considerably less sulfur and nitrogen. The spent shale contains substantially no kerogen residue. Operating conditions for Run 1 are shown below.

Synthesis gas generator 9:
  Feed to generator:

Heavy shale oil 27, °API 15 at 450°F.	17.5 lbs./hr.
Oxygen, 99.6 mol % at 160°F.	18.0 lbs./hr.
Steam at 800°F.	8.0 lbs./hr.
O/C ratio, mol O/mol C in HC feed	0.90
Temperature in reaction zone	2500°F.
Pressure in reaction zone	625 psig

  Composition of synthesis gas 10,

H_2	47.1 mol %
CO	46.5 mol %
CO_2	5.0 mol %
N_2	0.8 mol %
CH_4	0.2 mol %
H_2S and COS	0.4 mol %

Mixing tank 3:

Raw oil shale 1	980 lbs./hr.
Heavy shale oil 2	315 lbs./hr.

Contactor 8:

Synthesis gas 10	837 scfh
Recycle hydrogen-rich gas 12	4,305 scfh
Recycle water 13, lbs./ton raw shale 1	100
Oil shale–shale oil slurry 7	1,295 lbs./hr.

Noncatalytic tubular retort 15:

Pressure	500 psig
Retorting period	19.6 sec.
Turbulence level	2,800
Reaction temperature	925°F.
Hydrogen consumption, scf/ton of raw shale 1	520

Gas solids separator 17:

Velocity at inlet 19	33.6 ft./sec.
Temperature	925°F.
Pressure	500 psig

Catalytic reactor 49:

Light shale oil 45 at a temperature of 120°F.	15.8 gal./hr.

Hydrogen <u>39</u> at a temperature of 60°F.   1,200 scfh
Hydrogen consumption, scf/ton of raw shale <u>1</u>   1,040
Pressure   1,500 psig
Liquid hourly space velocity   1.5 bbl./hr./bbl.
Catalyst   Co/Mo

TABLE 1: RESULTS

	Run No. 1	Fischer assay
Gross water yield 64, gals./ton of raw shale 1	14.1	2.9
Make-up water 68, gals./ton of raw shale 1	1.2	N
Spent shale:		
Removal from gas stream 16 by separator 17, wt. percent	100	N
Spent shale 20, lbs./ton raw shale 1	1,630	1,670
Carbonaceous residue, wt. percent	3.5	5.0
Shale Oil Yield:		
Line 27 plus line 55, gals./ton of raw shale 1	39.0	31.2
Percent Fischer Assay	125	100.0
C₅ and lighter 58, gals./ton of raw shale 1		N
Product shale oil 57, gals./ton of raw shale 1	34.8	N
Heavy shale oil 60, gals./ton of raw shale 1	None	N
Treated shale oil 55 and Fischer assay shale oil:		
Gravity, ° API	32	24.1
Viscosity, SSU at 122° F.	43	70
Pour point, ° F.	60	75
Sulfur, wt. percent	0.02	0.98
Nitrogen, wt. percent	0.05	1.80
Conradson carbon, wt. percent	0.1	2.3
Characterization factor (K)	11.7	11.4
ASTM Distillation, ° F.:		
IBP	150	192
10%	270	336
30%	440	518
50%	510	655
70%	580	705
90%	640	--------
EP	680	--------

NOTE.—N=Not applicable.

Example 2:   This example will demonstrate the relationship between shale oil yields and pressure with respect to the continuous noncatalytic tubular hydrotort described previously. By maintaining all of the operating conditions described in Example 1 substantially the same with the exception of pressure in the tubular retort it may be shown from the data in Table 2 below that shale oil yields increase with pressure to a maximum at 500 psig in the tubular retort.   Then shale oil yields decrease with increasing pressure to 900 psig where they seem to level out.   The gross shale oil yields range from 111 to 125% of the Fischer Assay.

All of the hydrogen required in the catalytic reactor <u>49</u> is produced by a portion of the product shale oil being fed to the synthesis gas generator.   Consequently the net shale oil yields are lower.   The data represents the average of three runs at each pressure level. Lower yields would be expected at temperatures in the tubular retort which are higher than 950°F. due to cracking of the kerogen.

At temperatures lower than 900°F. incomplete cracking lowers liquid yields.   The low nitrogen and sulfur content of the product oil in line <u>55</u> as shown for the data in Table 2 indicates that maximum denitrification and desulfurization are obtained by the two-step hydrogenation process.

TABLE 2: EFFECT OF PRESSURE

Tubular retort pressure, p.s.i.g.	Gross shale oil yield, lines 27+55		Net shale oil yield—line 55			
	gal./ton	Percent F.A.	Gal./ton	Percent F.A.	Nitrogen wt. percent	Sulfur, wt. percent
300	34.5	111	30.3	97	0.1	0.05
400	37.2	119	33.0	106	0.1	0.05
500	39.1	125	34.9	112	0.1	0.05
600	37.9	122	33.7	108	0.1	0.05
700	37.2	120	33.0	106	0.1	0.05
800	36.2	116	32.0	103	0.1	0.05
900	35.7	114	31.3	100	0.1	0.05
1,000	35.5	114	31.1	100	0.1	0.05

Example 3:   This example will demonstrate the economic advantages of water injection in accordance with the process. The process as described in Example 1 is repeated at substantially the same operating conditions but with the exception that no water is injected into contactor 8 through line 13. Without water injection, very little CO will be converted to H_2 in tubular retort 15. Then, to maintain the same gross yield of shale oil (lines 55 + 27) it is necessary to supply more hydrogen to the system. This may be accomplished by increasing the quantity of synthesis gas introduced into the system through line 10 to about 1,685 scfh. This will of course increase the consumption of shale oil, oxygen, and H_2O fed to the gas generator. It will also increase the volume of gas processed through gas purifier 38.

In a related process, described by W.G. Schlinger, D.R. Jesse and J.P. Tassoney; U.S. Patent 3,617,471; November 2, 1971; assigned to Texaco Inc. hydrogen-rich gas, e.g., synthesis gas, and H_2O are injected into oil shale at a comparatively moderate pressure in the range of about 300 to 1,000 psig and at a temperature in the range of about 850° to 950°F., for producing high-quality shale oil in yields that exceed the Fischer Assay. The addition of H_2O reduces the hydrogen consumption and heat load required for a given yield of shale oil. The process can be self-sustaining in that the shale oil and water produced may be used for making the synthesis gas used in the hydrogenation and denitrification of the shale oil.

W.G. Schlinger, D.R. Jesse and J.P. Tassoney; U.S. Patent 3,617,472; November 2, 1971; assigned to Texaco Inc. also describe a process for recovering shale oil from oil shale by retorting with synthesis gas, i.e., a mixture of carbon monoxide and hydrogen, generated by partial combustion of by-product gas with oxygen, where part of the heat required for retorting is provided by the hot synthesis gas, and additional hydrogen is produced in the oil shale retort by the water-gas shift reaction, the shale acting as a catalyst; and the process being self-sufficient in requiring no external source of water.

Simultaneous Retorting and Hydrogenation

A process described by du B. Eastman and W.G. Schlinger; U.S. Patent 3,117,072; Jan. 7, 1964 and U.S. Patent 3,044,948; July 17, 1962; both assigned to Texaco Inc. relates to simultaneous retorting of oil shale to recover shale oil and hydrogenation of the recovered shale oil. The process results in the production of a recovered oil of reduced viscosity, lower sulfur and nitrogen content, and improved refinability as compared with oil recovered from shale by conventional retorting in the presence of relatively inert gases.

Oil Shale Refining Processes

In the process, a fluid mixture or slurry, of hydrogen, shale oil, and particles of oil shale is passed through an elongated tubular reactor of relatively great length in comparison with its cross-sectional area.

The volume of flow of feed material in the reaction zone is maintained at a rate such that velocities sufficient to completely disperse the shale particles in the oil-hydrogen composite fluid and obtain highly turbulent flow conditions is ensured.

Such velocities may be readily obtained by passing the slurry feed mixture through a tube of relatively small internal diameter, for example, one half to one inch tubular reactor. Under these conditions, the hydrogen diffusion distance is greatly reduced and the allowable rate of reaction correspondingly increased.

By the use of highly turbulent flow conditions, the hydrogenation reaction may be accelerated so that conversion of heavy shale oil to lighter products is accelerated and the shale oil product is considerably upgraded by increasing the yield of lower boiling products without the concomitant formation of high boiling polymers or coke.

In this process, oil feed rate, hydrogen recycle rate, reaction tube diameter, and operating conditions of temperature and pressure all tend to affect velocity of flow and turbulence. Temperatures of 700° to 1500°F. may be employed. A preferred range of temperatures is from 800° to 1000°F. Pressures of 1,000 to 20,000 psig may be employed, although pressures of 1,500 to 10,000 psig are preferred. Hydrogen feed rates of 1,000 to 100,000 scf/bbl. of slurry feed may be employed, but feed rates of 2,000 to 50,000 scf/bbl. are preferred. Hydrogen may be supplied in relatively pure form or in concentrations as low as 25 volume percent. Reaction times of 20 to 300 seconds are preferred.

Referring to Figure 2.3, moderately pulverized shale, e.g., shale having a particle size smaller than one-quarter inch in average diameter, is charged to a mixer 5 in which it is mixed with oil derived from the shale, optionally together with water to form a pumpable slurry. The addition of water to the slurry, as illustrated, and the addition of catalyst, e.g., iodine, a hydrogen halide, especially hydrogen iodide, organic iodine compounds, e.g., methyl iodide, and volatile halides of aluminum, zinc, boron or phosphorus, are optional.

The slurry is raised to an elevated pressure by pump 6, mixed with hydrogen under pressure from line 7 and passed through converter 8 at a velocity such that a turbulence level above 10, preferably above 25, is maintained in the converter. As illustrated, converter 8 comprises a helical coil of pipe, a preferred form of the converter. Alternatively, the converter may comprise a pipe still type furnace with straight tubes and 180° return bends of the general type employed in petroleum refining operations.

In coil 8, which serves the dual function of a retort for the oil shale and a hydrogenation reaction zone for shale oil, the kerogen in the shale is converted to shale oil and, at the same time, hydrogenation of the oil takes place. Heat from a suitable source, for example, furnace 9 is supplied to the heating coil to maintain the reaction temperature within the desired range of 700° to 1,500°F. Average pressure in the reaction coil 8 is of the order of several thousand pounds per square inch gauge, i.e., with the range of 1,000 to 10,000 psig and suitably 3,000 to 5,000 psig. In addition to the retorting and hydrogenation which take place in coil 8, a considerable amount of disintegration of the shale oil particles takes place within the coil due to the combined action of heat and highly turbulent flow. With some oil shales, disintegration takes place as a result of heating under pressure in the presence of oil, as described in U.S. Patent 2,793,194.

Additional pulverization of the oil shale particles results from the highly turbulent flow and resulting collisions of particles with one another and with the wall of the shale, shale oil, and residual hydrogen is discharged from conversion coil 8 through line 11 into separator 12 without reduction in pressure.

The primary purpose of separator 12 is to effect separation between residual solid and oil product. At the base of separator 12, hydrogen from a suitable source is introduced through line 14 effecting stripping of oil and oil vapors from the residual shale solids. All of the hydrogen required for the process is preferably introduced at this point.

Hydrogen, shale oil, and shale oil vapors are discharged from separator 12 through line 16 to a gas-liquid separator 17. In separator 17, which preferably is operated at the same pressure as separator 12, unreacted hydrogen is separated from liquid products and any entrained solids carried over from separator 12. Hydrogen from separator 17 is recycled by compressor 18 to line 7 from which it flows into conversion coil 8. Additional fresh feed hydrogen may be, if desired, supplied to the system through line 19.

Residual solid from separator 12, together with part of the oil, is withdrawn through line 21 to separator 22, preferably operated at the same pressure as separator 12, wherein hydrogen and oil are displaced from the residual solid by means of water. Water entering through line 23 preferentially wets the solid mineral residue from the shale, displacing oil and hydrogen through line 24 and pressure reducing valve 25 to separator 29. Spent shale and water are discharged through line 26 and discarded.

Separators 12 and 22 may be combined into a single vessel with hydrogen and water entering at intermediate points in the vessel and with hydrogen, vapors, and oil going overhead to separator 17 as illustrated in connection with separator 12 and with water and spent shale particles being withdrawn from the bottom of the vessel as illustrated in connection with separator 22.

The separations which are effected in separators 12, 17, and 22 preferably are carried out at elevated pressure, for example, substantially at the reactor discharge pressure. Liquid separated in separator 17, together with any entrained solid which may be present therein (usually a part of the oil shale fines), passes through reducing valve 28 into a fractionation system 29 where a final separation is made into various shale oil products. The shale oil recovered in the process is separated into various fractions according to product requirements.

A gaseous fraction is taken from the fractionation system through line 31. This gas may be processed for recovery of hydrogen in known manner, or used directly for fuel. Liquid products of intermediate boiling range are drawn from the fractionation system through line 32. Heavy oil, which may contain fine particles of oil shale residue which find their way through the various separators into the fractionation system, is withdrawn through line 33 for disposal in a suitable manner. This oil may be used directly as fuel, e.g., to supply heat for the process; it is also useful as fuel for the generation of hydrogen for the process by partial combustion with oxygen.

Recycle oil is drawn from the fractionation system through line 34 and supplied to mixer 5 for the preparation of the oil shale feed slurry for the process. Preferably the recycle oil is a fraction boiling below the heavy residuum, e.g., having a boiling range of 500° to 700°F.

The process described in U.S. Patent 2,809,104 is particularly useful for the conversion of the heavy oil to carbon monoxide and hydrogen. Carbon monoxide so produced may be subjected to a shift conversion operation in the presence of an iron catalyst effecting reaction with steam to produce carbon dioxide and hydrogen. Following removal of carbon dioxide, hydrogen is obtained which is suitable for use in the process.

Oil from separator 12, containing spent shale, may be withdrawn through line 37, and is suitable for use as fuel in the process or for the production of hydrogen. This oil may be treated for removal of solids or utilized directly as fuel. If oil is withdrawn from separator 12 through line 37 for use as fuel, it is preferable to separate hydrogen as by pressure reduction and heating, prior to its use as fuel.

Oil shale compositions from various sources vary considerable in recoverable shale oil content. The recoverable shale oil content may vary from 20 to 120 gallons per ton of shale. In general, the shale oil contents of commercial shales fall within the range of from about 30 to 60 gallons per ton. Oil shales having a shale oil content of at least 30 gallons of recoverable oil per ton, as determined by the Fischer assay method, are preferred for the process. The following examples illustrate the process.

Examples 1 through 4: Oil shale having a Fischer assay of 27.7 gallons per ton is treated by the process. The shale oil recovered from this shale by a conventional retorting procedure has the following characteristics:

API gravity	20
Viscosity:	
SUS at 130°F.	145
SUS at 210°F.	48
Pour point, °F.	+90
Sulfur in oil, wt. percent	0.7
Nitrogen in oil, wt. percent	2.6
Carbon residue, wt. percent	4.4
ASTM distillation:	
IBP , °F.	310
10%, °F.	493
50%, °F.	704
85%, °F.	760

The oil shale is crushed to minus 20 mesh (U.S. Bureau of Standards Standard Screen Series, 1919), mixed with an equal weight of treated oil from the process, and treated without a catalyst under the conditions and with the results indicated in the following table. In each instance, the hydrogen stream and the slurry of shale in shale oil are separately preheated to approximately reaction temperature. After combining the hydrogen with the slurry, the composite mixture is passed through a one thousand foot tubular reactor having an internal diameter of 0.312 inch.

	Examples			
	1	2	3	4
Average temperature, ° F	700	700	740	800
Average pressure, p.s.i.g.	3,000	5,000	5,000	5,000
Turbulence level, ave.	100	150	140	130
Total hydrogen feed rate std. cu. ft./ bbl. oil	27,400	21,000	26,000	29,000
Hydrogen feed purity, vol. percent	89	82	76	74
H₂ consumed, cu. ft./bbl. oil	430	580	665	1,630
Liquid yield, vol. percent [1]	99.7	100.7	96.9	81.6
API Gravity	27.7	26.5	28.7	36.7
Viscosity—				
SUS at 100 ° F	74.0	77.0	42.0	32.0
SUS at 210 ° F			32.5	
ASTM Distillation:				
I.B.P., ° F	166	200	158	110
I.B.P.-400 ° F., vol. percent	15	12	25	60
400-760 ° F., vol. percent	61	60	65	28
Above 760 ° F., vol. percent	24	28	10	12
Sulfur, wt. percent	0.34	0.68	0.27	0.13
Nitrogen, wt. percent	1.89	1.74	2.14	2.47
Carbon residue, wt. percent	2.83	2.99	2.77	2.70

[1] Basis Fischer assay yield.

FIGURE 2.3: SIMULTANEOUS RETORTING AND HYDROGENATION

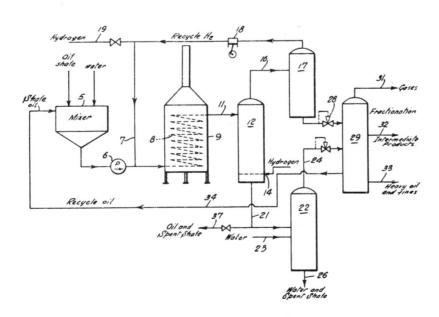

Source: du B. Eastman and W. G. Schlinger; U.S. Patent 3,117,072; January 7, 1964

Oil Shale Refining Processes

In a process described by W.G. Schlinger and du B. Eastman; U.S. Patent 3,224,954; December 21, 1965; assigned to Texaco Inc. an oil-bearing mineral is subjected to treatment with hydrogen containing gas at a pressure in the range of 1,000 to 2,500 lbs./sq. in. gauge and at a temperature in the range of 800° to 950°F. for a period of 20 minutes to 5 hours, preferably not more than 2 hours. High oil yields are obtained. Oil yields of more than 100%, and typically 125 to 135%, by volume, in comparison with the standard Fischer Assay, are obtained from commercial grade oil shales. The quantity of oil remaining in the residue is too small to support combustion. In addition, the recovered oil has lower viscosity, lower specific gravity and lower carbon residue than oils recovered by conventional retorting procedures.

Pyrolysis and Hydrogenation in Single Reaction Zone

G.B. Hoekstra; U.S. Patent 3,565,751; February 23, 1971; assigned to Standard Oil Co. describes a method for pyrolyzing oil shale and simultaneously hydrogenating the shale oil in the presence of a hydrogenation catalyst, and in a single reaction zone. This simultaneous pyrolysis and hydrogenation insures maximum yield of high quality product.

In carrying out the process, oil shale is introduced into a reaction zone which contains a conventional, fluidizable hydrogenation catalyst. The oil shale is heated in the reaction zone to pyrolysis temperatures, whereby to drive shale oil from the oil shale and to produce finely divided particles of spent shale as a result of the removal of the kerogen. Hydrogen is introduced into a lower portion of the reaction zone during the heating, under a pressure of about 200 to 2,000 psig and at an upward velocity sufficient to fluidize the catalyst and to carry the finely divided spent shale particles and shale oil upwardly out of the reaction zone. Because of the presence of the hydrogen and a hydrogenation catalyst, the shale oil is hydrogenated prior to removal from the reaction zone.

A process described by M.G. Huntington; U.S. Patent 3,475,317; October 28, 1969 involves the destructive distillation of hydrocarbonaceous materials. The apparatus and process include a means for feeding at least a solid supported catalyst and a crushed hydrocarbonaceous raw material through a lock and to a vertical reactor capable of withstanding temperatures of up to 2,000°F. and pressures to 30 atmospheres. The reactor contains a plurality of adjacent vertically positioned distillation zones, gaseous intake and offtake means for each zone, means for providing a gaseous diffusion barrier between zones, and a combination AC agglomerator and widening gaseous paths in each zone in front of the offtake means.

The reactor is further provided with a second lock to allow for the removal of the solid material which is subsequently passed to a system which separates effluent solids. Preheated hydrogen is fed into each zone, entrains the destructively distilled and stabilized product and is passed through a plurality of dephlegmators and catalyst beds. The catalyst in the reactor may be rejuvenated and recycled to the original feed means and a solid heating medium may be utilized in the reactor and continuously recycled. Complete details of process equipment are provided.

Use of Coarse and Fine Catalysts

N.C. Stewart; U.S. Patent 3,635,943; January 18, 1972; assigned to Cities Service

Oil Shale Refining Processes

Research and Development Company describes a method for treating oils in a simple reactor. By employing two differently sized particulate catalysts, two generally separate expanded catalyst beds are established in the single reactor. Basically, the process contemplates feeding regenerated fine catalyst together with the hydrocarbon oil feed and a hydrogen containing gas into a hydrotreating vessel, and passing the mixture upwardly through an expanded coarse catalyst bed in the reactor. Above the level of the coarse catalyst bed the fine catalyst, hydrocarbon reactant and gaseous mixture, passing upwardly into the upper portion of the reactor establishes an expanded fine catalyst bed.

A portion of the hydrocarbon reactant liquid is recycled back to the bottom of the reactor. Recycling effectively adds to the flow of fluids through the lower catalyst bed and the resultant velocity is sufficient to maintain the lower bed in an expanded state. The upward flow above the lower catalyst bed is reduced to a velocity which enables fine particulate catalyst to concentrate and form a fine catalyst bed in the upper portion of the reactor. Effluent is withdrawn from the reactor above the level of the fine catalyst bed.

The particulate coarse and fine catalysts may be of any suitable catalyst composition. Suitable catalyst compositions include a large number of materials such as cobalt, molybdenum, iron, nickel, tungsten, platinum, palladium, naturally occurring clays, as well as combinations of the same. For the particular application described here, a cobalt-molybdenum catalyst supported on alumina is the preferred composition.

The coarse particulate catalyst is in the form of either pellets or extrudates in the size range of from 1/32 to 3/8 inch in diameter. After becoming inactivated the coarse catalyst may be regenerated by calcining in an air or oxygen atmosphere, and then is either attrited or more preferably pulverized to a size below 600 microns, preferably in the size range of from 300 to 600 microns for use as fine catalyst in the process.

The feed may be any suitable hydrocarbon liquid for which a desired treatment is hydrogenation. For this reason naphtha and other oils boiling below 450°F. are not regarded as suitable. Preferably the feed is a liquid hydrocarbon boiling above 450°F., and more preferably above 650°F. Heavy hydrocarbon oils boiling above 950°F. such as vacuum or atmospheric residuums are preferred feeds, being particularly suitable for refining by hydrotreating. The term hydrotreating is intended to cover various reactions such as hydrocracking, hydrogenation, hydrodesulfurization and hydrodenitrogenation, all of which are obtainable in varying degrees by utilizing the process described herein.

Impregnation of Shale with Gasoline

A process described by C.D. Shields; U.S. Patent 3,503,868; March 31, 1970 comprises impregnating mined and crushed geological matrix, e.g., oil shale, with a hydrogen-containing solvent for the kerogen and maintaining the matrix in contact with the solvent for a period of time sufficient for the kerogen to be impregnated by the solvent. The solvent-impregenated matrix is then charged into a rotatable high pressure reactor which is provided with heating means and which contains crusher balls, preferably of heat conductive material, e.g., steel. The reactor is provided with a quick-opening vent valve which is connected to a line leading to a high pressure petroleum fractionating tower. The reactor is closed, heat in the range used for mixed phase petroleum cracking operations is applied and the reactor is rotated. The crusher balls grind the matrix into smaller particles, which are more readily accessible to the solvent and to the reactant agent. The crusher balls also serve conductively to heat the matrix. Pressure is permitted to rise in the closed reactor, causing increased solubilization of the heated kerogen by the hot solvent. The hydrogen from the solvent reacts with the kerogen to convert it into compounds volatile at 400° to 500°F. After a suitable grinding, heating, solvating, and converting period, a significant portion of the kerogen is made volatile.

The vent value of the reactor is opened suddenly to release the pressure. The sudden release of pressure causes the solvent in the matrix particles to expand almost explosively thereby pulverizing the ground particles into still finer particles. Solvent and low boiling kerogen products boil out of the reactor. The rapidly boiling materials entrain some higher boiling kerogen compounds and carry them out of the reactor. After the pressure in the reactor has dropped to a set limit, the vent valve is closed and more solvent is charged into the reactor.

A reactive chemical agent, which may be a hydrogenating agent, in alkylating agent, a cracking agent, or other petroleum converting agent is also charged into the reactor. Heating and rotating of the reactor and its contents are continued for a suitable reacting, cracking converting and solvating period while pressure again builds up in the reactor. At the end of this period, the pressure is again suddenly released from the reactor into the fractionating tower. The operating cycle of charging with solvent and with reactive chemical agent, rotating, reacting and sudden pressure releasing is repeated until substantially all the kerogen economically feasible to recover has been recovered from the matrix. The spent matrix is then discharged from the reactor and the unit prepared for the next charge of crushed solvent-impregnated shale oil matrix. The products vented into the fractionating tower are condensed and separated by distillation. Recovery of oil from the starting material by this process is about 130% of Fischer Assay.

Solvent Treating Before Hydrogenation to Prevent Plugging

A process described by R.A. Hanson; U.S. Patent 3,052,620; September 4, 1962; assigned to Union Oil Company involves a method for treating residual shale oils prior to hydrogenation in such a manner that the hydrogenation unit will not become plugged with gunk. The process involves solvent treating residual shale oils prior to the step of preheating the shale oil in the presence of hydrogen preparatory to catalytic hydrogenation. A preferred form of the process involves a combination of water washing and acetone treating residual shale oils prior to preheating the shale oil in the presence of hydrogen preparatory to catalytic hydrogenation. With this procedure, a total of 2 to 6% by weight is rejected by the solvent.

Example: Crude shale oil produced by the downflow process of U.S. Patent 2,501,153 was mixed with 3 volumes of acetone and agitated while being heated to 135°F. over a period of about 0.5 hour. The mixture was then permitted to settle and cool for about 16 hours, at which time it had cooled to about 80°F. The mixture was filtered through No. 40 Whatman filter paper at this temperature, leaving about 4% of the original weight of the crude oil as a solid residue on the filter paper. The filtrate was vacuum distilled to remove the acetone, and the remaining oil, which constituted about 96% by weight of the original crude, was tested in the filter bomb test described above in comparison with the crude oil feed. It was found that the original crude shale oil feed plugged the filter so quickly that substantially none of the oil could be filtered, whereas all of the acetone treated oil passed through the filter with no evidence of plugging and no perceptible precipitate. Photomicrographs of the feed and product were also taken, and whereas the feed showed evidences of many solid or semisolid particles of various sizes suspended in the oil, the product was substantially free of any particles.

When particles are referred to here it must be understood that these are not ordinary solid suspensions capable of removal by simple settling or filtration. These crude oils referred to have in many cases been stored for months and even maintained at temperatures of about 160°F. under a blanket of helium; and while there was in some cases a settling of a small amount of semisolid material, the photomicrographs remained substantially the same, as did the plugging tendency in the bomb test and in actual pilot plant runs. Even filtration after such long standing had no substantial effect on the appearance in the photomicrographs or on the plugging tendency. Yet the acetone treatment, which appears to remove primarily wax-like materials of relatively low melting point, not only clarified the oil but removed all tendency toward plugging or gunk formation during the subsequent hydrogenation. Since wax can be readily hydrogenated under the above conditions without causing any plugging of the hydrogenation reactor or preheater, the effect of the acetone treatment is quite surprising.

It is also interesting that when the crude shale oil feed is vacuum distilled to take 80% overhead, acetone treatment of the distillate as above resulted in rejection of substantially the same amount of waxy solid material, and had almost exactly the same effect of reducing pour point, i.e., a reduction of about 40°F.; yet this distillate is free from plugging tendency in the filter bomb and hydrogenation tests, so that acetone treatment is of little benefit to the distillate in this respect.

The acetone-treated crude oil described above was found to be substantially as corrosive as the crude shale oil feed, i.e., both exhibited corrosion of carbon steel at 600°F. amounting to about 0.068" per year. One volume of the product was mixed with one volume of water at room temperature and the mixture was agitated while heating to 180°F. over a period of one hour and allowed to settle for one hour at which time it had cooled to about 150°F. The oil was decanted from the water and recovered to the extent of about 99.5% by weight.

It was again tested for corrosivity and found to be substantially noncorrosive, i.e., its corrosion rate for carbon steel was only about 0.003" per year, which is well below the tolerable rate of about 0.008" per year. The water-washed oil remained equally free from plugging tendency in the filter bomb test, and was suitable for catalytic hydrogenation without plugging of the preheater or catalyst bed. Several modifications of the process are also described.

Conservation and Reuse of Hydrogen

A process described by M.G. Huntington; U.S. Patent 3,106,521; October 8, 1963; assigned to Huntington Chemical Corporation is concerned with the conservation and maximum recombination and reuse of the hydrogen which is initially contained in the hydrocarbonaceous constituent of oil shale and further concerns itself with hydrofining and hydrocracking of the condensable volatile matter in order to achieve maximum production of the more useful light oils while not requiring an outside source of hydrogen. Raw crushed shale of various sizes may be fed vertically downward through an internally heated retort in measured amounts over gyrating shelf feeders. The raw shale of various sizes is concurrently contacted and heated by a stream of hot hydrogen and the primary volatile matter is distilled. This primary volatile matter is taken off from a duct in the vertical retort and the solid particles of shale continue to be fed downwardly.

A moderate amount of unheated hydrogen is introduced to flow countercurrently through the spent, broken shale to effect the final stripping of volatile matter and to achieve at least partial heat recovery. Safety gas locks continuously purged with noncombustible gas are provided at both ends of the hydrogen contacting area of the retort to insure against ignition of the thermal carrier hydrogen. Heat recovery and preheating sections are provided outside of the safety gas locks at the bottom and top of the retort respectively.

The primary volatile matter offtake is connected to a multiple bed catalyzer and then to a fractionator and the entire stream passes through both vessels at system pressure. From the fractionator the heavy bottoms are recycled for contact coking in a portion of an auxiliary apparatus such as a coal still, the middle oils are passed through a high pressure hydrocracker and the overhead stream is passed to a condenser. After being scrubbed, uncondensable gases from the condenser are thermally cracked and reheated in an auxiliary apparatus and then are recycled to the oil shale retort. All of the heat supplied for heating the oil shale retort is supplied from an auxiliary source.

This auxiliary source for supplying all the heat may be a coal still in combination with the oil refining processes described. This coal still not only furnishes all of the heat but also may be the auxiliary apparatus which provides the means (hot char) for cracking hydrocarbon gases into hydrogen at substantial pressures and in substantial quantities and thus furnishes the thermal carrier gas to accomplish the destructive distillation of the oil shale.

The heavy oil bottoms from the fractionator are also recycled into the coal still where coking and redistillation are performed in contact with incandescent char. The flue gas produced from the coal still may be utilized as the noncombustible gas for the safety gas locks of the oil shale retort, and for heat recovery and preheating.

Thus, this process produces high quality petroleum products without requiring a source of hydrogen and without requiring internal firing of the oil shale retort. Furthermore, by utilizing a system in which the thermal carrier fluid is essentially hydrogen and wherein the partial pressure of hydrogen has a tendency to increase the yield of condensable liquids and to decrease the splitting off of permanent gases during the pyrolysis and distillation of the kerogen, also, the apparent yield of intermediate semirefined shale oil is substantially greater than 100% of that indicated by the modified Fischer Assay. A complete description of the process is presented.

OTHER PROCESSES

Combined Retort and Cracking Process

F.D. Hoffert; U.S. Patent 3,483,116; Dec. 9, 1969; assigned to Hydrocarbon Research, Inc.

describes a method by which shale in lump form may be subjected to retort or distillation conditions and where the volatile products from the retorting step, may be cracked to more desirable products within the same zone in which the retorting takes place. The shale fines produced from the retorting operation may be used as the heat transfer medium for both the distillation or volatilization step and the cracking step.

The process comprises passing lump shale downwardly through a contact zone containing a fluidized bed of hot shale fines. The temperature and inventory of the fluidized bed is maintained by introducing superheated fines at the top of the bed and removing cooler fines at the bottom. Thus, there is an overall downward flow of fines in the bed resulting in a temperature gradient vertically through the bed, the highest temperature being at the top and the coolest temperature being at the bottom.

As the lump shale travels downwardly through the bed, it is finally heated hot enough whereby the hydrocarbons contained therein begin to retort or distill out of the shale. Generally, the retorting doesn't begin until the lump shale is in the lower portion of the contact zone as it takes a finite time to heat it up to the required retorting temperature.

The vaporized materials travel upwardly into the upper superheated portion of the fluidized bed. The temperature in this upper portion is sufficiently high to result in substantial cracking of the distilled material into lower boiling and more valuable products which are removed from the upper part of the contact zone and cooled and fractionated in the usual manner. Thus, the bed is separated by function into two zones, a lower retorting zone where the lump shale is at its highest temperature and the fines are at their lowest temperature, and an upper cracking zone where the shale is at its lowest temperature and the fines are at their highest temperature. The bed of fines is normally fluidized by an external inert gas, however, the distilled vapors may be used to aid in the fluidization.

Thus, the process allows one to successfully and effectively remove the distillable hydrocarbon-containing materials from shale without having to grind the shale to a fine powder. Additionally, the process makes use of the fines which inevitably result even from a relatively crude grinding step to provide heat, not only for the distillation or retorting of the volatile constituents from the shale, but also for the subsequent thermal cracking of the distilled materials. The distilled lump shale is removed at the bottom of the contact zone and the fines are removed separately from the lump shale and may be reheated and recirculated to the upper portion of the zone.

Referring to Figure 2.4, granulated or lump shale having a nominal diameter size between 1/2 to 4 inches is introduced from hopper 10 through valve 12 and line 14 into the contact zone 16 which contains a fluidized bed of hot shale fines. The lump shale moves downwardly through the bed where it is heated by the fluid bed to distill the hydrocarbons and exits through stripper leg 20. Exit valve 22 controls the overall rate of flow of the lump shale through the zone. The hot distilled lump shale enters cooling chamber 48 through line 46 where it is cooled by the passage of air. The cooled distilled shale is then removed from the system through valve 52.

The fluidized bed is maintained by introducing superheated shale fines to the chamber through line 24 and gas-solids separator 26. The rate of passage of the fines through the chamber is

FIGURE 2.4: USE OF SHALE FINES AS HEAT TRANSFER MEDIUM IN CRACKING PROCESS

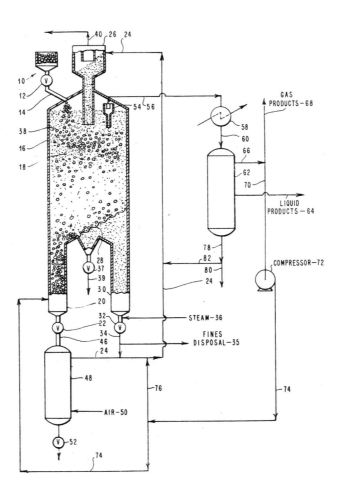

Source: F.D. Hoffert; U.S. Patent 3,483,116; December 9, 1969

a function of the heat transfer requirements of the system. The exiting fines are separated from the larger lumps of shale by screen 28. The fines enter stripper leg 30, are steam stripped using steam through line 36 to remove any adhering shale distillate oil and are then removed from the system through valve 32 and line 34. Fines disposal may take place either through valve 37 and line 39 or through line 35.

The bulk of the fines is introduced to line 24 where it is mixed with hot air from cooling zone 48. The air and fines with some residual oils adhering thereon, are passed upwardly through line 24 which constitutes a combustion zone, wherein the residual oils are burned in order to achieve superheating of the fines. The superheated fines are then recycled through line 24 into separator 26. The combustion or flue gas is separated from the fines in separator 26 and exits through line 40. The superheated fines entering the top of the contact zone through separator 26 provide the heat for the distillation of the hydrocarbon materials from the shale. It has been found that such fines have highly efficient heat transfer characteristics and, thus, provide a superior means for providing or transferring the heat source for the shale oil distillation.

The fines in bed 38 at the top of the contact zone are at a relatively high temperature. Thus, there is sufficient heat provided for the required cracking process. It is also noted, however, that a thermal gradient exists vertically through the reaction zone, since at the top of the zone, the lump shale is at its lowest temperature and the fines are at their highest temperature. As the lump shale progresses downwardly through the zone, it becomes hotter as it picks up heat from the fines. The fines thus become cooler. At a relatively low point in the contact zone, the lump shale is at its highest temperature and the fines are then relatively cool. The differential, however, at this low point between the lump shale and the fines is small, whereas, at the top of the reaction zone, the differential was quite high. Thus, the distillation of the hydrocarbons from the shale takes place at the lower portion of the contact zone, since it is at this point that the lump shale is the hottest.

The vapors then proceed upwardly through the lower portion of the bed, which constitutes the distillation zone and into the upper portion of the fluidized bed which constitutes the cracking zone. The vaporized hydrocarbons then exit the contact zone 16 through separator 54 wherein any fines are returned to the fluidized bed. The fines-free vapors removed from the separator 54 through line 56 are cooled in cooler 58 and enter fractionator 62 through line 60.

Fractionator 62, represents any known type of fractionation system which are normally used in the separation of multiboiling component mixtures. It may consist of either a single unit or units in combination including both atmospheric and subatmospheric thermal distillations.

From the fractionator 62, the various products or product fractions of the shale oil are removed. The liquid products are removed through line 64 and the gaseous products are removed through line 66 and fed to distribution through line 68. A portion of the gaseous products may be taken through line 70, compressed by compressor 72 and fed through line 74 into the stripper leg 20. This relatively high velocity compressed hydrocarbon gas serves a two-fold purpose. First, it removes the fines from the lump shale in and entering stripper leg 20 and assures that the distilled lump shale entering valve 22 is essentially dust-free. Second, the gas serves as a fluidizing means for the fines bed 38.

A unique aspect of the process, embodied in the fluid bed seal in the dip leg of separator 26, serves to prevent combustion gases from entering the distillation or cracking zone. As shown, the dip leg extends below the top surface or interface of the fluidized bed. A controlled differential pressure exists between the gases in the contact area and those leaving separator 26 through line 40, the pressure generally being lower in the separator such that the level of the fluidized bed in the dip leg of separator 26 is higher than in the contact zone. This additional depth of the bed, combined with the relatively small diameter of the dip leg compared to the reaction zone and the downward flow of solids being concentrated by the separator, acts to prevent the gases in the contact zone from escaping through the dip leg and, conversely, to seal the combustion gases in the separator from the contact zone.

Oil Shale Refining Processes

The bottoms products from fractionator 62 are removed through line 78 and may be sent to further downstream processing through line 80. If desired, however, a portion of the bottoms material may be introduced to the combustion zone in line 24 through line 82. The combustion of this bottoms material may then be used to incrementally supply the heat for the fines.

Generally, the conditions under which the process is carried out, would be a distillation zone temperature from 800° to 1000°F. and a system pressure from about atmospheric to about 100 psig.

Example: This example gives specific process conditions which have been used in applying the process to the production of oil from African and Australian shales.

Shale contact time retort, min.	20
Distillation temperature, °F.	950
Cracking temperature, °F.	1050
Lump shale feed rate, lbs./hr./sq. ft. of retort	2,400
Air circulation, scfh/sq. ft. of retort	16,400
Fines circulation rate (300°F. AT), lbs./hr./sq. ft. of retort	20,600
Heat release in retort, Btu/ cu. ft./hr.	51,000
Volatile matter in feed, %	40
Total oil product, bbl./ton of feed shale	2

In a process described by L.W. Fish and G.F. Pappas; U.S. Patent 3,093,571; June 11, 1963; assigned to Esso Research and Engineering Company both retorting and quality improving conversion of the liberated hydrocarbons are effected within a single combination system. A two-zone hydrocarbon conversion process, e.g., a fluid coker and burner, are integrated with a retorting zone in a manner such that a single burner supplies requisite heat for both the retorting and hydrocarbon conversion steps.

More particularly, carbon-coated fine particles are withdrawn from the hydrocarbon reaction stage and passed to the burner where they are subjected to combustion. A portion of the particles heated in this manner are passed to the reaction zone and a second solids stream passed to retorting zone thereby supplying requisite thermal energy. Liberated hydrocarbons pass directly from the retort to the hydrocarbon conversion stage where they are commingled with conversion vapors. A heavy ends portion of the total product vapors is condensed and circulated back to the reaction zone.

Simultaneous Separation and Cracking

L.P. Evans; U.S. Patent 3,281,349; October 25, 1966; assigned to Mobil Oil Corporation describes a process for the simultaneous separation and catalytic cracking of shale oil from crushed shale. The process comprises utilizing functionally integrated zones, including a retorting-cracking zone, a solids classifying zone, a catalyst regeneration zone and a shale fine separation zone. Within the retorting-cracking zone shale oil is separated from crushed shale particles upon being commingled with heated catalyst particles, and the resulting separated shale oil is cracked catalytically to more desired products. During this simultaneous retorting and cracking step organic matter is distilled from the shale particles; concurrently the cracking reaction deposits carbonaceous matter upon the solid catalyst particles and thereby reduces catalyst activity. Separation of organically depleted shale particles from the deactivated catalyst is effected in the solids classifying zone. Thereafter carbonaceous matter is burned from the catalyst in the regeneration zone; the catalyst is thereby heated and reactivated. After removal of entrained shale fines in the shale fine separation zone, the heated catalyst is recycled to the retorting and cracking zone for reuse.

Referring to Figure 2.5 there is shown a reactor 2 supported in an elevated position above a classifying chamber 4. The reactor 2 and classifying chamber 4 are positioned above regenerator 6 to permit gravity flow of solids. Positioned above a catalyst surge hopper 8 and connected by a gravity feed leg 10 is a separation chamber 12 into which lift gas and catalyst are discharged. A withdrawal conduit for standpipe 14 leads from the bottom of regenerator 6 to a lift feed chamber 16. A suitable lift gas inlet conduit 18 connects with the lift chamber 16 and an open-ended lift pipe 20 extends substantially vertically upward from a location within the lift chamber into the upper portion of the elevated separation chamber 12.

FIGURE 2.5: SIMULTANEOUS SEPARATION AND CRACKING OF SHALE OIL

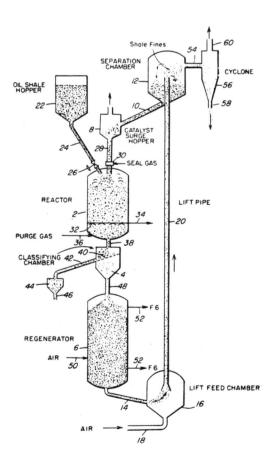

Source: L.P. Evans; U.S. Patent 3,281,349; October 25, 1966

Oil Shale Refining Processes

In the process, raw crushed shale particles, passed from oil shale hopper 22 by way of gravity feed leg 24 provided with flow control valve 26, are commingled with hot regenerated catalyst particles passed from an elevated catalyst surge hopper 8 by gravity feed leg 28 into reactor 2. The commingled mixture of catalyst and shale is passed through reactor 2 as a relatively dense, downwardly moving bed of particles. A suitable seal gas is introduced into gravity feed leg 28 or seal chamber 30 provided to maintain a seal pressure at the base of the feed leg 28 elevated sufficiently to permit flow of catalyst into reactor 2.

Oil shale and hot regenerated catalyst contact is effected within reactor 2 under conditions and a manner which accomplishes a separation or distillation of hydrocarbonaceous material from the oil shale and a catalytic cracking of separated hydrocarbonaceous material to provide useful products of a more desired nature. The endothermic heat required for effecting the above separation of hydrocarbonaceous material and the catalytic cracking thereof is supplied at least in part by recycled regenerated catalyst particles. The ratio of hot catalyst to cold shale is controlled to allow heating of the shale upon commingling with the catalyst particles to a temperature of 850° to 950°F. at the top of the bed.

The separated hydrocarbonaceous material flows concurrently with the relatively dense, downwardly moving bed in reactor 2, is cracked simultaneously to more useful constituents and emerges from reactor 2 by vapor outlets 32 through conduit 34 to a shale oil recovery section. The deactivated catalyst and organically depleted shale particles are purged free of hydrocarbonaceous vapors by means of a suitable inert purge gas supplied through conduit 36. The spent catalyst and shale particles then pass by gravity flow via conduit 38 into classifying chamber 4.

The mixture of spent catalyst and shale particles is separated in classifying chamber 4 by means of a suitable separating device 40, such as a grate, vibrating screen, shaker table, or other classifier. Preferably a catalyst is used in the method which is of a substantially different particle size from that of the spent shale particles, to allow an effective physical separation of the spent shale. A major portion of the spent shale particles is separated from the main catalyst stream and removed from classifying chamber 4 through conduit 42 into a coarse spent shale hopper 44 and discarded through conduit 46. If economics warrant, the spent shale may undergo heat recovery before discarding. The deactivated catalyst particles and entrained small shale particles then pass by gravity flow via conduit 48 into regenerator 6.

The catalyst and small shale particles pass through regenerator 6 as a relatively dense, downwardly moving bed being contacted with air or other oxygen-bearing gas introduced via conduit 50. Carbonaceous deposits are burned from the catalyst and shale particles under conditions to heat the catalyst particles to a temperature of at least 1100° to 1200°F. Under such conditions the entrained shale is rapidly disintegrated into fines. Gas combustion products are withdrawn from regenerator 6 via conduits 52.

Hot regenerated catalyst and disintegrated shale fines pass by gravity flow via conduit 14 into lift feed chamber 16. A suitable lift gas is introduced via conduit 18 at a temperature sufficiently elevated to preclude any significant cooling of the regenerated catalyst particles and at a velocity sufficient to elevate the regenerated catalyst particles and shale fines via lift pipe 20 to the separation chamber 12. Regenerated catalyst particles fall by gravity to the bottom of separation chamber 12 and are removed by gravity flow via conduit 10 to catalyst surge hopper 8. Virtually all of the buoyant shale fines are removed overhead by the lift gas from separation chamber 12 via conduit 54 into cyclone 56 wherein the shale fines are separated from the lift gas and removed by gravity flow via conduit 58 while the lift gas is removed overhead via conduit 60. Preferably the retorting-cracking zone is maintained at a temperature of between 500° and 1000°F. and the regeneration zone is maintained at a temperature of between 1000° and 1400°F.

Zeolite Catalysts

H.C. Maryland; U.S. Patent 3,654,141; April 4, 1972; assigned to Atlantic Richfield Co. describes a process for catalytically cracking of oils derived from oil shale which contain high amounts of nitrogen, i.e., over about 1%. The catalytic cracking is conducted at temperatures of about 975°F. up to 1200°F. At these temperatures the adverse effects of nitrogen poisoning of the catalyst are substantially negated.

A test was made in a laboratory catalytic cracking unit which contained a small fluidized bed reactor with provisions for continuously feeding oil and the catalyst, the oil being a 625° to 925°F. boiling range distillate shale oil (without hydrogenation) containing 2.2 weight percent nitrogen. The cracking temperature was 1000°F., the shale oil feed rate was 5 weight units per hour per weight unit of catalyst in the reactor hot zone, i.e., 5 WHSV, and the catalyst was fed at the rate of 16 weight units per hour per weight unit of shale oil, i.e., a 16 to 1 catalyst to oil ratio. The catalyst used was a rare earth (including cerium) exchanged crystalline aluminosilicate-containing catalyst, containing 0.5 to 0.9 weight percent Na, calculated as the free metal, about 0.6 weight percent rare earth, calculated as the free metal, a silica to alumina mol ratio of about 4.5 to 1, a pore radius of about 13 angstroms, and containing about 10% crystalline aluminosilicate mixed with an amorphous $SiO_2 \cdot Al_2O_3$ cracking base, part of which is derived from clay.

The product distribution showed about 11 weight percent coke on the feed and substantial yields of 430°F. EP gasoline and 430° to 600°F. distillate cuts. The 600°F. plus cut contained 4 ppm Ni, 6 ppm V and 1ppm Fe which is satisfactory for most purposes. The gasoline contained 0.85 weight percent nitrogen and the 430° to 600°F. cut contained 1.43 weight percent nitrogen. These nitrogen levels indicate that the gasoline could be improved by denitrogenation by hydrogen treatment and then catalytic reforming to increase its octane rating.

R.L. Clampitt; U.S. Patent 3,551,322; December 29, 1970; assigned to Phillips Petroleum Company describes a destructive distillation process for recovering hydrocarbons from oil-yielding solids where liquid hydrocarbons and noncondensible gas are recovered, the noncondensible gas is separated from the liquid distillation product and passed to a hydrocarbon conversion zone where the hydrocarbon contained in the noncondensible gas is converted, the converted hydrocarbon product is then separated and recovered from the noncondensible gas.

One form of the process comprises catalytically cracking the noncondensible gas stream over a silica-alumina catalyst at from 950° to 1150°F., condensing the cracked product, recovering the liquid product from the noncondensible gas stream, and recycling the gas stream to the retorting zone to cool residue solids and act as heat transfer media.

Asphalt Treating

<u>V. Mekler; U.S. Patent 2,846,361; August 5, 1958; assigned to The Lummus Company</u> describes the treatment of the class of material known as asphaltites to provide a suitable feed for a contact coking operation.

The asphaltites are natural asphalt-like substances characterized by their high fusing points. They are generally grouped into three classes, namely gilsonite, glance pitch and grahamite. This process is particularly concerned with solid gilsonite, which has a softening point in the order of 270° to 400°F., normally containing less than 5% volatile matter and having a fixed carbon content in the range of 10 to 20%. Gilsonite is particularly characterized by the fact that when heated to a temperature above 600° to 700°F., there is formed a considerable quantity of gas and the release of substantial quantities of heat.

Normally if a powdered form of gilsonite is mixed with a liquid hydrocarbon and heated to temperatures below the 600° to 700°F. temperature, it is possible to remove the undesired gaseous components, particularly nitrogen, and produce an asphalt-like charge that can be ultimately reduced to dry coke. This reduction to dry coke can be accomplished by charging the asphalt to apparatus such as delayed or continuous coking units suited for that purpose without unwarrented frothing or foaming in the apparatus and without unwarranted formation of coke in the system.

It has been found that a liquid having a boiling range of between 350° to 600°F. will provide a means of carrying the hot gilsonite to a fractionation operation in which the gaseous components produced on heating the gilsonite will be effectively separated from the gilsonite charge. A liquid of such a boiling range will be distilled along with the components of gasification from which the liquid can be condensed , separated and returned to a melting tank. The temperature of the returned liquid should be maintained sufficiently high to melt the powdered gilsonite charge without additional heating.

If desired, a liquid of lower boiling range may be used. However, the relatively high softening point of the gilsonite requires a carrier of the stated preferred range. A liquid of considerably higher end point could conceivably be used, but operations with such a liquid could require distillation temperature in the critical temperature area 600° to 700°F. at which the exothermic reaction of the gilsonite may occur.

Referring to Figure 2.6 ground or pulverized gilsonite obtained from a collection source such as a hopper is introduced at a desired rate by conveying mechanism 10 into a melting tank 12. The capacity of tank 12 can be varied in accordance with the amount of gilsonite charged. To enhance the mixing of the powdered gilsonite and the liquid hydrocarbon carrier, agitators 14 are provided.

A suitable quantity of liquid carrier is introduced into the tank 12 by means of line 16 from a make-up source not shown, or is recycled from the fractionation operation as hereinafter described. It is desirable to maintain the liquid carrier at a temperature of approximately 500°F. The powdered gilsonite will at temperatures in this range form a pumpable slurry. The slurry or mixture of powdered gilsonite and liquid hydrocarbon is withdrawn from the tank 12 by way of line 18 and passed to a conventional heater 20 having appropriate coils or tubes 22. The liquid carrier used should have a boiling range of between 350° to 600°F. and is generally used in an approximate ratio of one part by weight of carrier to one part by weight of the powdered gilsonite. The temperature of the slurry in heater 20 is maintained at about 600°F., sufficient to cause the gaseous components to be removed from the gilsonite charge. It is essential that the temperature be kept below 700°F. at which temperature decomposition of gilsonite begins, causing the formation of coke and plugging of the coils in the heater.

It has been found that if sufficient amounts of carrier are present during the heating stage and the temperatures of the heating operation is controlled so that the undesired exothermic reaction is avoided, substantially complete removal of gaseous components of the gilsonite can be obtained.

The effluent from the heating operation, which is passed by way of line 24 to an atmospheric distillation tower 26, has the general appearance or a fuel oil. This material is introduced into the column at a temperature of approximately 600°F. The introduction of the effluent into the tower results in a considerable frothing or foaming due to the presence of the undesired constituents which include nitrogenous, oxygenated and sulfurous compounds. This mixture, including substantially all the vaporized hydrocarbon solvent is withdrawn as a tower overhead by line 31 and passed through condenser or cooler 32 and into a separator 33.

In the separator 33 noncondensible gasification products, such as nitrogen, sulfur dioxide, carbon dioxide and possibly carbon monoxide are withdrawn through line 34 and vented to the atmosphere or to a further separation apparatus, if desired. The condensed hydrocarbon vapors are in part returned as a tower reflux through line 36 by means of pump 37. The remaining portion of the condensed carrier is returned by way of line 35 to the melting tank 12 to be added to fresh gilsonite.

It is one of the features of the process to provide a continuous recycle of the liquid hydrocarbon carrier as a means of carrying the gilsonite through the gasification treatment with little loss of carrier. Carrier make-up line 16 is provided for adding carrier lost in the cycle during long periods of operation.

The heavier boiling portion of the heater effluent having the properties of a heavy fuel oil or asphalt is withdrawn as a bottoms product from the fractionation tower by way of line 39 and passed to a coking reactor 40.

The reactor 40 may be of a continuous contact type as described in U.S. Patent 2,600,078, or a fixed bed coking apparatus, if desired. In the coking reactor the treated gilsonite is contacted with the coke particles present in the reactor. This results in a continuous vaporization of the lighter ends of the charge by the heated coke. The coke particles in a moving bed coker are transferred from the coking reactor through a reheater wherein the temperature is raised to a level sufficient to substantially vaporize, crack and convert the gilsonite charge into gas, gasoline, gas oil and coke.

The products of the coking including the gas, gasoline and gas oil distillate are introduced into tower 44. The light components are taken over head as a product through line 45, passed through condenser 48 and into a separating tank 49. The gaseous components or light ends

FIGURE 2.6: ASPHALT TREATMENT FOR FEED TO CONTACT COKING OPERATION

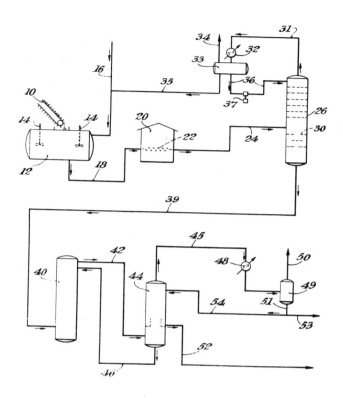

Source: V. Mekler; U.S. Patent 2,846,361; August 5, 1958

are withdrawn by way of line 50 and passed to a gas holder or other treatment, as desired. Unstable gasoline separated in 49 is withdrawn through line 51 and passed to further recovery through line 53. A part of the condensed overhead may be returned to column 44 by line 54 as reflux. Gas oil is withdrawn from an intermediate part of the column 44 and passed to storage through line 52. The gilsonite, when handled in accordance with the process, has yielded the following:

Material	B./D.	G. P. H.	API	Lb./Hr.	Percent Wt.
Gilsonite Feed [1]	6,000	10,500	3.0	92,000	100
Products:					
Gas C$_3$ and Lighter				8,380	9.0
Gasoline	1,540	2,700	60.0	16,560	18.0
Gas Oil	2,050	3,580	27.0	26,660	29.0
Coke (485 T/D)				40,400	44.0
				92,000	100.0

[1] Not including liquid carrier.

W.J. Bloomer; U.S. Patent 2,726,196; December 6, 1955; assigned to Lummus Company has found that if the gilsonite is heated in the presence of a liquid hydrocarbon of selected boiling range in such ratios that the exothermic heat can be largely dissipated by the vaporization of the hydrocarbon, it is possible to heat the gilsonite to a sufficiently high degree so that it can be ultimately reduced to a dry coke by charging it to apparatus suited for that purpose without unwarranted formation of coke in the heater coil or vapor lines to such apparatus. During the heating, it is possible to recover valuable gaseous end-products of the lower boiling range such as nitrogenous and other base materials.

It will be apparent that it is necessary to have a liquid which will have a boiling range substantially above the temperature of incipient coking of the gilsonite, which is around 500° to 550°F. In addition, there must be enough of the liquid having sufficiently high latent heat present so that enough of the exothermic heat is absorbed to prevent excessive gassing and temperature rise of the mixture. For this purpose, it is preferred to use a gas oil of about 700° to 900°F. end point. Such a liquid has the advantage that it will tend to partially dissolve the gilsonite and being an adjacent fraction may be readily handled not only in a cracking heater, but in fractional distillation equipment and in a continuous coking operation.

Pour Point Depressant

D.K. Wunderlich and J.H. Frankovich; U.S. Patent 3,532,618; October 6, 1970; assigned to Sinclair Oil Corporation describe a process for producing a pour point depressant for shale oil which comprises mixing a deasphalting solvent, under deasphalting conditions, for instance, at a temperature of up to about 250°F. at a pressure up to 500 psig, with a shale oil which has had its viscosity and pour point lowered as a result of contact with hydrogen under hydrovisbreaking conditions. The mixture of shale oil and deasphalting solvent is then separated into deasphalted shale oil and a heavier portion containing the pour point depressant for shale oil. The following example illustrates the process.

Example: Raw shale oil was passed up-flow, in contact with hydrogen under hydrovisbreaking conditions, through a 3/8 inch, schedule 40 pipe which was held at reaction temperature in an electrically heated furnace. Feedstock properties, reaction conditions and product inspections are contained in the following table.

	Raw shale oil	Hydrovis- breaking
Reactor temperature, ° F		825
Pressure, p.s.i.g		1,000
Gas ratio, s.c.f./b		2,000
Oil feed rate, gm./hr		300
Cold oil time, min		10
Wt. percent liquid recovery	100	94.0

	Feed	Product
Liquid Inspections:		
Gravity, ° API	18.9	19.7
Pour point, ° F	+85	−45
Viscosity, kv. at 122° F	31.01	14.15
Percent Ramsbottom carbon	4.5	5.46
Wt. percent hydrogen	11.27	11.11

	Raw shale oil	Hydrovis- breaking
ASTN (vac.) distillation, ° F.:		
I.B.P	393	375
5%	457	421
10	505	454
20	590	521
30	670	587
40	741	662
50	802	738
60	856	809
70	920	895
80	990	1,017
Trap, ml		17.0

The shale oil of lowered viscosity having a pour point of −45°F. produced by the hydrovisbreaking process was mixed at ambient temperature and pressure with an equal volume of normal pentane. After thorough mixing, the mixture was centrifuged and a heavy viscous layer amounting to 2.5 weight percent of the shale oil of lowered viscosity and pour point was centrifuged from the lighter deasphalted shale oil layer. This heavy viscous layer contained the pour point depressant for shale oil.

The deasphalting solvent contained in the deasphalted shale oil layer was evaporated from the deasphalted shale oil. The resulting deasphalted shale oil had a pour point of 0°F. The removal of the heavy viscous layer, therefore, actually increased the pour point of the shale oil of lowered viscosity and pour point from the initial value of −45° to 0°F. The heavy viscous layer obtained from the deasphalting step and containing the pour point depressant was mixed thoroughly with a volume of raw shale oil having a pour point of +85°F. which was equal to the volume of shale oil of reduced pour point and viscosity from which the heavy viscous layer was obtained.

The resulting mixture of raw shale oil and the heavy viscous layer containing the pour point depressant had a pour point of 0°F. Thus, the pour point depressant was effective in reducing the pour point of raw shale oil from +85° to 0°F.

Thermal Treatment to Reduce Pour Point

W.J. Culbertson, Jr., T.D. Nevens and W.D. Schnackenberg; U.S. Patent 3,284,336; November 8, 1966; assigned to The Oil Shale Corporation describe a method for treating a heavy fraction separated under substantially noncracking conditions from a crude oil derived by thermal treatment of solid carbonaceous material, to produce the heavy fraction and at least one light fraction, which method comprises heat treating the separated heavy fraction alone at a temperature above about 600°F. and below the point of incipient thermal decomposition of the heavy fraction for a period of time which is inversely proportional to the temperature to produce a product which, when combined with at least part of a light fraction, results in an oil having a pour point lower than that of the original crude oil; the heat treatment producing substantially no noncondensible hydrocarbons and substantially no elemental carbon.

While the precise effect of the heat treatment of the heavy high molecular weight fraction containing the waxes, asphaltenes, and the like is not completely clear, it is theorized that some portion of the heavy fraction undergoes a molecular modification and/or rearrangement which results in a marked improvement in pour point and reduction in thixotropy after combination with lighter hydrocarbon oil fractions.

The molecular weight of the heavier hydrocarbons is not appreciably affected by any such alteration in molecular structure. Moreover, the pour point of the heavy fraction which has been treated in accordance with the process in not appreciably changed from that of the heavy fraction prior to treatment. The temperature and conditions utilized avoid appreciable formation of light gases or of coke. These substances represent undesirable loss in yield in processing oils, and in the process are not formed even as by-products. The pour points were determined by ASTM D97-47. Pour points were taken to the nearest 5°F. The distillations were conducted according to ASTM D-1160-52T.

Example 1: In order to demonstrate the effectiveness of the method in lowering the pour point of oils derived by thermal treatment of solid carbonaceous materials by thermal means, runs were carried out on samples of a crude Colorado shale oil having a pour point of 80°F. where each sample of the oil initially was fractionated to provide a light fraction consisting of 70% by volume of the crude oil and a residue. Portions of the residue then were heated to and maintained at temperatures of about 650°, 700°, and 750°F., for a time period of about 1 hour.

No discernible amount of noncondensibles or elemental carbon were produced. At the end of the heating period each treated residue was cooled to 70°F., tested for pour point properties, and recombined with its corresponding, previously removed light fraction. Each oil resulting from the recombination was then tested for its pour point characteristics. The results of the various runs are set forth in Table 1.

TABLE 1

Run	Temp., °F.	Coke and Gas Losses	Residue Pour Point, °F.		Final Oil Pour Point, °F.
			Before Soaking	After Soaking	
1	650	None	80	80	50
2	700	do	80	80	15
3	750	do	80	80	5

Example 2: The general procedure of Example 1 was repeated in a series of runs where various residues were heat treated for a period of 1 hour following removal of the light fractions indicated in Table 2. Runs 1, 2 and 3 of Example 1 are included for comparative purposes. There was no dicernible production of either noncondensible hydrocarbons or elemental carbon. The results are set forth below.

TABLE 2

Temperature, °F	650			700							750
Run	1	4	5	6	7	2	8	9	10	11	3
Light Fraction Removed, Percent by Volume	70	50	30	90	80	70	65	60	50	30	70
Residue Pour Point Before Soaking	80	95	90	----	----	80	90	95	95	90	80
Residue Pour Point After Soaking	80	90	90	----	95	80	85	95	----	85	80
Final Oil Pour Point, °F	50	70	75	55	45	15	20	15	35	50	5

Example 3: Example 1 was repeated in a series of runs with the same shale oil, temperature and treating time varied as indicated in Table 3. A light fraction of 70% by volume was removed and the residue treated as indicated in the table. Runs 1, 2 and 3 are shown for comparison. There was no discernible production of noncondensibles or elemental carbon.

Oil Shale Refining Processes

TABLE 3

Time, hr	.25			1.0			2.0	
Run	12	13	14	1	2	3	15	16
Temp., °F	650	700	750	650	700	750	650	700
Residue Pour Point °F. Before Soaking	80	80	80	80	80	80	80	80
Residue Pour Point, °F. After Soaking	----	80	75	80	80	80	85	----
Final Oil Pour Point, °F	70	40	15	30	15	5	61	25

Example 4: The general procedure of Example 1 was repeated except for removing a light fraction of 36 volume percent and employing a soaking time of 2 hours at 600°F. The pour point of the final recombined oil was 55°F. No discernible noncondensibles or elemental carbon were produced.

Example 5: A Colorado shale oil having a pour point of about 80°F. was fractionated to produce a heavy residue constituting a 70 to 100% fraction, i.e., 30% by volume, and various lighter fractions as set out in Table 4. The residue was heat treated in accordance with the process at a temperature of about 700°F. for a period of about 1 hour. The pour point of the residue before and after heat treatment was 80°F. There was no discernible production of either noncondensible hydrocarbons or free carbon. The treated residue was combined with varying amounts of the various lighter fractions and pour point determinations made. The results are set forth below.

TABLE 4

Run No.	Volume Percent of Residue	Volume Percent of 0-20% Fraction	Pour Point of Combined Mixture, °F
17	0	100	−70
18	25	75	−65
19	40	60	−65
20	55	45	−35
21	70	30	0
		Volume percent of 20-70% Fraction	
22	0	100	80
23	25	75	80
24	40	60	80
25	55	45	80
26	70	30	85
		Volume Per-cent of 0-35% Fraction	
27	0	100	0
28	15	85	−30
29	25	75	−35
30	40	60	−30
31	55	45	−15
32	70	30	10
		Volume Per-cent of 35-70% Fraction	
33	0	100	90
34	25	75	90
35	40	60	85
36	55	45	90
37	70	30	85

Run No.	Volume Percent of Residue	Volume Per-cent of 0-50% Fraction	Pour Point of Combined Mixture, °F
38	0	100	40
39	10	90	15
40	20	80	−5
41	30	70	−10
42	40	60	−10
43	50	50	5
44	60	40	20
45	70	30	40
		Volume Percent of 50-70% Fraction	
46	0	100	100
47	30	70	95
48	40	60	95
49	50	50	95
50	60	40	95
51	70	30	95
		Volume Percent of 0-70% Fraction	
52	0	100	65
53	20	80	65
54	25	75	55
55	30	70	40
56	35	65	10
57	40	60	10
58	45	55	10
59	50	50	15
60	60	40	25
61	65	35	30
62	75	25	40
63	100	0	80

From the data given it is apparent that by combining the treated residue with various amounts of the lighter fractions, especially the lighter ends of the originally separated light fraction, oils of extremely low pour point may be produced.

Treatment of Raw Oil with HCl

C.N. Kimberlin, Jr., and H.G. Ellert; U.S. Patent 2,966,450; December 27, 1960; assigned to Esso Research and Engineering Company have found that shale oil is effectively upgraded by treatment with an acidic gas in the presence of a hydrocarbon solvent under certain conditions. There is obtained a sludge or precipitate representing substantially all of the more undesirable coke-forming nitrogen-containing constituents; this sludge nonetheless being extremely small in amount. There is further obtained as an extract a maximum amount of high quality cracking stock.

Referring to Figure 2.7 raw shale oil obtained by retorting oil shale at a temperature of 800° to 1200°F. for a period of 0.1 to 2 hours is fed by means of line 2 to precipitation zone 4. Though the shale oil may be given a preliminary thermal treatment or subjected to visbreaking conditions, this is normally not necessary. In fact, it is one of the advantages of the process that the visbreaking operation may be dispensed with.

Zone 4 may be an upright vessel provided with means for providing intimate contact of counterflowing streams, such as agitators, packing or perforated plates. Alternately, vessel 4 may be a mixer-settler of conventional design. The shale oil is treated in vessel 4 with from 0.5 to 10 volumes of a hydrocarbon fraction boiling in the range of from -45° to 250°F. Pentane, hexane, propane, butane or naphtha fractions give good results. This hydrocarbon is introduced through line 5. The temperature is in the range of 0° to 300°F., preferably 50° to 150°F., and pressure sufficient to keep material in the liquid phase.

An anhydrous acidic gas, such as HCl, HBr or BF_3, but preferably HCl, is passed into vessel 4 through line 7 in amounts sufficient to saturate the oil. 0.5 to 4.0, but preferably 0.9 to 1.5, equivalents of acid per equivalent of nitrogen in the oil may be used. The oil-solvent-gaseous acid mixture is maintained in a state of agitation, preferably for a residence period of from about 1 to 60 minutes, and then passes to settling zone 8.

The extract, containing the oil and solvent, is removed from zone 8 through line 10 to flash distillation zone 12 where the low boiling hydrocarbon solvent is distilled overhead by flash or fractionation and recycled via line 14 to precipitation zone 4. The shale oil fraction may then advantageously be passed to a catalytic cracking zone 18 for conversion by conventional means into valuable fuels and lubricants.

Returning to settler 8, the lower layer is a sludge-like material comprising in part high molecular weight hydrogen-deficient material known as Conradson carbon, and also the salt-like reaction product of the HCl and the nitrogen compounds. About 7 to 15 lbs. of HCl per barrel of oil are required in this process.

This low quality sludge, amounting to some 25 to 35% of the total shale oil, may also be utilized to increase the overall yield of motor fuel and lubricants. In one example of the process, it is withdrawn as a lower layer from vessel 8 and passed to a hydrogenation zone

FIGURE 2.7: SHALE REFINING PROCESS EMPLOYING HCl TREATMENT

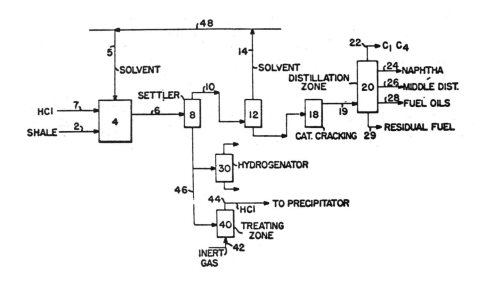

Source: C.N. Kimberlin, Jr. and H.G. Ellert; U.S. Patent 2,966,450; Dec. 27, 1960

<u>30</u>. By operating at about 3,000 psig in a conventional manner and at 650° to 1000°F., preferably 700° to 850°F., the nitrogen content of the sludge is reduced from 5 to 0.5% or less. Alternately, this sludge may be partially hydrogenated at less severe conditions and the product recycled through the precipitation zone.

Example 1: A sample of shale oil was treated in accordance with the process described in the presence of n-hexane. Four types of acidic treating agents were employed, with the following result as shown in Table 1.

TABLE 1

		Solvent (3 volumes n-hexane)			
		Acid			
Treatment	Raw Shale	Anhydrous HCl	60% H_2SO_4*	SO_2 (Gas)	BF_3
Yield, volume percent	–	70	63	86	51
Product Quality:					
Gravity, °API	20.6	28.2	25.6	21.6	26.6
Nitrogen, wt. percent	1.9	0.4	0.3	1.5	0.5
Sulfur, wt. percent	0.7	0.5	0.8	0.7	0.7
Con. carbon, wt. percent	4.3	0.9	1.2	4.3	1.7

*4 mols/mol N_2 in oil.

These data demonstrate the excellent results obtained by the process in upgrading shale oil to a catalytic cracking feed stock. It is to be noted that aqueous acid provides a substantially lower oil yield without quality improvement.

Example 2:   The necessity of maintaining a solvent in the mixture being acid treated with gaseous HCl is shown by the following data.

TABLE 2

Treatment	None	HCl* at 400°F.	Hexane + HCl
Yield, vol. percent	-	67	70
Product quality:			
Gravity, °API	20.6	27.3	28.2
Nitrogen, wt. percent	1.9	1.2	0.4
Con. Carbon, wt. percent	4.3	3.9	0.9

*Added to saturation.

TAR SANDS SEPARATION PROCESSES

HOT WATER PROCESSES

<u>Treatment with Inorganic Phosphates and Alkylene Oxide Surfactants</u>

A process described by <u>G.P. Canevari and R.J. Fiocco; U.S. Patent 3,331,765; July 18, 1967; assigned to Esso Research and Engineering Company</u> involves the recovery of oil from tar sands where in a first or initial stage a substantial amount of the sands are removed by treatment of the sands with water and an oil froth is produced. This oil froth in essence comprises an emulsion of oil and water containing an appreciable amount of solids. This froth is treated in a secondary phase or stage with additional water to remove more solids from the emulsion of oil and water. In a tertiary stage the emulsion, containing some solids, is treated with a chemical mixture to break the emulsion so as to secure an oil phase free of water and solids.

A desirable chemical mixture comprises a transfer agent, a chelating agent and a demulsifying agent used in combination with a hydrocarbon solvent. The additive mixture preferably contains from 0.1 to 2.0%, preferably 1% by weight based on the froth, of a transfer agent such as tetrasodium pyrophosphate, or sodium tripolyphosphate. Other equivalent chemicals which may be used for example potassium pyrophosphate, sodium hexametaphosphate and sodium silicate. These transfer agents promote the transfer of the solid fines from the oil-water interface into the aqueous phase by establishing a uniform electropotential over the entire surface of the particle. In general inorganic builders and condensed phosphates act as transfer agents.

A second constituent of the chemical mixture is a demulsifying additive. These demulsifying additives are nonionic surface active compounds, as for example a polyethoxyalkylene compound known as Nalco D-1645 produced by the Nalco Chemical Company. Another preferred demulsifying solution comprises a mixture of (1) one part of the reaction product of diethyl ethanol amine with premixed propylene oxide and ethylene oxide (propylene oxide-ethylene oxide can range from 40/60 to 60/40, preferably 55/45) and (2) approximately three parts of a palmitic acids ester of the reaction product of an alkyl phenol formaldehyde resin with ethylene oxide

$$\left(\frac{\text{alkyl phenol formaldehyde}}{\text{ethylene oxide}} = \frac{1}{1.5} \right).$$

The mixture may be varied in the range from one part of the reaction product to two parts of the acid ester to one part of the reaction product to four parts of the palmitic acid ester. Other satisfactory demulsifiers are Pluronic polyols. These Pluronic compounds are poly-oxypropylene glycols having a chemical structure as follows

$$HO(CH_2—CH_2—O)_a(\underset{\underset{CH_3}{|}}{C}H—CH_2—O)_b(CH_2—CH_2—O)_c H$$

where a = molecular weight range of 50 to 7,000, b = molecular weight range of 900 to 4,000 and c = molecular weight range of 50 to 7,000. These compounds have molecular weights ranging from 1,000 to over 16,000. The amount of demulsifier used is in the range from 0.01 to 0.5%, for example 0.2% by weight based on the weight of the total emulsion. In instances where the froth may contain heavy minerals, for example sometimes as high as 2 to 5% by weight of heavy minerals as for example zircon, rutile, ilmenite, tourmaline, apatite, staurolite, garnet, etc., it may be desirable to employ chelating agents in addition to a demulsifier and transfer agent. For example, chelating agents which may be used as part of the chemical mixture are ethylenediamine-tetraacetic acid, sodium gluconate, gluconic acid, sodium oxalate and diethylene glycol.

The chemical mixture may contain a hydrocarbon solvent boiling in the range from 250° to 600°F., preferably in the range from 250° to 450°F. Preferred solvents are xylene and naphtha boiling in the range from 250° to 450°F. The amount of solvent used is in the range from 10 to 100% by weight of the froth, preferably 50%.

In related work, S. Ross, G.P. Canevari and R.J. Fiocco; U.S. Patent 3,296,117; Jan. 3, 1967; assigned to Esso Research and Engineering Company describe a process for the recovery of oil from tar sands where the oil is removed from the sands in an initial stage or phase comprising a treatment with water to produce a froth containing an appreciable amount of water and solids (sand/clay) particles. This froth is subsequently treated in a secondary stage with water containing a selected chemical transfer agent. In a third stage the substantially solids-free oil and water phase are separated by treatment with a selected chemical demulsifier.

Tetrasodium pyrophosphate is one such transfer agent; other examples are trisodium poly-phosphate and sodium silicate. The amount of tetrasodium pyrophosphate added to the water is in the range from 0.1 to 2.0%, preferably 1.0%. The demulsifying solution comprises a mixture of (1) one part of the reaction product of diethyl ethanol amine with premixed propylene oxide and ethylene oxide (the propylene oxide/ethylene oxide can range from 40/60 to 60/40, preferably 55/45) and (2) approximately three parts of a palmitic acid ester of the reaction product of an alkyl phenol formaldehyde resin with ethylene oxide

$$\left(\frac{alkyl\ phenol\ formaldehyde}{ethylene\ oxide} = \frac{1}{1.5}\right).$$

The mixture may be varied in the range from 1 part of the reaction product to 2 parts of the acid ester to 1 part of the reaction product to 4 parts of the palmitic acid ester. A preferred mixture is 1 part by weight of the reaction product to 3 parts by weight of the palmitic acid ester. In order to illustrate the process, a froth comprising 46.6% by weight of bitumen, 42.6% of water and 10.8% sand was contacted in a number of operations; namely, A, B,

C, D and E. The results of these operations are illustrated in the following table.

Effects of Transfer Agents and Demulsifying Agents on Unwashed Froth

Operations	Water, percent wt.	Solids, percent	Bitumen
A. Untreated Sample (Control)	42.6	10.8	46.6
B. Water Washing With 1% TSPP Solution [1]	36.0	1.79	62.21
C. Water Washing+Addition 0.4% Demulsifying Mixture [2]	18.0	---------	---------
D. Water Washing With 1% Na$_2$SiO$_3$ +Addition 0.4% Demulsifying Mixture [2]	7.5	---------	---------
E. Water Washing With 1% TSPP Solution [1]+Addition 0.4% Demulsifying Mixture [2]	0.3	0.1	99.6

[1]Tetrasodium pyrophosphate.
[2]Mixture of the process.

From the above, it is apparent that far superior results are secured if the froth is contacted initially with water containing a transfer agent to remove substantially all the solid and then contacted in the subsequent stage with a demulsifying agent.

In Operation B a substantial amount of solids was removed but the bitumen contained an appreciable amount of water. The same situation occurred in Operation C, as well as in Operation D.

However, when employing the technique of the process by washing the froth in an initial phase containing tetrasodium pyrophosphate and then removing the sand and treating the same in the secondary phase, the oil phase was 99.6% oil, containing only 0.1% by weight of solids and 0.3% by weight of water.

The palmitic acid ester is preferably secured from a phenol formaldehyde resin where the alkyl group contains from 3 to 4 carbon atoms and is secured from isopropyl alcohol or alkyl butyl alcohol. The molecular weight is in the range from 1,200 to 1,600, preferably 1,400.

Recovery of Oil from Middlings Layer

A process described by P.H. Floyd, R.C. Schenk, H.L. Erskine, Jr. and J.V.D. Fear; U.S. Patent 3,401,110; September 10, 1968; assigned to Great Canadian Oil Sands Limited, Canada comprises the combination of a hot water separation step for primary recovery of oil from the sands together with a scavenger step for further treatment of the middlings layer obtained from the primary separation step to recover an additional amount of oil.

The process also involves regulating the amount of water introduced to the primary separation step and the rate of transfer of middlings layer to the scavenger step so as to maintain the density and/or viscosity of the middlings layer. The process involves the following procedure.

(1) Forming a pulp of the bituminous sands with a minor amount of water in a pulping zone while heating the mixture with steam.

(continued)

(2) Removing pulp and mixing it with hot water and hereinafter specified recycle steam in a dilution zone, the amount of the hot water plus the water added to the bituminous sands in forming the pulp being 0.2 to 3.0 lbs./lb. of the bituminous sands.

(3) Flushing the mixture from the dilution zone into a separation zone.

(4) Settling the mixture in the separation zone at a temperature in the range of 130° to 210°F., more preferably 170° to 210°F., to form an upper oil froth layer, a middlings layer comprising water, clay and oil, and a sand tails layer.

(5) Separately removing the oil froth layer and the sand tailings layer.

(6) Removing a stream of middlings layer from the separation zone and passing it to the dilution zone as the recycle stream.

(7) Passing a second stream of middlings layer to a scavenger zone and subjecting it to air flotation to recover an additional amount of oil froth.

(8) Regulating the amount of water incorporated with the bituminous sands in Step (1) and the rate of passage of the second stream to the scavenger zone in Step (7) to regulate and maintain the density of the middlings layer in the range of 1.03 to 1.50 and/or the viscosity thereof in the range of 0.5 to 10 cp.

(9) Removing from the scavenger zone and discarding from the system middlings material of depleted oil content comprising clay dispersed in water.

Referring to Figure 3.1 the bituminous oil sand is fed to the system through line 10 where it first passes to a conditioning drum or muller 11. Water is fed to the muller via line 12 and steam is introduced through line 13. The total water so introduced in liquid and vapor forms is a minor amount based on the weight of the tar sands processed and generally is in the range of 10 to 45% by weight of the mulled mixture.

The conditioning drum 11 is provided with suitable kneading or mixing means to give the desired mulling action. Enough steam is introduced through line 13 to raise the temperature in the conditioning drum to within the range of 130° to 210°F. and preferably to above 170°F. Mulling of the tar sands produces a pulp which then passes from the conditioning drum as indicated by line 14 to a screen indicated at 15. The purpose of screen 15 is to remove from the tar sands pulp any debris, rocks or oversized lumps as indicated generally at 16.

The conditioned tar sands pass from screen 15 to a pulp box 17 which serves as a zone for diluting the pulp with additional water before passage to primary separation zone 18. Hot water from heater 27 is passed through line 19 to pulp box 17 and additional steam is fed through line 20 if necessary to maintain the temperature in the range of 130° to 210°F. and preferably above 170°F. Also a middlings stream which is withdrawn from the primary separator 18 is recycled through lines 21 and 19 to the pulp box. This recycle stream serves to provide sufficient liquid to flush the tar sands pulp from the pulp box and effect transfer

FIGURE 3.1: RECOVERY PROCESS EMPLOYING PRIMARY HOT WATER SEPARATION AND SCAVENGER ZONE

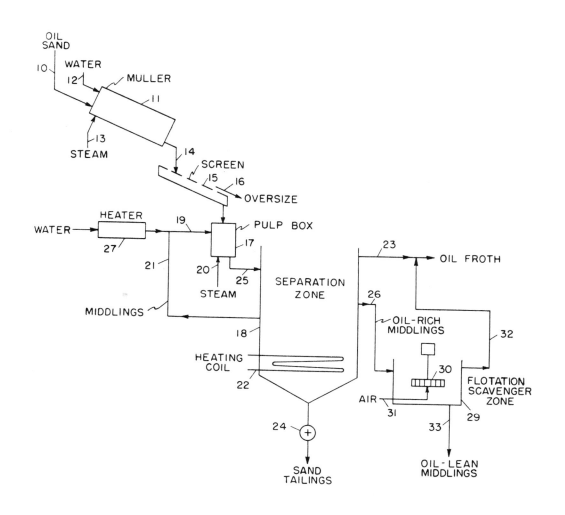

Source: P.H. Floyd, R.C. Schenk, H.L. Erskine, Jr. and J.V.D. Fear; U.S. Patent 3,401,110; September 10, 1968

of the pulp to the separator. Another important function of the recycle stream is to cause dispersion of the pulped material as it is fed into separation zone 18. However, such recycling of middlings is not essential in all cases, particularly when the clay content of the tar sands is high. In this event a relatively high rate of fresh feed water introduction through heater 27 can be employed to compensate for the high clay content while a correspondingly high rate of transfer of middlings layer through line 26 can be maintained; and under these circumstances recycling of the other stream of middlings through lines 21 and 19 to pulp box 17 is not required. Modifications that may be made in the process as above described include sending a minor portion of the middlings recycle stream from line 21 through a suitable line to muller 11 to supply all or a part of the water needed therein other than that supplied through condensation of the stream which is consumed. Also, if desired, a stream of the middlings recycle can be introduced onto the screen 15 to flush the pulp through and into pulp box 17. Separation zone 18 can comprise a large cylindrical or rectangular tank, or battery of tanks, which may, if desired, be provided with heating coils 22 for maintaining a temperature in the range of 130° to 210°F., and preferably above 170°F. The separator is supplied with an oil froth withdrawal line 23 adjacent the top and a sand tailings removal line having star valve 24 or any other suitable control discharge means at the bottom. Separator 18 also has an intermediate withdrawal line 26 through which a stream of middlings layer is removed in addition to that recycled through line 21. The following example illustrates the process.

Example: The process is utilized to recover the oil from Athabasca tar sands containing by weight 10% bituminous matter and 89% mineral matter. 25% of the latter consists of particles having diameters less than 44 microns. On an hourly basis 100 lbs. of the tar sands, 0.1 lb. of concentrated caustic soda solution, 30 lbs. of water and steam are fed into a conditioning drum and the mixture is heated to 180°F. while being mulled.

The resulting pulp is passed through a screen and then to pulp box 17 as shown in the drawing. Hot water at 190°F. in amount of 74 lbs. and a middlings recycle stream in amount of 200 lbs. are passed through line 19 into the pulp box and the mixture continuously flushes into separator 18 where the temperature is maintained at 190°F. The pH of the middlings is held at 8.4 by the addition of caustic soda at the rate above specified. From the separator sand tailings are removed at a rate of 78 lbs./hr. from the bottom and froth is removed from the top at a rate of 10 lbs./hr. The tailings are composed of 74% mineral matter, 25% water and 1% oil by weight. The froth is approximately composed by weight of 50% oil, 10% mineral matter and 40% water. The oil content corresponds to a recovery of 50% of oil in the original tar sands.

A stream of oil rich middlings in amount of 112 lbs./hr. and composed of 4 lbs. of oil, 27 pounds of mineral matter and 81 lbs. of water is withdrawn from separator 18 and is transferred to a scavenger zone where it is subjected to air flotation in a subaeration type air flotation cell 29. This rate of transfer of the oil rich middlings from separator 18, in combination with the previously specified rates, maintains the middlings at a viscosity of 1.5 cp. and a density of 1.14. From the flotation cell additional oil froth is obtained in amount of 7 lbs./hr. and 104 lbs./hr. of oil lean middlings are withdrawn and discarded. Use of the flotation cell increases the recovery of oil from the tar sands to an overall value of 85%.

In related work, E.W. Dobson; U.S. Patent 3,594,306; July 20, 1971; assigned to Great Canadian Oil Sands Limited, Canada describes a process which involves the hot water process for extracting bitumen from tar sands produces. A secondary recovery is conducted on the middlings from the separation cell to produce additional froth which usually is combined with the primary froth and treated. It has been found that the froth from the secondary recovery operation can be upgraded in bitumen content by gravity settling. By the process, secondary recovery froth is settled to produce an upper layer upgraded in bitumen content over the secondary froth. This upgraded bitumen layer is then added to the primary froth for further processing.

Addition of Tar Sand Oil to Slurry

S. Andrassy; U.S. Patent 3,208,930; September 28, 1965 describes a process for the separation of oil from tar sands which comprises forming a mixture of tar sands, oil of the same consistency as the oil in the tar sands and water in an amount sufficient to form a water layer on top of the tar sands, needling the water and oil-tar sand mixture and heating the water-oil-tar sand mixture and heating the water-oil-tar sand mixture to the boiling point of water thereby causing oil trapped in the tar sands to separate from the tar sands and float to the top of the water layer, maintaining the temperature at 190° to 200°F. so as to allow the separated oil to accumulate on the top of the water layer, and recovering the oil from the water layer.

One of the essential features in the process is the addition to the tar sands of oil of the same constituency as the oil trapped in the tar sands. It has been found that the addition of this oil, preferably oil previously extracted from the tar sand itself has a profound effect upon the oils present in the tar sands and allows for virtually complete stripping of the oil trapped in the tar sands so as to leave clean white tailings of sand behind. The best results are obtained when 15 to 25% of oil based on the weight of the tar sands is added to the tar sands prior to heating the mixture. When less than 15% oil is added, the process takes longer, and when more than 25% oil is added no particular advantages were found.

It is believed that one of the primary reasons for the efficacy of this process is that the added oil has an affinity for the entrapped oil thereby helping to strip the entrapped oil from the sands. The increased volume of the oil, which changes the proportions of the basic material, may also be a contributing factor. During the heating process, the specific gravity of the crude oil trapped in the sand becomes less than that of the water itself and consequently floats to the surface of the water where it may be easily removed.

Water at 60°F. has a specific gravity of 0.9990 and at 212°F. has a specific gravity of 0.9584. The crude oil trapped in the sands generally has a specific gravity at 60°F. of 1.002 to 1.02 and has a specific gravity at 212°F. of from 0.926 to 0.944. Thus the addition of excess oil from a previous extraction plus the increase in temperature to near the boiling point of water causes the specific gravity of the oil trapped in the sands to decrease below that of water and consequently permits it to rise to the surface. The following examples illustrate the process.

Example 1: 100 parts by weight of Athabasca oil sands were mixed with 20 parts by weight of oil previously extracted from oil sands and with 100 parts by weight of water. The mixture was heated to the boiling point of water and held at 212°F. for two minutes. The heating was stopped and the oil which had floated to the surface of the water was skimmed off. 46 parts by weight of the oil and water were skimmed off. Upon drying, 37 parts by weight were obtained. This yielded 17 parts by weight of the recovered oil on a dry basis. The Athabasca tar sand deposits have an oil content of 10 to 17% (D.S. Pasternak, Chem. Eng. Progress, Vol. 56, April, 1960). On the basis of the tar sands tested, the recovery appears practically theoretical.

Example 2: 25 parts of oil recovered from a previous batch of tar sands were mixed with 300 parts of water and heated until the oil floated to the surface. The mixture was then cooled to slightly below 190°F. and 100 parts of tar sands were added to the mixture. The mixture was then needled and heated to 212°F. until the oil began to separate from the tar sands and rise to the surface. The temperature was then decreased to between 190° to 200°F. and maintained until the oil accumulated on its surface of the water. The separation of the oil from the tar sands took somewhat longer than usual and was not as effective since some oil still remained in the tar sands.

The temperature was decreased and the free oil permitted to settle to the bottom of the reaction chamber. The mixture was then reheated with needling in the manner previously described. A clean separation of the oil from the tar sands was obtained.

Referring to the Figure 3.2, tar sand is introduced into a hopper 11 which is connected directly to the tank 10. Prior to introducing the oil sands into the hopper, the sands are heated by discharging hot gases. From the inner side of the hopper through orifice 12, excess oil is charged to the hopper and mixes with the tar sands. Water is continuously introduced into the tank through orifice 38 and is maintained at the desired level. The oil enriched tar sands fall by gravity into the partly water-filled needling compartment 13.

Plungers 18 are individually sprung so that in case they hit stones, etc., they will not break. These plungers which are driven by motor means 19, needle the oil enriched tar sand-water mixture to form a homogeneous mass and facilitate floatation of oil to the surface. Heat is applied from the bottom of the tank by heating means 37 and the temperature is raised to the boiling point of water. At this temperature, the added oil is helpful in stripping the oil from the sands.

As soon as the boiling starts, the oil rises to the surface and flows to settling compartment 17. The gradual flow of the oil enriched tar sands into compartment 17 is somewhat retarded by partition wall 14 which has an opening on both the top 15 and the bottom 16. The heavier than water particles sink to the bottom of this compartment and move toward the bottom exit 20 of partition wall 24 conveyed by hot water jets 21 while the oil floats over the top opening 22 to the next compartment 23. In compartment 23, additional oil separates from the pockets of tar sands remaining in the heavier sand being freed by the constant grinding action induced by the bottom heating and flows over top opening 25 of partition wall 26 while the sand particles move through bottom opening 27.

In Figure 3.2a, three compartments are shown but this number can be increased if desired. In the last compartment 28, no heat is applied from the bottom of the tank thereby permitting settling of fine particles and silt. The separated sand is continuously pushed by water jets 21 into compartment 28. The solids and water are discharged through outlet 32 and removed by conventional means.

The floating oil is continuously moved toward the oil off-take 29 by hot air or stream jets 30. Gaseous products are withdrawn at off-take 31. The flue gases generated by the burners are discharged through flue gas duct or chimney 33 and are used to preheat the incoming tar sands. The feed water is preheated through a heat exchanger using the heat of the sand tailings. Referring to Figure 3.2b which shows a top view of the apparatus, it will be seen that before

FIGURE 3.2:   HOT WATER SEPARATION PROCESS

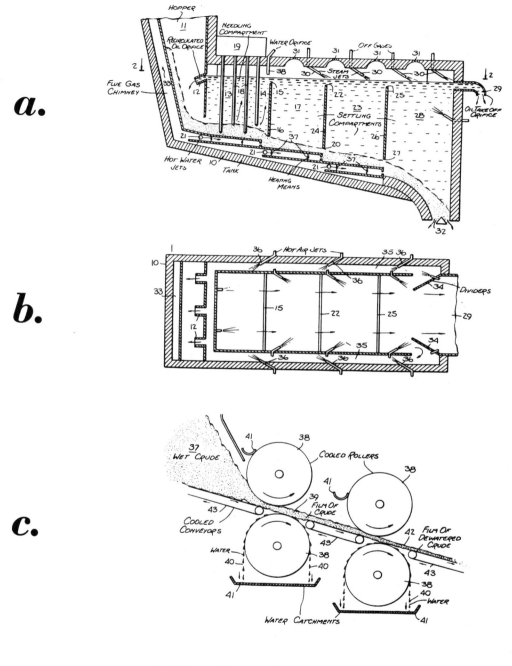

(a) Cross-Sectional View of Apparatus
(b) Sectional View Along Line 2—2 of Figure 3.2a
(c) Water Removal Apparatus

Source: S. Andrassy; U.S. Patent 3,208,930; September 28, 1965

the separated oil flows out of the tank 10, a regulated quantity of oil is returned to the hopper 11 through excess oil orifice 12 (Figure 3.2a). This is accomplished by causing a portion of the oil to flow through dividers 34 positioned in the front of the tank adjacent oil off-take 29 and channels 35 located along the sides of tank 10. Hot air or live steam jets 36 positioned in the channels 35 keep the oil moving in the desired direction towards excess oil orifice 12. In the hopper, the hot and purified oil is continuously fed into the incoming stream of raw material thus providing a continuous self-feeding and self-enriching system for the recovery of oils from the tar sands.

The recovered wet crude oil is cooled to below 70°F. or until it becomes semirigid but still of plastic consistency. Referring to Figure 3.2c, it will be seen that the plastic mass of wet crude oil 37 is passed between a system of slanted cooled rollers 38 where it pressed into a thin film 39. During this process, the water 40 which is entrapped in the oil, is pressed out and discharged to receptacle 41. The dewatered film 42 is then conveyed to storage or further treatment on slanted conveyor 43. This process may be repeated, if necessary, to remove additional water from the crude oil.

Water Washing and the Use of Fluid Bed Combustion Chamber

A process described by C.E. Hemminger; U.S. Patent 2,940,919; June 14, 1960; assigned to Esso Research and Engineering Company involves recovering oil from oil-bearing solids, particularly tar sands, by the use of hot liquid extraction procedures. Experimental work has indicated that when the tar sands are subjected to a hot aqueous wash, e.g., 150° to 200°F., oil is liberated from the oil sands and passes into the aqueous phase and it is ultimately separated and recovered as product.

In the process, spent washed tar sands are passed from the washing zone preferably after a drying step, to a fluidized solids combustion zone, e.g., a fluid bed burner. The tar sands as mined generally range from 10 to 200 mesh in size and thus are naturally suited to fluidization. By utilizing a fluidized combustion zone as opposed to other types of furnaces or burners, it is possible to effectively burn the less than 2 weight percent residual bitumen in the sand, thus liberating thermal energy.

Such fluidized combustion zones have been found to burn materials having carbonaceous contents of as low as 0.1 to 0.7 weight percent. The heat liberated from the fluidized combustion zone is then utilized to supply the thermal requirements of the overall system, e.g., heating the wash medium, effecting drying of spent sands, preheating fresh sand feed, etc. Additionally, it can be converted into mechanical or electrical energy for the mining and transportation of the sand as well as providing power for the washing system itself.

Referring to Figure 3.3 there is depicted a system for treating oil-bearing solids, e.g., Athabasca tar sands, by the process. Basically, there is shown a washer-separator zone 10, settler 11, and a burning and drying vessel 12. While a distinct settling unit and drying zone are not absolutely necessary, it is normally desired to utilize settling and drying of spent solids in order to minimize their water content before being introduced into the burning zone. Fresh tar sand, which may be heated to 50° to 100°F. in external equipment, is introduced into washer vessel 10 by line 15. By way of example, the fresh tar sand contains 3 weight

FIGURE 3.3: WATER WASHING PROCESS EMPLOYING FLUID BED COMBUSTION CHAMBER

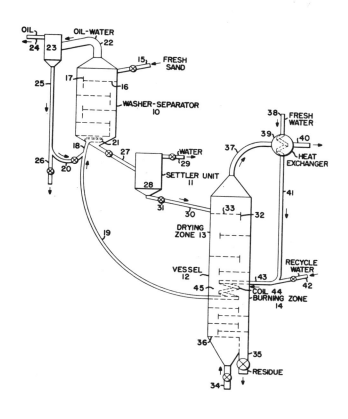

Source: C.E. Hemminger; U.S. Patent 2,940,919; June 14, 1960

percent water, 10 weight percent oil, the balance being mineral matter, e.g., clay, quartz, etc. Generally, tar sands of this type contain from 10 to 17 weight percent oil. As mined from the ground, the sands are less than 1,000 microns in size, predominantly ranging from 70 to 400 microns in diameter. Washing vessel 10 is provided with a series of distributing grids 16 and downcomers 17 in order to promote countercurrent contact between the tar sands and the hot water wash introduced at the bottom of the vessel by multiple injector 21. The tar sands are thus contacted in several stages with hot water passing up through the distributing grids, partially depleted sands passing through the downcomer into the next stage.

Though washing by relatively high water velocity, e.g., 0.05 to 0.5 feet/second, countercurrent flow is preferred, cocurrent flow or merely batch mixing may be employed. Means, not shown, may be provided in the vicinity of outlet 22 of the contactor for removing entrained fine sand particles. For example, one or more cyclones may be used to remove fine solids from the withdrawn water-oil mixture. The water temperature in the contactor may range from 150° to 180°F. at atmospheric pressure. It is desired to utilize pressures of up

173

to 200 psi, in order to allow water washing at temperatures of 300° to 350°F. By using the higher temperature, better separation of clay and oily particles is obtained because viscosity of tar is reduced a hundredfold as compared to only a four fold decrease in viscosity of water in going from 150° to 350°F. Undesirable froth formation is also avoided.

During the washing step, oil material passes into the washing fluid forming an oil-rich, aqueous phase which is withdrawn through outlet 22 and passed into an oil recovery unit 23. The oil recovering unit may be a conventional distillation zone or decanter, oil product being withdrawn by line 24. Wash water is removed by line 25 and may be discarded, directly recycled to washer 10 by line 20. In the example, shown, the residence time (60 minutes), temperature, etc., are controlled to give a rather good wash recovery of the oil, only 1% of residual bitumen remaining on the tar sands as they are withdrawn through outlet 27. Generally, residence times of 30 to 200 minutes are used, depending upon the source of the tar sand.

The spent tar sand-water mixture passes to settler unit 11 where separation is effected by the sands gravitating to form mass 28 in the bottom of the settler. Water is withdrawn through conduit 29 and may be discarded or further recycled to the washing zone. Partially dried spent tar sand is removed by line 30 and passed to vessel 12. Valve 31 is an expansion valve through which the liquid suspension of sand is flashed to essentially atmospheric pressure and a vapor solid mixture.

Vessel 12 consists essentially of drying zone 13 and burner zone 14, zone 13 being superimposed directly upon the fluidized combustion zone. As shown, spent sands are introduced into zone 13 onto perforated plate or distributing grid 33. As they pass along grid 33, they contact upflowing hot flue gases from the burner zone, residual adhering liquid flashing off overhead with the combustion gases. The sands then pass through downcomer 32 onto the next grid plate where additional solids-hot gas contact is obtained. The dry solids pass into burner zone 14, normally similarly fitted with a series of grid-downcomer configurations for promoting stagewise contact with good gas distribution.

Air or other oxygen-containing gas is introduced in vessel 12 by inlet 34, the air being preheated to a temperature of 160°F. by contact with hot combusted spent solids as they pass along grid 36 into withdrawal conduit 35. The air is introduced at a superficial velocity of 0.5 to 3 feet per second and serves to maintain the burning solids in the form of relatively dense turbulent beds having the appearance of a pseudo-liquid. The fluidized bed or beds of the burner zone have an apparent density of 40 to 100 pounds per cubic foot.

In the example described, the spent tar sands contain 1 weight percent residual bitumen as they enter the burning zone and approximately 90% of this bitumen fraction is consumed in the combustion step and converted to thermal energy. Thus, the solid residue removed through line 35 contains only 0.1 weight percent bitumen. While the heat liberated in the burning zone can be utilized in many ways to supply requisite energy for the hot water washing, e.g., as by passing hot flue gas into the washing zone, preheating fresh tar sands, etc., a particularly desirable method of supplying heat for the overall process will now be detailed. Fresh water at ambient temperature is introduced into the system through line 38, the water being preheated in heat exchanger 39 to a temperature of 125°F. by contact with the burner-drying zone gaseous effluent (at a temperature of 200°F.) taken overhead from unit 12 by line 37. The cooled gases, e.g., at a temperature of 150°F., may be discarded or further circulated by line 40 to additional heat exchange with, for example, fresh tar sand. The fresh makeup water then passes through lines 41 and 43 into a heat exchanging coil immersed in the fluidized combustion bed in section 45. In addition to the fresh water, recycle water, emanating from the settler unit 11 and/or oil-water separator 23, is added by line 42 and is heated in coil 44. The passage of the relatively cool water streams maintains the fluidized solids mass in section 45 at a temperature of 400° to 600°F. while the water is heated under pressure to 350°F.

Partial vaporization of the water is practiced to increase the heat transfer from the burner vessel 12 to the separator 10 for the same mass of water. Additional combustion takes place above section 45 so that the temperature of the flue gases passing to the drying zone is 900°F. so that substantially complete combustion of the bitumen is attained. The hot water, partially in the form of steam, is withdrawn from unit 12 and is passed to the washer by line 19, from where it is injected into the washer by nozzle 21. Part of the hot water-steam mixture can be removed to a steam turbine. The steam is separated from the water in a separator, and the steam expanded through a turbine for power and the condensate pumped back to line 42. The following table is a compilation of pertinent conditions with respect to the system described.

	Broad Range	Preferred
Washing Zone:		
Temperature, °F.	150–375	190–225
Pressure, p.s.i.g.	0–300	0–50
Wt. Ratio of Water to Fresh Solids	0.1 to 3	0.3 to 1.0
Burner Zone:		
Bitumen on Solids Sent to Burner, Wt. Percent	0.5 to 3	1 to 1.5
Bitumen on Solids Discharged, Wt. Percent	0.1 to 0.5	0.2 to 0.4
Apparent Density of Fluidized Solids, lbs./ft.³	40–100	60–80
Superficial Fluidizing Velocity, ft./sec.	0.5 to 3.0	1.2 to 1.8
Temperature, °F., in Areas without Cooling Coils	700–1,500	850–950

In a process described by L. Clark; U.S. Patent 3,052,621; September 4, 1962; assigned to Cities Service Research and Development Company crude hydrocarbon oil is separated from bituminous sand containing the same by the process which comprises mixing the sand with sufficient water to form a slurry, introducing the slurry into the lower portion of a mixing tower, and adding additional water to the slurry in the lower portion of the mixing tower. The slurry, together with the added water, is then flow upwardly through the mixing tower and hydrocarbon diluent is introduced at an intermediate point in the mixing tower.

The mixture of crude oil, sand, hydrocarbon diluent and water then passes to the upper portion of a sand separation tower in which it is allowed to flow downwardly over a series of downwardly slanted baffles. Due to its lower specific gravity oil tends to collect under the baffles and an oil-rich mixture of oil and water is drawn off from under the upper portions of the baffles. This oil-rich mixture may be treated by conventional methods such as flotation for separation of oil and water. The remainder of the mixture in the sand separation tower preferably continues downwardly through the tower and is contacted in the lower portion of the tower with a countercurrent flow of water introduced into the lower portion of the tower. This water serves to strip the sand and stripped sand may be withdrawn from the bottom of the tower. Slanted baffles similar to those in the upper portion of the sand separation tower are preferably contained also in the lower and intermediate portions of the tower and stripping water containing small amounts of oil may be withdrawn from under the baffles at the lower part of the tower while water containing slightly greater quantities of oil may be withdrawn from under baffles in the intermediate part of the tower.

The oil-rich mixture of oil and water from the upper portion of the sand separation tower is preferably passed to the upper portion of a surge tower located at a slightly lower elevation than the separation tower. The mixtures of oil and water withdrawn from the intermediate and lower portions of the separation tower may then be passed to an intermediate portion of the surge tower. The use of a surge tower in this manner serves to minimize the effects of variations in flow rates, etc., and to insure a uniform pressure drop in removing liquid streams from the separation tower. By maintaining a uniform, relatively low pressure drop across the valves or outlets through the possibility of forming undesirable emulsions is substantially reduced.

The lower portion of the surge tower preferably contains slanting baffles similar to those used in the sand separation tower and oil tends to become trapped under these baffles as the oil water mixtures from the intermediate and lower portions of the sand separation tower move towards the bottom of the surge tower. Such oil may be withdrawn from under the upper portions of these baffles and allowed to pass through a bypass conduit to the upper portion of the surge tower. A product mixture of oil and water may then be withdrawn from the upper portion of the surge tower for recovery of oil by suitable processes such as flotation while a stream of water is withdrawn from the lower portion of the surge tower. Part or all of this water is preferably recycled for forming the original slurry with the bituminous sand as described above.

Thermal Dehydration of Emulsion

R.A. Given and M.P. du Plessis; U.S. Patent 3,338,814; August 29, 1967; assigned to Imperial Oil Limited, Canada, Atlantic Richfield Company and Royalite Oil Company Limited, Canada describe a process where the separation of oil from the emulsion is effected by thermally dehydrating the emulsion to remove water and applying specific gravity separation to the dehydrated oil to divide the oil into portions having a high and a low solids concentration to permit processing of each portion separately.

The process comprises thermally dehydrating the bituminous emulsion under elevated temperature and pressure, dividing the dehydrated emulsion by specific gravity separation into a first fraction having a concentration of mineral solids substantially less than the first fraction, and separately treating each fraction to recover a hydrocarbon product substantially free of mineral solids and a residue. The reaction conditions, the hydrocarbon products, or the residue, differ for each of the separate streams which are treated.

The dehydration temperature and pressure can vary over wide ranges such as temperatures of from 225° to 550°F. and pressures from 4 to 1,000 psig. Preferably, the temperature can be from 350° to 450°F. and the pressure from 100 to 300 psig. The dehydrated emulsion can contain from 0 to 5% water and preferably from 0 to 2% water. Additionally, the dehydrated emulsion contains from 5 to 40% solids; these values generally being from 5 to 25% solids and from 79 to 94% bitumen. The dehydrator can be any suitable vessel for separating the vaporized water from the emulsion under the specified temperatures and pressures. The heat removed from the dehydrator in the vapor overhead is utilized by direct use of the stream in the extraction process, or to produce clean steam by using heat exchangers. In this regard the dehydrator conditions of pressure and temperature can be set, within the limits specified above, so as to produce steam of high enough temperature and pressure to be suitable for use elsewhere.

After dehydration, the mixture of bitumen, mineral solids and small quantities of water is subjected to specific gravity separation to divide the mixture into a portion having a high solids concentration and a portion having a solids concentration substantially less than the first portion. Since the mineral solids contain large amounts of fines, it is extremely difficult to make a good specific gravity separation between oil and solids. Preferably, the concentration of mineral solids of the separated streams or portions of the dehydrated emulsion is at least 10% higher in the high solids portion as compared to the low solids portion and it is particularly desirable that the difference in concentrations of mineral solids in the different portions be at least 20%.

Thus, with a minimum differential of 10% solids, one portion of the dehydrated mixture can contain from 35 to 70%, 29 to 64% bitumen, and no more than 4% water; whereas, the second can contain from 1 to 10% solids, 97 to 89% bitumen and no more than 4% water. In the specific gravity separation a larger concentration of water will be found in the portion having the lower solids concentration. The specific gravity separation of the dehydrated mixture is preferably effected at elevated temperatures such as those of from 300° to 700°F. and preferably from 400° to 700°F., so that the bitumen viscosity is greatly reduced.

Cycloning is a preferred method for achieving specific gravity separation in the dehydrated mixture of bitumen and mineral solids in order to effect the desired separation. In cycloning the dehydrated mixture, conventional hydrocyclones and procedures can be employed. Two stake cycloning can be employed when it is desirable to do so; such as when the mineral solids in the dehydrated mixture encompass a large range of particle size. Two stage cycloning is accomplished by first feeding the dehydrated mixture into a large diameter cyclone, or cyclones operating in parallel. The ensuing centrifugal force applied to the mixture in the cyclone(s) causes a small portion thereof, containing a relatively high concentration of mineral solids, to underflow from the cyclone(s).

The mineral solids in the underflow are primarily from the larger sized mineral particles in the feed. The remainder of the mixture, comprising the bulk of the fluid in the mixture and a relatively low concentration of mineral solids, overflows from the cyclone(s). The overflow from the large diameter cyclone(s) is fed into smaller diameter cyclones operating in parallel. This feed is separated into overflow and underflow streams which exit from the cyclones. The underflow stream comprises a relatively small portion of the feed, but it contains a relatively high concentration of mineral solids. The overflow from the small diameter cyclones contains the bulk of the hydrocarbon in the feed stream to the large diameter cyclone, but much of the mineral solids contained in the feed stream have been removed in the underflow streams effluing from the large and small diameter cyclones. The streams underflowing the smaller diameter cyclones and larger diameter cyclone(s) are combined and processed to recover the hydrocarbon value.

Micellar Dispersions for in Situ Treatment

J.T. Kelly and F.H. Poettmann; U.S. Patent 3,648,771; March 14, 1972; assigned to Marathon Oil Company have found that oil from subsurface tar sands having an injection means in fluid communication with a production means is recovered by injecting an oil-external micellar dispersion at a temperature above 100°F. into the tar sands and displacing it toward the production means to recover hydrocarbon.

The micellar dispersion can be preceded by a slug of hot water (e.g., above 100°F.) and the water can have a pH greater than 7. Also, the water within the micellar dispersion can have a pH of 7 to 14; and, preferably the dispersion is at a temperature greater than 150°F. The oil-external micellar dispersion is comprised of hydrocarbon, surfactant, and aqueous medium. Optionally, alcohol and/or electrolyte can be incorporated. Examples of volume amounts include 4 to 50% hydrocarbon, 10 to 90% aqueous medium, at least 4% surfactant, 0.01 to 20% cosurfactant, and 0.001 to 5% by weight of electrolyte. In addition, the dispersion can contain other additives such as corrosion inhibiting agents, bactericides, sequestering agents, etc. The following example illustrates the process.

Example: This example is presented to show specific examples of micellar dispersions useful with this process. These examples are prepared at room temperature with minimal agitation. The compositions of the micellar dispersions are indicated below.

Sample	Surfactant Percent	Surfactant Type	Hydrocarbon Percent	Hydrocarbon Type	Aqueous medium Percent	Aqueous medium Type	Cosurfactant Ml. 100 ml.	Cosurfactant Type
A	5.2	Ammonium petroleum sulfonate (average EqW=440, 81% active).	24.75	Crude oil	70	{60% Henry plant water.[3] 40% Palestine water.[4]}	0.08 0.25	n-Amyl alcohol. Isopropanol.
B	10	"Pyronate 50"[1]	20	...do...	70	{60% Henry plant water. 40% Palestine water.}	3.25	n-Hexanol.
C	10	"Petronate L"[2]	20	Straight-run gasoline.	70	{60% Henry plant water. 40% Palestine water.}	4.25	n-Amyl alcohol.
D	20	"Duponol WAQE"	10	...do...	70	Distilled water	14	i-Amyl alcohol.
E	10	"Energetic W-100"	20	...do...	70	...do...	8.5	Do.
F	10	"Triton X-100"	20	...do...	70	...do...	5.5	Do.
G	20	"Arquad 12-50"	10	...do...	70	...do...	17.0	Do.
H	16.6	Sodium petroleum sulfonate (avg. EqW=465, 62% active).	16.6	...do...	66.6	...do...	1.3	Isopropanol.
I	10	Ammonium petroleum sulfonate (avg. EqW=440, 81% active).	5	Crude oil	85	{60% Palestine water. 40% Henry plant water.}	2.5	n-Amyl alcohol.
J	7.4	Sulfonate defined in Example H..	49.6	Straight-run gasoline.	43	Water containing 500 p.p.m. dissolved solids.	---------	
K	11.6	...do...	60.6	...do...	24	Water defined in Example J.	---------	3.8% isopropanol.
L	12 6	...do...	51.0	Pentane	33	...do...	---------	3.4% isopropanol.

[1] Pyronate 50, a sodium petroleum sulfonate, average equivalent weight 350. Sold by Sonneborn Chemical Co., 300 Park Avenue South, New York, New York, 10010.
[2] Petronate L, a sodium petroleum sulfonate, average equivalent weight 422. Sold by Sonneborn Chemical Co., 300 Park Avenue South, New York, New York, 10010.
[3] Henry plant water is obtained from the Henry lease in Illinois; contains about 18,000 p.p.m. of dissolved salts.

[4] Palestine water is obtained from the Palestine water reservoir in Palestine, Illinois; contains about 420 p.p.m. of dissolved salts.

NOTE.—The amount of cosurfactant is based on ml. of cosurfactant per 100 ml. of liquid containing surfactant, hydrocarbon and aqueous medium—except in examples K and L wherein the amount of alcohol is based on percent of the total volume of dispersions.

In related work J.T. Kelly and F.H. Poettmann; U.S. Patent 3,637,018; January 25, 1972; assigned to Marathon Oil Company have found that oil from subsurface tar sand having an injection means in fluid communication with a production means is recovered by injecting a water-external micellar dispersion at a temperature above 100°F., into the tar sands, displacing it toward the production means and recovering the oil. The micellar dispersion can be preceded by a slug of hot water which can optionally have a pH greater than 7. Also, the micellar dispersion can have a pH of 7 to 14 and preferably a temperature greater than 150°F. The micellar dispersion contains hydrocarbon, surfactant, aqueous medium, and optionally cosurfactant and/or electrolyte.

Water-External Micellar Dispersions

J.T. Keely and F.H. Poettmann; U.S. Patent 3,644,194; February 22, 1972; assigned to Marathon Oil Company have found that oil within tar sands can be recovered by contacting the tar sands, preferably comminuted, with a water-external micellar dispersion in amounts sufficient to solubilize economically feasible portions of the oil from the tar sands. Thereafter, the micellar dispersion containing the solubilized oil is separated from the spent tar sand and subsequently the oil is recovered. The water-external micellar dispersion is preferably at a pH of 7 to 14, preferably 12 and also can be at temperatures in excess of 100°F. and preferably 150°F. or more. Volume amounts of from 0.05 to 30 volumes of the micellar dispersion per volume of tar sand is useful.

The water-external micellar dispersion useful in this process is comprised of hydrocarbon, surfactant, aqueous medium, and optionally cosurfactant and/or electrolyte. Examples of volume amounts include 1 to 50% hydrocarbon, 40 to 95% aqueous medium, at least 4% surfactant, 0.01 to 20% or more of cosurfactant, and 0.001 to 5% by weight of electrolyte. In addition, the dispersion can contain other additives such as corrosion inhibiting agents, bactericides, sequestering agents, etc. The surfactants useful with the micellar dispersion can be nonionic, cationic, and anionic surfactants. Specific examples of useful surfactants include those found in U.S. Patent 3,254,714.

Specific examples of useful cosurfactant include alcohols, amino compounds, esters, aldehydes, and ketones. Useful examples include isopropanol, n- and isobutanol, amyl alcohols such as n-amyl alcohol, 1- and 2-hexanol, 1-octanol, decyl alcohols, alkaryl alcohols such as p-nonyl phenol, alcoholic liquors such as fusel oils, etc. Preferably the electrolyte is an inorganic base or inorganic salt, e.g., sodium hydroxide, sodium chloride, sodium sulfate, sodium nitrate, ammonium chloride, ammonium hydroxide, potassium chloride, etc. Examples of specific electrolytes useful with the process include those found in U.S. Patent 3,330,343. Specific examples of useful water-external micellar dispersions are found in U.S. Patents 3,506,070 and 3,506,071.

Centrifugal Separation

G.R. Coulson; U.S. Patent 2,968,603; January 17, 1961; assigned to Can-Amera Oil Sands Development Ltd., Canada describes a process which involves the clarification of the water of the quiescent bath, and of the separation of the froth or overflow product of quiescent bath into relatively pure constituents, by the application of centrifugal force rather than by settling tanks or thickeners. In the process, the froth or overflow product from the quiescent bath and oil sludge from plant water are first mixed with a suitable diluent, i.e., a hydrocarbon oil capable of dissolving the oil constituent of the froth or overflow product, and of substantially lowering its specific gravity. While relatively low boiling hydrocarbons such as benzene, xylene, toluene, gasoline, naphtha or the like may be used, it is preferred to use diluents having an initial boiling point of 350° to 400°F. or higher such as kerosene, furnace distillates or diesel fuels, etc. to prevent substantial losses by evaporation. The diluent should be thoroughly mixed with the froth or overflow product and oil recovered from plant water to ensure uniform distribution therethrough. The diluted product is then subjected to the action of centrifugal force.

It is essential, during the process of separation through the application of centrifugal force, that sufficient water be present to form a continuous layer or barrier between the oil constituent and the solids constituent as well as completely saturating the voids in the solids component. It has been found that if the solids and oil are allowed to contact each other, they will, in many cases, recombine and require additional centrifuging to reseparate them. If the froth or overflow product contains sufficient water to ensure the maintenance of such a barrier and saturation of sand void space, it may be introduced without further addition, but if the water content is not sufficiently high, it will be necessary to add further water to the diluted product prior to the application of centrifugal force.

Under operating conditions in the centrifuge, a water layer or barrier of at least one inch should be continuously maintained between the oil and the solids. If water is to be added, the lower limit of water addition is the least amount at which the solids removed are virtually oil free, and the oil is virtually solids free. This point may be readily determined when the process is in operation. The only upper limit on the amount of water to be added is determined by the efficiency of the process, for when sufficient water is added to form the water barrier, no additional amount of water will influence the recovery, but a large excess of water would be uneconomical to handle in the centrifuge.

The application of centrifugal force will result in a three way separation of the constituents by densities, namely, an outer layer of solids, an intermediate layer of water and an inner layer of diluted oil. The oil recovered is of a high grade, substantially water free, virtually solids free and may be further processed in a standard refinery without the necessity for settling, thickeners or evaporators. The water recovered will be found to be substantially solids free and may be recycled into the process for recovery of the heat content thereof.

COLD WATER PROCESSES

Addition of Kerosene and Recycled Oil

In a process described by G.R. Coulson; U.S. Patent 2,825,677; March 4, 1958 the bituminous sands are mixed with a solvent which must be capable of dissolving substantially all of the bituminous constituents and also of reducing the specific gravity of these constituents so that the oil-solvent mixture has a specific gravity substantially below that of the aqueous phase. While relatively low boiling, normally liquid hydrocarbons such as benzene, xylene, toluene, gasoline, either cracked or straight run, petroleum naphtha, coal tar naphtha or the like may be employed provided precautions are taken to prevent loss thereof by evaporation, it is preferred to employ solvents having an initial boiling point of 350° to 400°F. or higher, for example, the higher boiling petroleum naphthas, kerosene, gas-oil in the boiling range of furnace distillates or diesel fuels, etc. This obviates to a large degree the loss difficulties which might be encountered with the lower boiling materials and the recoveries of crude oil obtained are satisfactory. When lower boiling solvents are used, a vapor proof system should be used to avoid loss of solvent. Oils of an aromatic or olefinic character are the most efficacious since certain constituents of the tar-sand oils are more soluble in these than in predominantly paraffinic distillates. Indeed, where the tar-sand oil is of an asphaltic base, some constituents may be almost entirely insoluble in paraffinic solvents, particularly the lower boiling ones, and hence would not be recovered.

It is advantageous to recycle a portion of the recovered oil mixed with the solvent since this, in some instances, appears to increase the ultimate recovery of oil from the sand. This reduces the proportion of solvent used, which, however, must be present in sufficient amounts to product the specific gravity within the desired range of the recovered product. It is preferred to employ the more unsaturated and/or aromatic distillates, either alone or mixed with some of the recovered oil which may be produced during the thermal or catalytic cracking or coking of hydrocarbon oils. The constituents of the tar-sand seem to be somewhat more compatible with solvents of this character and hence the degree of recovery is increased.

Where such cracked distillates are available on the premises they may be used in the form of side streams such as that normally employed as recycle stock in the cracking process. Thus, if the recovered oil is being cracked or coked at or near the recovery site, a side stream may be taken from the cracking or coke plant fractionating tower, mixed with the sands, the oil recovered and then the entire mixture returned to the cracking or coking operation, if desired by way of the fractionator. In view of the fact that the crude oil recovered is too viscous for transportation through a pipeline, it is necessary to convert it to a more fluid form. A particularly desirable way of doing this is to subject a portion or all of the crude oil to a coking operation and the crude oil can be reduced to a gravity and viscosity suitable for transporting through a pipeline.

A particularly suitable diluent comprises the overhead distillate from such an operation. The lighter gravity oil thus produced may be used as such or in a mixture with a portion of the oil as recovered from the sands. Instead of using all of the overhead distillate from the coking operation, a lower boiling fraction of the coke distillate, such as that boiling in the range of heavy naphtha, kerosene, or light gas oil, may be employed, alone or in admixture with the recovered crude oil. The solvent performs the function of dissolving the oil and reducing its viscosity and making it more mobile and susceptible to the stripping forces of the aqueous phase. It also reduces the specific gravity to a point below that of the aqueous phase, thus facilitating separation. This has the effect of reducing power and equipment requirements.

The amount of the solvent or diluent which is added will vary with the raw sands, and factors influencing the amount to be added are the porosity of the sand where the voids between the grains are filled to a greater or lesser extent; the degree of saturation, i.e., the amount of bituminous matter present in the sand; the density, fluidity and melting point of the bitumen; the specific gravity of the diluent; and the viscosity of the resulting mixture of diluent and oil. The best separation takes place when the specific gravity of the bitumen is reduced to between 0.79 and 0.95 by the addition of a suitable amount of the lower gravity diluent.

If the specific gravity of the bitumen is 1.025 (a common value for oils in sands found in the Athabasca River area and containing 10 to 20% by weight of oil) and if a kerosene of 0.75 specific gravity is used in equal parts by volume, the mixture of oil and kerosene will have a specific gravity of 0.887, which is in the desired range and has been found to be highly useful in this process.

The following comparative results, run as a batch, show the effect of varying degrees of dilution, and of the addition of a surface active agent and were arrived at through the following procedure. A uniform sample of raw Alberta oil sand was divided into a number of equal portions. In each case two volumes of water were added after dilution, and the diluted sand and water thoroughly agitated before centrifuging. The first table below shows the results using kerosene (specific gravity = 0.81) as the solvent. The second table shows the results using recycled diluted oil recovered from the process (specific gravity = 0.87) as the solvent.

Kerosene as Solvent, 2 Volumes of Water

Percentage Solvent by Weight of Oil Sands	Specific Gravity of Diluted Oil	Ratio by Volume Diluent: Oil	Net Oil Recovery (Percentage of Oil Content by Weight)	S. A.,[1] Percent
50	0.842	5.25	91	---------
30	0.859	3.15	91	---------
25	0.865	2.63	91	---------
10	0.910	1.05	87	98
7.5	0.923	0.78	63	77
5.0	0.942	0.52	54	71
2.5	0.973	0.26	44	44
0	1.02	0.00	Nil	Nil

[1] Surface active agent Ethomid HT/60, 1 part to aqueous phase 40,000 parts.

Recycled Diluted Oil as Solvent, 2 Volumes of Water

Percentage Solvent by Weight of Oil Sands	Specific Gravity of Diluted Oil	Ratio by Volume Diluent: Oil	Net Oil Recovery (Percentage of Oil Content by Weight)	S. A.,[1] Percent
50	0.892	4.88	91	---------
30	0.905	2.93	87	---------
25	0.912	2.44	96	96
20	0.920	1.95	98	91
15	0.928	1.46	63	86
5.0	0.966	0.49	54	71
2.5	0.988	0.25	34	62
0	1.02	0.00	Nil	Nil

[1] Surface active agent Ethomid HT/60, 1 part of aqueous phase 40,000 parts.

The above data shows that when no solvent is used, the recovery of oil from the sands is nil. However, when the solvent is added in proportions amounting to 0.5 to 5 volumes of diluent per volume of oil contained in the sands, recoveries of from more than 50% of the oil up to more than 90% of the oil can be obtained. It should also be noted that when a surface active agent is added in the areas of lower diluent ratios substantial improvement in oil recovery is obtained. This means that by use of a surface active agent in conjunction with the diluent and water a lower amount of diluent can be added than is otherwise necessary. Similar results are obtainable when using a portion of the recovered diluted oil as the solvent.

In related work G.R. Coulson and L. Clark; U.S. Patent 2,885,339; May 5, 1959; assigned to Can-Amera Oil Sands Development Ltd., Canada have found that coarse sand may be separated from the oil, water, clay and fines by treatment in a fluidizing tower subjected to a countercurrent flow of water through a sand column. Generally, the method consists in feeding downward, into the top of a tower, a slurry of oil bearing sand, diluent and water, maintaining a constant level of sand in the tower by constantly withdrawing sand from the bottom, and forcing a stream of water upward through the sand column, countercurrent to the slurry, and withdrawing the overflow of oil, clay and other fines, and water.

The raw oil-bearing sand may conveniently first be mixed with a diluent oil capable of dissolving the oil content. The use of such a diluent has the effect of reducing the viscosity and the specific gravity of the oil constituent thus permitting a separation in the manner hereinafter described. In their natural state specific gravity of the oil content varies from 1.000 to 1.025. It is desirable to dilute the oil constituent to such an extent as to reduce the specific gravity of the diluted constituent substantially below 1.000 and preferably in the range of from 0.79 to 0.95.

This slurry is fed into the upper portion of the body of a column in which a constant sand level is maintained. To the bottom of the tower, water is supplied under pressure to create an upward flow at a rate of approximately 0.2 to 1.5 feet per minute free water velocity in the column, more or less as determined by the size of the sand grains. In order to ensure even distribution of the water stream over the entire cross-sectional area of the column, the water may conveniently take the form of a plurality of upwardly or downwardly projecting jets located near the bottom of the tower and disposed at regular intervals over the cross-section of the tower.

Sand is continuously withdrawn from the bottom of the column to maintain the sand level in the column, while the overflow from the column, consisting of oil, clay and other fines, and water is continuously withdrawn from the top of the column. In an installation of this type, the sand in the column may be considered as settled and initially motionless. As the rate of flow of the rising fluid is increased, the bed particles begin to move due to the lifting effect of the rising fluid. As the flow is increased, the motion of the particles increases. At a certain upward velocity, the sand becomes fluidized to a point where the abrasive action of the sand particles on each other causes rupture of the surrounding oil films, without however being sufficient to carry the solid particles upward in the stream.

The oil thus released is carried upward with the rising water and discharged from the tower as an overflow product together with the clay and other fines of the raw sand. In a continuous column with slurry feed at top and with sand grains descending against the rising water, the rising water velocity required is reduced in part by the rate of descent of the sand in order to maintain good attrition condition. This process is continuous, the oil-sand water slurry being continuously charged into the top, the water countercurrent from the bottom, the sand removed continuously from the bottom and the oil, clay, water and fines removed continuously by way of overflow, all at such rates as to maintain constant operating conditions in the tower.

Alkali Metal Silicate Treatment

A process described by R.J. Stegemeier and P.W. Fischer; U.S. Patent 2,924,565; February 9, 1960; assigned to Union Oil Company of California involves a low temperature process using a warm aqueous solution of a special alkali metal silicate, with or without other reagents, and a moderately heavy hydrocarbon diluent to separate the heavy oil from the bituminous sands, and in which process special procedures and apparatus are used in handling the effluent from the mixing step in which these materials are heated and agitated with one another to effect the separation of the heavy oil from the sand. Referring to Figure 3.4a, the essential equipment elements employed in the process include pulper or mixer 10, primary separator 12, sand washer and drier 14, thickener 16, and the product settler 18.

FIGURE 3.4: OIL RECOVERY FROM SAND USING SILICATE TREATMENT

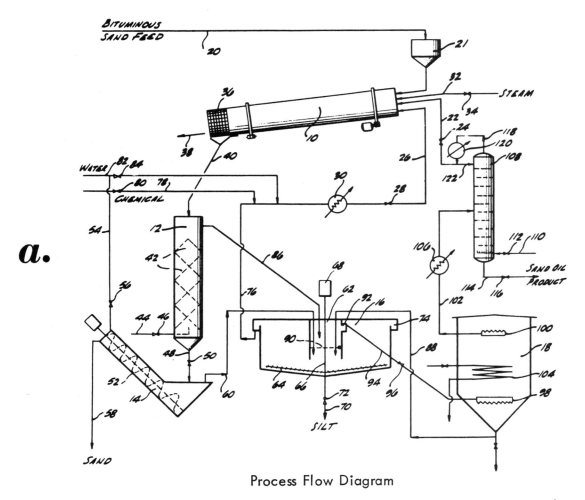

Process Flow Diagram

(continued)

FIGURE 3.4: (continued)

b.

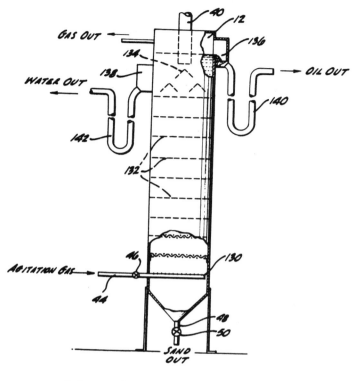

Primary Separator

c.

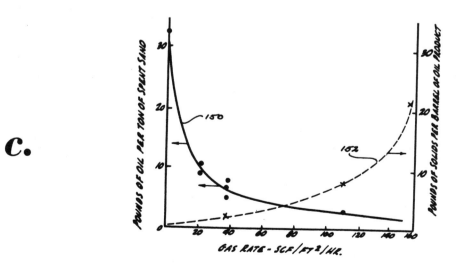

Efficiency of Process as a Function of Aeration Rate

Source: R.J. Stegemeier and P.W. Fischer; U.S. Patent 2,924,565; February 9, 1960

The subsequent discussion in connection with Figure 3.4a will be conducted as a typical example of the process as applied to the treatment of Sisquoc bituminous sand at a rate of 200 tons per day. Although the tar sand may contain between 20 and 40 gallons of oil per ton and have a gravity of from 2 to 10° API, typical bituminous sand contains about 30 gallons per ton of 4° API gravity bitumen.

The freshly mined bituminous sand is introduced into pulper 10 by means of conveyor 20 at a rate of 200 tons per day controlled by solids feeder 21. A light coker gas-oil as diluent oil is introduced at a rate of 191 barrels per day and a temperature of 180°F. through line 22 at a rate controlled by valve 24. Also introduced into the pulper is an aqueous alkali metal silicate solution (with or without other reagents) which flows through line 26 at a rate of 286 barrels per day controlled by valve 28. This material is maintained at a temperature of 180°F. by means of heater or exchanger 30. To maintain a pulper temperature of 180°F. in pulper 10, steam at the rate of 482 pounds per hour is also introduced through line 32 at a rate controlled by valve 34.

The relative rates at which the ingredients are introduced into pulping zone 10 are specific to one typical operation. In general however they are preferably maintained in certain limits in order to effect the most rapid and efficient liberation of the bituminous material from the sand or other solid grains. Pursuant to this the diluent hydrocarbon rate is that sufficient to produce an oil phase having an API gravity above 10° and is preferably maintained between limits of 0.1 and 2.5 barrels per ton of raw bituminous sand feed. The aqueous silicate solution is introduced at a rate maintained between 0.75 and 5.0 barrels per ton of raw sand feed, and preferably between 1.0 and 1.5 barrels per ton.

This aqueous solution contains between 0.5 and 20 and preferably between 0.75 and 10.0 pounds of an aqueous sodium silicate concentrate per barrel. This concentrate is a 34% by weight aqueous solution and is a special material known as "Silicate 120". It has an Na_2O to SiO_2 ratio of 0.55 mol per mol. Other high basicity sodium silicates may be substituted provided this ratio is above 0.4 and preferably greater than 0.5. The commercial water glass of commerce is not satisfactory since it has a ratio of 0.25.

The pulping temperature must be maintained higher than 160°F. and preferably is maintained above 180°F., although it ordinarily should not run above 250°F. The operation of the pulping zone is controlled relative to the set rate and the size of the pulper so that the raw bituminous sand is subjected to the action of steam, the aqueous silicate, and the hydrocarbon diluent within the pulping zone for a period of between 0.1 and 2.0 hours. Under the conditions given previously a pulping time of 0.25 hour will liberate substantially all of the bitumen from the sand and produce a spent sand containing less than 3 pounds of hydrocarbon per ton.

The discharge end of pulping zone 10 is provided with trash screen 36 by means of which rocks and nondisaggregated lumps of tar sands are discharged from the system by means of conveyor 38. The fluid pulp discharges through the screen 36 and flows by means of line 40 into the top of primary separation zone 12. This stream contains 58 tons per day of water, 55 tons per day of oil and 172 tons per day of sand. Primary separation zone 12 operates at a temperature a few degrees below that of the pulper. This is attained by making line 40 as short as possible and providing for the immediate transfer of the pulp from the pulper into the primary separator. Preferably line 40 is an inclined pipe having a slope of not less than 60° relative to the horizontal. The interior of primary separation zone 12 is provided with a plurality of baffles 42 over which the settling sand progresses in sequence to provide the gentle agitation necessary to liberate mechanically trapped oil drops from the sand stream. Additional agitation is provided by introducing fluid, hereinafter more fully described, into the bottom of primary separation zone 12 through line 44 at a rate controlled by valve 46.

From the bottom of primary separation zone 12 the treated sand discharges through line 48 at a rate controlled by valve 50, which may be a density valve responsive to the density of the sand and water slurry collecting in the bottom of primary separation zone 12. In any event, the sand discharges at a rate of 172 tons per day into washer 14 along with 193 barrels per day of water. The sand is picked up and conveyed upwardly by means of conveyor 52 where a gravity separation of the aqueous phase is provided. Preferably, part or all of the makeup water to the system is introduced by means of line 54 controlled by valve 56 as wash water to the washer-drier. The clean oil-free sand is discharged from washer-drier 14 by means of line 58 and is conveyed to a suitable disposal point.

The aqueous phase removed with the sand from the primary separation zone 12 is separated from washer-drier 14 through line 60 and is discharged into the central well 62 of thickening zone 16. This stream flows at 160°F. at a rate of 1,168 barrels per day, containing 5 tons per day of sand and 1 barrel per day of oil. Thickener 16 is an essentially cylindrical vessel provided internally with a coaxial central well 62 into which all of the fluids for treatment are introduced. The floor of thickener 16 is provided with a plurality of radial rake arms 64 rotated by means of a vertical central shaft 66 or by other means, driven by rotating means 68.

In the example the central well is such that the fluid residence time is one hour devoted to the settling of silt from the oil phase as well as the separation of the oil and water phases. The annular volume outside well 62 is sized to give a water residence time of 6 to 8 hours during which time substantially all of the silt settles from the aqueous phase. Rake arms 64 are provided with rakes inclined at such an angle so that rotation of the rakes move the settled silt as a thickened sludge radially inward toward silt outlet 70. The thickened silt is removed through line 70 at a rate controlled by valve 72, the silt concentrate containing 87 barrels per day of water and 15.0 tons per day of solids.

The clear water effluent is removed from collector 74 surrounding the upper periphery of thickener 16 by means of line 76 at a rate of 1,821 barrels per day. This material actually constitutes the aqueous silicate solution to which makeup aqueous silicate concentrate is introduced by means of line 78 at a rate of 2.5 gallons per hour controlled by valve 80. Fresh water is introduced by means of line 82 at a rate of 355 barrels per day controlled by valve 84. This may, if desired, flow into the clear aqueous stream in line 76. As previously indicated this is preferably employed, wholly or partly, as wash water for the spent sand and is introduced through line 54 previously described. The total aqueous stream from thickener 16 continues through heat exchanger 30. It is heated to 180°F. and is introduced into pulping zone 10 through line 26. The overflow of the wet oil phase from primary separator zone 12 passes through line 86 also into central well 62 of thickener 16. This stream flows at a rate of 1,081 barrels per day and includes 754 barrels per day of water, 327 barrels per day of oil, and 12 tons per day of silt and sand. The temperature of the stream is 175°F. Also introduced into the central well 62 at a temperature of 155°F. is a relatively small stream of water from the bottom of settling zone 18. This passes through line 88 into central well 62 and contains 67 barrels per day of water, 1 barrel per day of oil, and a trace of silt and sand.

In central well 62 broken line 90 indicates the approximate position of the oil emulsion-aqueous phase interface. This is maintained at a distance about two-thirds of the way down in the central well. The aqueous streams flowing through lines 60 and 88 from washer-drier 14 and settling zone 18 respectively are introduced below this level because they contain only slight quantities of oil. The primary separator effluent flowing through line 86 and containing 30% by volume of oil is introduced above level 90 into the supernatent phase consisting of separated oil and possibly a layer of oil-water emulsion.

Preferably the interface denoted by line 90 is detected continuously and the rate of removal of the supernatant wet oil phase from weir box 92 or other removal means is controlled so as to maintain a substantially constant position of the interface. In any event, residence time for the oil phase is one hour and the wet oil stream is removed from weir box 92 through line 94 at a rate of 409 barrels per day controlled by valve 96 or other means. The temperature of this stream is approximately 168°F., and it contains 328 barrels per day of oil, 81 barrels per day of water, and 2 tons per day of sand.

This wet oil stream is discharged into separator zone 18 by means of distributor 98 disposed in the lower portion of the settling zone. Heating coil 104 is provided within settling zone 18. Preferably the volume of settling zone 18 is sufficient to give the wet oil a residence time of 12 hours permitting it to separate into dry oil and aqueous phases. The separated aqueous phase is removed from the bottom of settling zone 18 through line 88 and contains a trace of solids, but is otherwise essentially all water. The dry oil is removed from the top of settling zone 18 by means of takeoff weir 100. This stream is pumped by means of a pump not shown through line 102 to distillation facilities which may be located at the plant site or at a remote area where it is associated with oil refining facilities for treating the recovered oil.

This stream flows at a temperature of 153°F. and contains 321 barrels per day of oil, 2 barrels per day of water and 0.1 tons per day of solids. The effluent dry oil is heated in exchanger means 106 and is distilled in distillation column 108. A stripping gas such as steam is introduced into the bottom of distillation column 108 through line 110 at a rate controlled by valve 112. The overhead vapor flowing through line 118 from still 108 is condensed in condenser 120, part of the condensate is returned through line 122 as reflux, and the remainder is pumped by means of a pump not shown through line 22 into pulping zone 10. The stripped diluent oil free bitumen is removed through line 114 at a rate of 137 barrels per day controlled by valve 116. This product oil has the following properties.

Viscosity, SUS at 180°F.	50,200
Carbon residue, percent by wt.	16.05
Sulfur, percent by wt.	4.4

(continued)

Nitrogen, percent by wt.   0.95
Gravity, °API   4.4

By means of the above described process, bituminous sands are readily treated to effect better than 96% by volume of the bitumen contained therein at moderate temperatures and pressures and with only slight consumption of chemicals. The sand discharged from the system contains less than 5 pounds per ton of residual oil.

Referring to Figure 3.4b, an enlarged detail drawing of primary separator 12 is shown in which the details of the internals and particularly the baffles are shown. As previously described, a lower outlet line for treated sand is provided in the form of line 48 controlled by valve 50. Also a lower inlet line 44 controlled by valve 46 is further provided with a distributor 130 by means of which an aeration gas is introduced and broken up into small bubbles distributed uniformly throughout the entire cross-sectional area of the primary separator zone.

In primary separator vessel 12 there is superimposed above each other a series of transverse perforated baffles, such as relatively small meshed screens 132 having mesh sizes between 0.1 and 1.0 inch, supported internally from the walls of the column. As a specific example, excellent success was attained in removing residual oil from the sand in a column which was 10 feet in height, and 22 inches in diameter which contained 9 screens having 0.25 inch mesh spaced apart from one another by a distance of 10 inches, or between 0.25 and 1.0 column diameters. The pulp introduced from pulping zone 10 flows through line 40 into the top of separator 12 where it contacts several conical distributors 134.

From the distributors the sand flows downwardly successively through the superimposed screens countercurrent to a rising stream of aeration gas bubbles. If desired, the aqueous and oil phases may be removed together in the manner shown in Figure 3.4a by means of line 86. However, in the specific apparatus shown it was found that an excellent separation of the aqueous and oil phases could be obtained and accordingly separate weir boxes 136 for the oil and 138 for the aqueous phases were provided. A gooseneck line 140 opens from weir box 136 through which the oil discharges as fast as it accumulates at the top of separator 12. A second gooseneck takeoff line 142 opens from weir box 138 by means of which the aqueous phase is removed at a controlled liquid level within the column.

Where the sand separated by simple settling in an unbaffled tank to which no aeration gas was provided contained 60 pounds of residual oil per ton, and sand from the screen baffled tank with no gas aeration contained 32 pounds of oil per ton, the process of aeration gas agitation in the presence of superimposed screens described above successfully reduced the residual oil content to 4 pounds per ton at 150°F. and with a gas rate of 75 scf/ft.^{2}/hr. (standard cubic feet per square foot of column cross-section per hour).

Referring to Figure 3.4c, experimental data obtained in the semicommercial size apparatus are shown plotted to illustrate the variation in the degree of contamination of the sand with residual oil and the variation in the degree of contamination of the product oil with solids, each as a function of aeration gas rates. Curve 150 graphically illustrates the rapid reduction in residual oil content in the spent sand with the introduction of aeration gas into the bottom of separation zone 12. As little as 20 scf/ft.^{2}/hr. aeration gas reduces the residual oil content to 25% of its original value in the absence of aeration. Further reductions are obtained with moderate increases in the gas rate and contaminations less than 3 pounds per ton are readily obtained at aeration gas rates of 100 scf/ft.^{2}/hr. In the process, the increases in gas rate may not be continued indefinitely since simultaneously with the reduction in oil concentration in the sand, there is an increase in the solids or silt contamination of the product oil. This is represented by curve 152 also shown in Figure 3.4c.

Accordingly in the process the aeration gas rate must be limited between values of 20 and 140 scf/ft.^{2}/hr. and preferably the aeration rate is restricted to between 50 and 100 scf/ft.^{2}/hr. There is also a limitation on the sand rate, and desirably the solid grains have a falling retention time of from 1.5 to 5 minutes. The solids rate should be maintained between 0.5 and 5.0 tons per square foot of column cross-section per hour, and preferably between 1.5 and 2.5 tons per square foot per hour.

In related work P.W. Fischer, V. Kenny and J.W. Scheffel; U.S. Patent 2,903,407; September 8, 1959; assigned to Union Oil Company of California treat and recover hydrocarbon oil from tar sand by pulping it with a mixture of aqueous sodium silicate and a hydrocarbon solvent at slightly elevated temperatures to separate the oil from the sand. Briefly, the process comprises the mining of surface or near surface deposits of tar sand by the usual procedures to produce a raw tar sand material consisting of chunks of tar sand not exceeding 12 inches in average dimension.

The mined material is immediately transferred without excessive exposure to the atmosphere to one or more storage basins into which it is introduced and kept submerged in an aqueous medium. Although water alone prevents many of the disadvantages of storage, preferably this aqueous medium is a dilute solution of sodium silicate. This storage maintains the material out of contact with air of the atmosphere, prevents water evaporation from the tar sand itself, and further prevents oil wetting of the sand grains.

The temperature of this pretreatment is preferably atmospheric or slightly above, such as between 60° and 160°F. At the higher temperatures evaporation losses of water become high, but a partial digestion and pretreatment of the tar sand is also accomplished, a result which is accelerated with increases in temperature. At the lower temperatures, the chunks of tar sand are completely inhibited from coalescing and hardening into a single mass similar to that to which they were mined. The stored and pretreated material is removed from storage and is fed to the treatment process.

J.W. Scheffel and P.W. Fischer; U.S. Patent 3,075,913; January 29, 1963; assigned to Union Oil Company of California have found that, in a process where clay-containing bituminous solids are reduced to a fluid pulp by agitation in the presence of aqueous sodium silicate at slightly elevated temperatures and the resulting pulp is mechanically treated, for example, by gravity settling or by centrifuging, to separate a solids fraction, a hydrocarbon oil fraction, and an aqueous sodium silicate fraction which is recycled to the pulping step, the buildup of clay in the sodium silicate recycle stream can be substantially prevented by introducing into the process system a small amount of an ionizable calcium compound. The calcium ions produced by the latter in aqueous solution serve to flocculate the clay which otherwise remains colloidally suspended in the circulating stream of sodium silicate, and allows such clay to be separated along with the nonclay solids in the separation step.

A number of other modifications of the above recovery process, using alkali metal silicates in the pulping operation are described by J.E. Sherborne; U.S. Patent 2,921,010; January 12, 1960, A.E. Kelley; U.S. Patent 2,980,600; April 18, 1961, R.P. Vaell and P.W. Fischer; U.S. Patent 2,924,566; February 9, 1960; all assigned to Union Oil Company of California.

Aqueous Extraction Using Sea Water

J.H. Barkman, Jr., R.M. Jorda and J.V. Vogel; U.S. Patent 3,547,803; December 15, 1970; assigned to Shell Oil Company describe a process for recovering oil from a tar sand where pulverized tar sand is mixed with a liquid hydrocarbon diluent. The diluted tar sand is then mixed with a first volume of hot brine at a controlled pH. The materials which float in the first volume of hot brine are isolated and mixed with a second volume of hot brine containing a surfactant. The second volume of hot brine is also at a controlled pH. Finally, any hydrocarbon materials that are substantially free of solids and aqueous liquids and float in the second volume of brine are isolated. The process provides a method of separating or breaking oil from bituminous sands by aqueous extraction using neutral or acidic brine or sea water. Referring to Figure 3.5, tar sand ore is pulverized as by crushing or grinding in any conventional manner at a pulverizing station 10.

FIGURE 3.5: AQUEOUS EXTRACTION OF TAR SAND USING SEA WATER

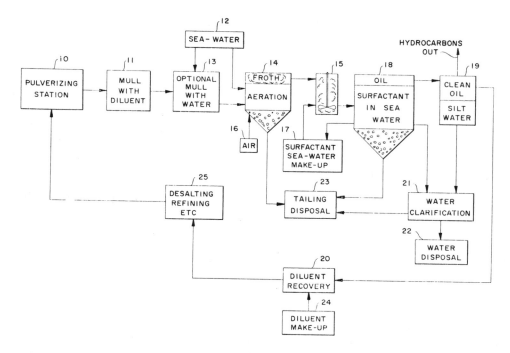

Source: J.H. Barkman, Jr., R.M. Jorda and J.V. Vogel; U.S. Patent 3,547,803; December 15, 1970

Tar Sands Separation Processes

The pulverized ore is next mulled at mulling station 11 with a suitable hydrocarbon diluent in a conventional manner for a period long enough to allow the tar and diluent to mutually dissolve. The tar sand is substantially uniformly diluted to an oil phase exhibiting a viscosity of less than 100 cp. at a temperature of less than 200°F.

At this point, if desired, the ore-diluent mixture may be mulled at station 13 with hot liquid brine or sea water, received from a sea water source 12, having a pH of not more than 7 and a volume sufficient to extend between materials which float and sink in the brine or sea water so as to change the slurry characteristics of the ore. The resulting ore-diluent mixture (or slurry) at station 13 is introduced into a flotation stage or process comprising one or more flotation cells (such as skimming stage 14, countercurrent washer 15, and aeration cell 16) which may employ in cell 16 aeration from any convenient air source or other conventional techniques as indicated to create a froth or emulsion upon the introduction of brine or sea water into the cell.

The froth or emulsion is then treated by countercurrent washing at washer 15 with a preferably hot liquid brine or sea water solution of a detergent or surfactant received from a surfactant-sea water makeup station 17. The surfactant used is one that exhibits a significant amount of solubility in both brine and oil, the second volume of brine also having a pH of not more than 7, and a volume sufficient to extend between materials which float and sink in the brine or sea water.

The washed froth-surfactant slurry from washer 15 is separated, by conventional settling, into a solid and aqueous-free oil, surfactant in sea water and tailings mixture at station 18. The oil is removed and, at station 19, any hydrocarbons that are as substantially as volatile as the hydrocarbon employed as the diluent are evaporated and the remaining oil is recovered by passing it to a diluent recovery station 20. The silt-water, separated from the solid-free oil at station 19, is clarified with water at station 21 and the water and tailings are disposed of by conventional disposal means.

Thus, the water is passed to a water disposal station 22 and the tailings to a tailings disposal station 23. The sea water removed from the oil-surfactant-sea water slurry at station 18 is also clarified with water at station 21 while the tailings are disposed of to station 23, indicated in the drawing. The surfactant in the sea water is passed from station 18 to surfactant makeup station 17. Finally, at the diluent recovery station 21, any necessary diluent is added from a diluent makeup station 24 while any surplus diluent is passed to a processing station such as a desalting and refining station 25 for further processing by conventional means. The necessary diluent for mulling station 11 is supplied from the diluent recovery station 20. Tailings from skimming stage 14 are also passed to tailings disposal station 23.

Thus, as can be seen from the above, a clean hydrocarbon product with good recovery yields is obtained at the diluent recovery station 20. The diluent from station 20 contacts the tar sand at mulling station 11 before any water is added. This is an important feature of the process since, if the diluent is added after water is introduced, recovery may be reduced. Once the diluent has been added, and well mixed, water may be added from station 12, as desired, to improve the slurry characteristics. It is also important that the surfactant used to upgrade the froth or emulsion produced in the flotation stages is not added at an earlier stage in the process, such as during the mulling process at station 11 and 13 or the skimming stage 14. In these cases, such an addition would be ineffective for improving the froth quality and may actually interfere with the flotation process by causing an increase in the amount of solids being floated and in the volume of froth due to inclusion of excess air. Suitable surfactants for use in the froth upgrading of the process are described in U.S. Patent 3,553,100.

Such surfactants may comprise an aqueous solution of an anionic surface-active material which is a free acid or salt of a complex organic phosphate ester (as for example, Gafac RE-610 and described in U.S. Patents 3,331,896 and 3,168,478). Further, any suitable closely related compound, as for example, any surfactant material in which ethylene oxide groups, acyl radicals and from about 10 to 22 carbon atoms are contained in each of the molecules of a surfactant that exhibits a significant amount of solubility in both oil and brine in addition to having a pH of not more than 7 and a volume sufficient to extend between materials which float and sink in the brine may be used.

The addition of water or brine from water source 12 to station 13 is optional since certain tar sand ores, such as those from the Edna, California region, as well as other regions, commonly contain from 3 to 10% water by weight in their natural state. The addition of more water, especially before contact with the hydrocarbon diluent, either reduces the recovery of tar from the sand or, if it is a very small amount, has no effect. It is believed that, in the former case, it hinders adequate solution of the tar and diluent by filling and blocking the pore volume. The diluent is generally required to effect complete separation of tar, although, with some tar sands, it may be possible to obtain separation without diluent by careful operation of the flotation process.

In related work R.M. Jorda, J.H. Barkman, Jr. and H.F. Young; U.S. Patent 3,553,100; January 5, 1971; assigned to Shell Oil Company describe a process for breaking or separating an emulsified mixture of liquid hydrocarbon, insoluble fluid and finely divided solid material. The emulsified mixture is mixed with a volume of hot brine having controlled pH and containing a surfactant material in which ethylene oxide groups, acyl radicals, and from 10 to 22 carbon atoms are contained in each of the molecules of a surfactant that exhibits a significant amount of solubility in both oil and brine. Hydrocarbon materials that are substantially free of solids and aqueous liquids and float in the brine are isolated and the hydrocarbon components of the isolated materials are recovered.

Utilization of Methane as Flotation Gas

R.M. Butler, J.L. Tiedje and J.A. Bichard; U.S. Patent 3,203,888; August 31, 1965; assigned to Esso Research and Engineering Company describe a method of securing the separation of bitumen particles from sand particles which, in essence, comprises the utilization of a hydrocarbon gas as, for example, methane which will function to change the apparent density of the bitumen particles to less than the density of water. The process is particularly adapted for use in conjunction with a water technique conducted at ambient temperatures where from 40 to 400% by weight of water is added to the tar sands. It has been found that when tar sand is intermittently mixed with sufficient cold water, such as 200 wt. percent of water at 70°F., a mixture containing small particles of bitumen and sand is obtained. Under these conditions, the sand particles in such a dilute suspension are essentially bitumen-free. This is the case even when, under certain mixing operations, a relatively small amount of the water as, for example, from 30 to 50 wt. percent is added and mixed under a shearing action and then the remaining quantity of water added to the slurry in order to dilute the slurry. This latter technique helps to break down any large particles in the sand.

However, in such a process as described, the dilute cold suspension in general tends to produce a settled layer containing both the particles of bitumen as well as the particles of sand. The reason there is no sharp separation of sand from the bitumen is that the bitumen has a density slightly higher than that of water and, thus, does not float. For example, specific gravities of Athabasca bitumen vary from 1.007 to 1.022 at 77°F. Even higher apparent specific gravities may be obtained if some fine clay is contained within the bitumen particle.

By this process, the apparent densities of the bitumen particles are lowered to less than that of water, thereby producing a very effective separation between the sand particles and the bitumen particles. Figure 3.6 specifies that natural tar sands are introduced into zone $\underline{3}$ and mixed with water which is introduced by means of line $\underline{2}$. In zone $\underline{3}$, the mixture is subjected to a mixing-shearing action.

FIGURE 3.6: UTILIZATION OF METHANE GAS TO CHANGE THE APPARENT DENSITY OF BITUMEN PARTICLES

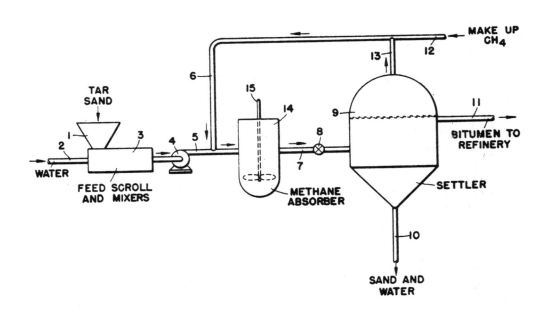

Source: R.M. Butler, J.L. Tiedje and J.A. Bichard; U.S. Patent 3,203,888; Aug. 31, 1965

The slurry is then passed by means of pump 4 through line 5 into a gas absorption zone 14. In this zone, the slurry is thoroughly mixed with the gas as, for example, methane, or ethane, which is introduced by means of line 6. A preferred adaption is to maintain the zone 14 at a pressure in the range from 5 to 50 lbs./sq. in. gauge. Thorough mixing is secured in zone 14 by means of stirrer or equivalent means 15.

By contacting the tar sands with a normally gaseous hydrocarbon under a moderate elevated pressure, the tar sand tends to dissolve the hydrocarbon gas, thereby changing its apparent specific gravity. The mixture is then passed by means of line 7 through valve 8 into a settler 9 which is maintained at a pressure below that of the pressure in zone 14 as, for example, from 5 to 20 lbs./sq. in. less. In zone 9 the hydrocarbon gas as, for example, methane, comes out of solution and forms gas bubbles attached to the bitumen particles. This decreases the average specific gravity of the bitumen particles and causes the same to float.

Thus, the bitumen particles may be removed as a bitumen phase by means of line 11 while the sand and water phase is removed as a bottoms stream by means of line 10. Gas particles are removed overhead by means of line 13 and repressured as a recycle stream. Makeup gas may be added by means of line 12. A further advantage of the process is that, even if clay is present in the bitumen particles, these clay-containing particles can also be made buoyant by the employment of adequate hydrocarbon pressure. In general, it is preferred that the pressure in zone 14 be in the range from 20 to 30 lbs./sq. in. gauge, preferably 25 lbs./sq. in. gauge. It is preferred that the pressure in zone 9 be 10 to 15 lbs./sq. in. gauge below the pressure existing in zone 14.

In a process described by M.C. Lowman, Jr. and E.J. Fisch; U.S. Patent 2,871,180; January 27, 1959; assigned to Shell Development Company an aqueous pulp of the bituminous sand is supplied to a vertical extraction zone and a liquid low molecular weight paraffinic solvent flows in an upward direction of the vertical extraction zone in countercurrent direction to the downwardly descending sand. During the countercurrent movement of the aqueous pulp and solvent, there is formed a deasphalted oil and solvent phase, an asphaltene phase diluted with a lesser portion of the solvent, a water phase and a substantially oil-free sand. The several phases and sand are then separated into distinct layers with the asphaltene-enriched layer being disposed below the point of introduction of the hydrocarbon solvent and the water layer immediately below the asphaltene layer. The sand settles to the bottom of the water layer. A deasphalted-oil enriched solvent layer forms above the point of introduction of the aqueous pulp.

Addition of Granulated Carriers During Mixing

J.A. Bichard; U.S. Patent 3,153,625; October 20, 1964; assigned to Esso Research and Engineering Company describes an integrated process where in an initial operation, the concentration of the bitumen is increased on a certain quantity of sand and then this bitumen-rich sand is handled in a coking operation such as a fluid type coking operation. The carrier particles or granulated carriers may be nonporous as for example stones, but are preferably a hydrocarbon adsorbent as for example coke particles such as are secured in a fluid coking operation. In essence, the operation comprises mixing the carrier which preferably comprises coke particles with the tar sands which mixture is then treated with an optimum amount of water and mixed so as to cause separation of oil-free sands and the enrichment of the remaining sands. Figure 3.7a illustrates the process. Tar sands as mined are introduced into a shearing-mixing stage or zone 3 of the sand separation phase by means of line 1. Water is introduced by means of line 2 and mixed with the sands. This water may be introduced directly into the shearing-mixing zone 3. As a specific example, the composition of the sand introduced into zone 3 comprises 6% by weight connate water, 15% by weight of bitumen, 80% by weight of sand and 5% clay. The clay content varies from 0 to 30% in these sands but, in the specific example given, the clay comprises 5% by weight of the total.

The tar sands as mined are mixed with granulated particles, preferably coke particles secured from a fluid coking operation, which are introduced by means of line 12. While it is preferred that these coke particles be mixed with the tar sands prior to the introduction of the water, it is possible to add the granulated particles also by means of line 13 after the addition of the water. Under certain conditions, it may also be desirable to introduce the granulated particles directly into mixing zone 3 by means of line 14.

The mixing operation in zone 3 is carried out under conditions where a shearing thrust is imparted to the sands being mixed with the added water. Under these conditions, substantially oil-free sands separate and the entire mixture is passed into the second stage or zone of the sand separation phase which comprises a mechanical separation zone 5. The sands are introduced into zone 5 by means of line 4.

This mechanical separation zone may comprise any suitable mechanical means for separating the substantially oil-free sands from the bitumen-rich sands. For example, the mixture introduced by means of line 4 may be sieved in order to separate the oil-free sand which oil-free sand is removed by means of line 11. The bitumen enriched sands and granulated particles in a plastic physical state are removed by means of line 6 and passed into the second phase of the integrated process which preferably comprises a thermal operation, such as a fluid coking operation. This second phase, however, may comprise a solvent treating operation of the bitumen enriched sands. Stages 3 and 5 are preferably conducted at temperatures in the range from 32° to 160°F., preferably at temperatures in the range from 50° to 90°F. It is preferred that zone 7 comprise a fluid coking operation such as described in U.S. Patent 2,881,130.

The effectiveness of the technique for the separation of oil-free sand and the resulting production of bitumen-enriched sand in the initial phase is illustrated in Figure 3.7b. Referring to Figure 3.7b, the amount of water added is plotted along the abscissa and the amount of sand removed plotted along the ordinate. The connate water of the sand in Figure 3.7b is 7%. In all cases, the sand removed was substantially completely free from oil. It is apparent from Figure 3.7b, that when less than 40% of water is added, no oil-free sand separated where when the water added exceeded 40% by weight, the amount of sand removed rose rapidly to a point in excess of 65 to 75% bitumen-free sand.

Thus, the remaining 35 to 40% of the sand contains the total amount of oil originally present on the total sand. As the water addition is increased, the amount of oil-free sand recovered

FIGURE 3.7: SEPARATION PROCESS EMPLOYING GRANULATED CARRIERS TO OBTAIN BITUMEN-RICH SANDS

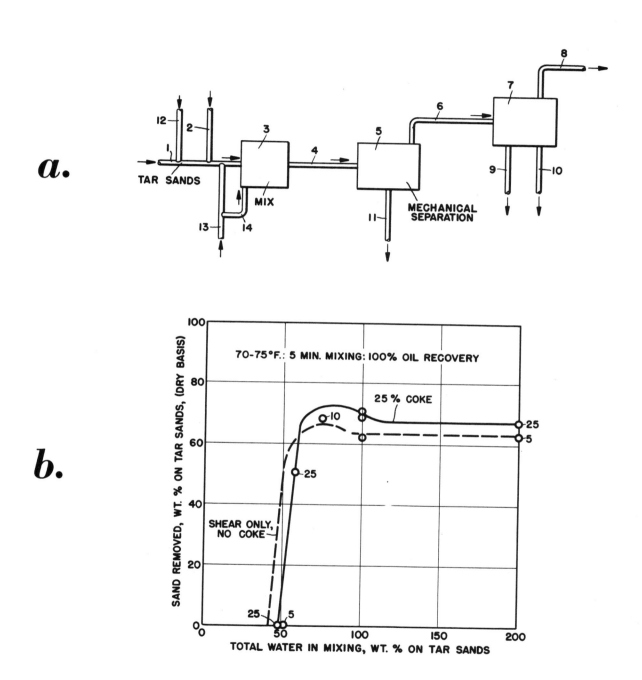

Source: J.A. Bichard; U.S. Patent 3,153,625; October 20, 1964

decreases somewhat. Thus, it is preferred that the amount of water added in the process be in the range from 40 to 400% of water, preferably in the range from 50 to 100% of water by weight based upon the tar sands being processed and that the preferred temperature be 50° to 90°F. It is also noted that, when utilizing approximately 25% of coke particles (8 to 14 mesh), increased quantities of oil-free sand were removed.

The process is illustrated by the following example. In operation A, the mined tar sands were mixed with water and handled in a manner as described. Operation B was similar to that with respect to operation A except that approximately 8 unit weights of coke particles were added per 25 unit weights of dry tar sands. The temperature at which the operation was carried out was in the range from 70° to 75°F. The results of these operations are as follows.

Operation	A	B
	Mixing with Water	Mixing With a Carrier and Water
Tar sands, units	25	25
Water, units	12	18
Carrier, units (Coke 8–14 mesh)		8
Clean dry sand recovered, units	12.5	17.5

From the above it is apparent that the effectiveness of operation B was 50% greater than operation A since 17.5 weight units of oil-free sand was removed as compared to 12.5 weight units in operation A.

Vacuum Separation Technique

R.A. Hemstock; U.S. Patent 3,139,397; June 30, 1964; assigned to Esso Research and Engineering Company describes a recovery technique which employs a vacuum separation step. The following examples illustrate the process.

Example 1: A 100 g. of a sample of tar sands (dry basis) containing 7 wt. percent connate water and 13 wt. percent oil was mixed with 30 wt. percent water for half a minute to effect disintegration of the tar sands into sand and very small oil particles distributed in water. This was carried out at 45°F. The mixture was transferred to a flask containing excess water and the pressure was reduced. When the pressure reached 200 mm. of mercury, oil floated to the surface. At lower pressure, increasing amounts of oil floated to the surface. Complete separation was obtained, with clean sand remaining at the bottom of the vessel, in less than half a minute from starting the evacuation. Very small oil particles that floated to the water surface immediately coalesced, forming large agglomerates, thus reducing the water content of the oil mass. These agglomerates were skimmed off the water.

Example 2: The sand reduction in this operation can be compared with that from mixing with water and mechanical separation. This is shown in the table on the following page. From the table it is apparent that a better oil recovery is secured in a shorter time period when utilizing a vacuum separation technique.

198

Tar Sands Separation Processes

Good Sand Reduction is Accomplished at Lower Temperatures and with Lower Amounts of Water in Premixing and Minimum Premixing Time

(Tar Sands Contained 7 Wt. Percent Water, 13 Wt. Percent Oil)

Process	This Process	Sand Reduction [3]
Temperature, °F	45	70
Premixing Time, Minutes	0.5	5
Premixing Water, Wt. percent [1]	30	75
Sand Removed, Wt. percent [1][2]	66	80
Oil Recovery, Wt. percent	90	88

[1] On tar sands (dry basis).
[2] Also contains oil not recovered in oil phase.
[3] Use of mechanical separation at atmospheric pressure.

Use of Shearing-Mixing Zone to Obtain Bitumen-Rich Sand

J.A. Bichard and J.W. Wunder; U.S. Patent 3,159,562; December 1, 1964; assigned to Esso Research and Engineering Company describe an integrated process for the recovery of oil from tar sands where in one operation or an initial phase, at relatively low temperatures, the process comprises removing substantially oil-free sand from a quantity of tar sands as mined, thereby increasing the concentration of the tar or bitumen on the remaining sands. The bitumen-rich sand is then further handled in a secondary phase utilizing steam and relatively high temperatures in order to produce an oil phase containing a relatively small amount of sand.

Referring to Figure 3.8 which illustrates the process, tar sands as mined are introduced into a shearing-mixing stage or zone 3 of the sand separation phase by means of line 1. Water is introduced by means of line 2 and mixed with the sands. This water may be introduced directly into the shearing-mixing zone 3. As a specific example, the composition of the sand introduced into zone 3 comprises 6% by weight connate water, 15% by weight of bitumen, 80% by weight of sand and 5% clay. The clay content varies from 0 to 30% in these sands but, in the specific example given, the clay comprises 5% by weight of the total.

The mixing operation in zone 3 is carried out under conditions where a shearing thrust is imparted to the sands being mixed with the added water. Under these conditions, substantially oil-free sands separate and the entire mixture is then passed into the second stage or zone of the sand separation phase which preferably comprises a mechanical separation zone 5. The sands are introduced into zone 5 by means of line 4.

This mechanical separation zone may comprise any suitable mechanical means for separating the substantially oil-free sands from the bitumen-rich sands. For example, the mixture introduced by means of line 4 may be sieved in order to separate the oil-free sand which oil-free sand is removed by means of line 11. The bitumen enriched sands in a plastic physical state are removed by means of line 6 and passed into the second phase of the integrated

FIGURE 3.8: TWO PHASE SEPARATION PROCESS

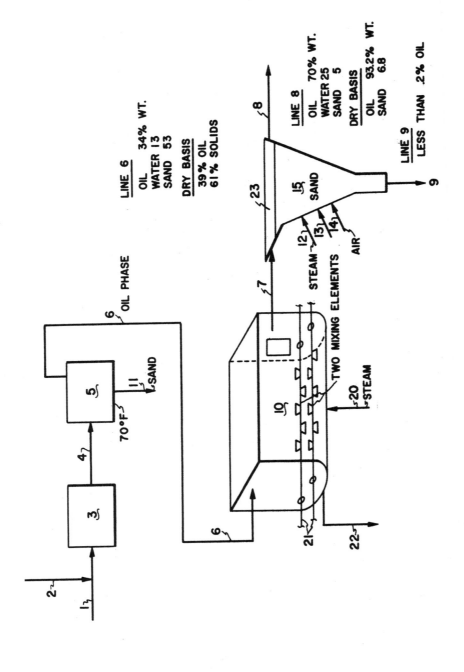

LINE 6
OIL   34% WT.
WATER 13
SAND   53

DRY BASIS
39% OIL
61% SOLIDS

LINE 8
OIL   70% WT.
WATER 25
SAND   5

DRY BASIS
OIL   93.2% WT.
SAND   6.8

LINE 9
LESS THAN .2% OIL

Source: J.A. Bichard and J.W. Wunder; U.S. Patent 3,159,562; December 1, 1964

process which comprises a relatively high temperature operation. Stages 3 and 5 are preferably conducted at temperatures in the range from 32° to 110°F., preferably at temperatures in the range from 50° to 90°F. It is also preferred that the amount of water utilized in stages 3 and 5 be in the range from 40 to 400% of water by weight, preferably in the range from 40 to 150% of water by weight based upon the tar sands being processed.

Under the conditions of the process, the oil phase removed from stage 5 by means of line 6 contains from 30 to 50% of oil. This phase is introduced into separation zone 10 which preferably comprises a pug mill where steam is injected by means of line 20. Zone 10 may be any desirable type of pug mill as, for example, one which contains mixing elements 21 at the bottom with paddles in order to remove the sand countercurrent to the introduction of the feed stream. The sand stream is removed by means of line 22.

The temperature in zone 10 is maintained in the range from 140° to 210°F., preferably at a temperature in the range from 185° to 195°F. The amount of steam introduced into zone 10 is adjusted so that there exists in this zone 20 to 160% of water, preferably 30 to 100% of water by weight based upon the oil present. The mixed oil phase is withdrawn from pug mill 10 by means of line 7 and introduced into a separation zone 15. In this zone an oil phase 23 formed on the top which is removed by means of line 8. Sand collects in the lower area of zone or cell 15 and is removed by means of line 9. In accordance with this example, steam and/or water is introduced into cell 15 by means of lines 12 and 13 and air by means of line 14 in order to bring the sand in a fluidized condition. A plurality of addition points may be used. In order to further illustrate the process the following example is given.

Example: In one operation, a sand containing 6% by weight of connate water, 15% by weight of bitumen, 80% by weight of sand and 5% clay was processed in zones 3 and 5 at a temperature of 70°F. in a manner as described. The oil phase removed from zone 5 comprised 34% by weight of oil, 13% by weight of water, and 53% by weight of sand. This feed was introduced into zone 10 at a temperature of 190°F. under conditions where approximately 40 to 100% by weight of water is present.

The streams were then introduced into zone 15 maintained at a temperature of 190°F. and an oil phase removed by means of line 8 and a sand phase by means of line 9. Under these conditions of operation, the oil phase removed by means of line 8 comprised 70% by weight of oil, 25% by weight of water, and 5% by weight of sand on a wet basis. The oil content was 93.2% by weight, while the sand was 6.8% by weight on a dry basis. In the same operation, the sand removed by means of line 9 contained less than 0.2% by weight of oil. Thus, overall, the process is concerned with a two-phase operation where in the first phase tar sands are subjected to shearing-mixing agglomeration action at relatively low temperatures, and in a second phase the oil phase is treated at a relatively high temperature utilizing injected steam and air. Under these conditions of operation, the oil phase is relatively pure and substantially no oil is lost in the sand phase.

In related work J.A. Bichard, R.M. Butler, J.R. McEachern and J.W. Wunder; U.S. Patent 3,152,979; Oct. 13, 1964; assigned to Esso Research and Engineering Co. describe an integrated process for the recovery of oil from tar sands, which utilizes a a shearing-mixing stage and then employs a particular technique in a secondary separation stage. In the latter stage, air is utilized for the more efficient separation of the oil phase.

Hydrogenation of Emulsion

E.W. White; U.S. Patent 3,291,717; December 13, 1966; assigned to Cities Service Athabasca, Inc., Imperial Oil Limited, Atlantic Richfield Company and Royalite Oil Company Limited has found that water can be effectively separated from bituminous emulsions by a relatively mild hydrogenation of the emulsion. Further, such a mild hydrogenation serves as a convenient point for further hydrogenating and separating the bitumen to more useful products such as those having an API gravity above 15 or above 20. Hydrogenation of the bituminous emulsion of froth destroys many of the surfactants and reduces the specific gravity, viscosity and surface tension of the bitumen. Also it is believed that hydrogen sulfide released from hydrogenated sulfur compounds in the emulsion decreases the pH of the mixture which also tends to favor separation.

The process comprises feeding the products of a heated bituminous emulsion to a reactor maintained under suitable hydrogen pressure and reaction conditions for reacting hydrogen with such feed and particularly the bitumen when it is desired to effect hydrocracking in addition to merely breaking the emulsion. The major portion of the water vaporizes in the reactor whereas the bitumen remains in the liquid phase. During hydrogenation much of the surfactant content of the emulsion is destroyed. The oil is then separated from water by various techniques such as cooling the effluent from the reactor to a temperature below about 400°F. and flashing to reduced pressure.

The hydrogen which is supplied to the reaction system can be substantially pure hydrogen or of a gaseous stream containing other constituents such as carbon oxides, nitrogen, methane, ethane, and steam. The hydrogen-containing gas introduced to the reaction zone is adjusted to provide sufficient hydrogen for reaction of about 600 scf per barrel of bitumen feed to about 1,500 scf/bbl. of bitumen feed. Preferably, the hydrogen consumption for hydrocracking of the bitumen is from about 800 scf/bbl. to 1,000 scf/bbl. of bitumen feed. When it is principally desired to merely make a separation of the emulsion into the oil and water phase with minimum cracking of the feed, the hydrogen consumption of the feed can vary from about 600 scf to about 800 scf per barrel of bitumen in the feed.

The hydrogen partial pressure in the reactor can vary over a wide range such as that from about 800 psig to 2,000 psig and preferably from about 1,000 psig to 1,500 psig. The total pressure in the reactor will be substantially greater than that of hydrogen, particularly due to vaporization of water in the reactor although the total pressure preferably varies from about 1,000 psig to about 3,500 psig. The temperature in the reactor can vary from about 700°F. to about 900°F. and preferably from about 775°F. to about 880°F. Since water is the more easily vaporized major constituent of the feed and for the most part vaporizes in the reactor, the lower and intermediate portions of the reactor are enriched with oil.

Hydrogenation of the bitumen is in the liquid phase, preferably without the addition of a catalyst. However, conventional hydrogenation catalysts can be employed. After hydrogenation the water is separated from the oil by cooling and flashing the effluent. Water can then be recovered as overhead vapor or condensed as a bottom liquid layer, depending on temperature and pressure of the effluent.

Hydraulic Cyclone

M.R. Tek and S.J. Marwil; U.S. Patent 2,910,424; October 27, 1959; assigned to Phillips Petroleum Company describe the use of a hydraulic cyclone in the separation and recovery of oil from oil sands.

The process comprises introducing a suspension or slurry of the oil sand into a hydraulic cyclone, subjecting the slurry to the forces developed in the cyclone, withdrawing a stream consisting essentially of sand from one end of the cyclone, and withdrawing a stream of oil and water from the other end or base portion of the cyclone. The stream of oil and water is then processed for the recovery of the oil. The following example illustrates the process.

Example: 120 pounds per minute of Athabaska oil sand having an oil content of about 14 percent by weight is crushed to the extent that the particle size was less than 60 mesh. The crushed sand is introduced into a mixing tank agitated with a motor driven stirrer and is there mixed with 60 gallons per minute of water introduced at a temperature of 170°F. to produce a slurry or suspension containing about 19.3 percent by weight of solids. 80 cc per minute of Aerosol MA are introduced into the mixing tank to aid in the formation of the suspension or slurry. The residence time in the tank is about 21 minutes.

The suspension or slurry is pumped at a rate of 66 gallons per minute and a pressure of 60 pounds per square inch gauge through a three-quarter inch i.d. inlet orifice and tangentially into the base portion of a four inch diameter cyclone with a ten inch cone section which gradually and uniformly tapers to a five-eighth inch underflow or apex nozzle. The cyclone has a three-quarter inch i.d. overflow orifice axially positioned in the base portion or feed section. A stream containing about 3 percent by weight oil and about 97 percent by weight water together with a small amount of finely divided sand is removed through the overflow orifice. The remainder of the slurry introduced into the cyclone is removed through the underflow or apex orifice.

The overflow stream of oil and water is filtered to remove the sand and then passed to a phase separation vessel where a surface active agent of the "emulsion breaker" type is introduced at a rate of about 30 cc per minute. The surface active agent employed is the type G-2854 produced and sold by the Atlas Powder Company. A stream of oil in an amount of about 15 pounds per minute or 900 pounds per hour is recovered from the phase separator.

Sound Wave Induced Separation

A.G. Bodine; U.S. Patent 3,123,546; March 3, 1964 describes a process and apparatus for separating the petroleum constituent from tar-sand mixtures by use of high intensity sound waves.

One typical treatment apparatus in accordance with the process constitutes a batch container, with the walls functioning as a sound wave generation and/or transmission system. A liquid may simply be added to the tar-sand in the container. The added water, or other liquid, is apparently helpful in that it provides a fluid medium of intermediate density and impedance. It is additionally very helpful and important in that it very greatly increases the degree of acoustic coupling between the sound wave source, e.g., the walls of the container, and the mixed sand and petroleum material. In the operation of the process, assuming the tar-sand material to be placed in a container, and intense sound waves passed through, the oil quickly migrates to the surface of the sand.

With liquid added to the batch, the material disintegrates as the sound wave action drives the liquid into the material, and the oil leaves the sand more completely, undoubtedly as a result of the sound waves being transmitted more effectively to and through the mass. The oil rises to the surface of the water (if water is used as the added liquid), and the sand collects in the bottom of the container. The sand settlement occurs no matter what the nature of the added liquid may be. Complete details of the apparatus are provided.

Mechanical Separation Technique

R.T. Eyre; U.S. Patent 2,790,750; April 30, 1957 describes a process which involves mulling the bituminous sand with a minor amount of water until the pulp has reached a certain state. The pulp is then vigorously mixed with a large volume of water and the mixture is fed into an inclined conduit which functions as the separating zone, the conduit being inclined at an angle of 28° to 35°. The dispersion of mulled tar sands in water is fed at a low temperature, below 50°F., into the conduit which is maintained filled with liquid, and the conduit is subjected to vibrations to aid the flow of material down the inclined bottom of the conduit. This causes the mixture to separate effectively into a lower layer of sand particles, an intermediate layer of oil and an upper water layer containing the clay or silt which was present in the tar sands charged. The lower layer of sand is trapped and drawn off, while the oil and water layers are also separately withdrawn from the separation zone.

NONAQUEOUS PROCESSES

Use of Soluble Oils

A process described by F.H. Poettmann and J.T. Kelly; U.S. Patent 3,392,105; July 9, 1968; assigned to Marathon Oil Company comprises contacting the oil sands with "soluble oils," then diluting the tar sand-soluble oil mixture with a solvent-diluent, and separating the sand from the resulting relatively low viscosity solution. The term "soluble oil" refers to solutions of surfactants in nonpolar solvents with the ability to emulsify water.

The process involves a combination of separation and dilution steps which are to be carried out aboveground. In the process, comminuted oil sands are contacted with a soluble oil to form a slurry in a mixer unit. The slurry is then mixed with a solvent-diluent and separated.

This process is illustrated with reference to Figure 3.9 where conveyer 1 passes comminuted oil sands 2 into hopper 3. Comminuted oil sands 2 pass through star feeder 4, or other suitable valving mechanism, into slurry preparation tank 5. Soluble oil from storage tank 6 passes through valve 7 in line 8 to slurry preparation tank 5 where it is rapidly mixed with oil sands 2 by stirring devices 9. Normally, from at least about 0.1 to 10, preferably at least from about 0.5 to 15, volumes of soluble oil per volume of oil sand produce a desired slurry.

FIGURE 3.9: EXTRACTION PROCESS USING SOLUBLE OILS

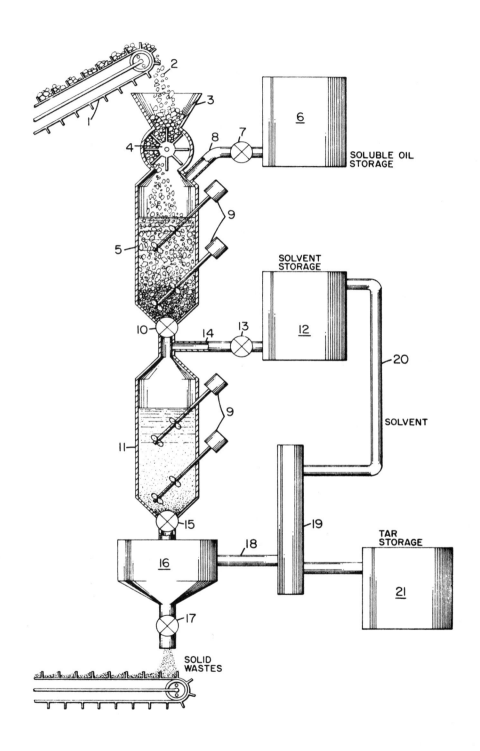

Source: F.H. Poettmann and J.T. Kelly; U.S. Patent 3,392,105; July 9, 1968

A mixture of four parts tar sand and one part of a soluble oil comprising straight run gasoline, isopropanol (about 4%), and water (about 25%) creates a loose slurry on mixing. After a slurry of suitable viscosity, preferably from about 500 to about 50,000 cp., is prepared, it passes through valve 10 into dilution tank 11 where it is mixed with solvent. Solvent from solvent storage 12 passes through valve 13 in line 14 into dilution tank 11 where it serves to further reduce the viscosity of the slurry. A mixture of four parts of the above loose slurry and one part straight run gasoline gives a solution which appears to have a viscosity approximating that of kerosene.

Normally, from at least about 0.5 to 15 volumes of solvent are added per volume of slurry. The amount of solvent added depends upon the viscosity of the solvent, the temperature of the solvent and the slurry, etc. Solvents such as straight run gasoline, liquefied petroleum gases, xylene, isopropanol, dimethyl formamide, furfural, phenol, etc., can be used in this process. When diluted to a desired degree, for example, from about 30 to about 1,000 centipoises, the diluted mixtures pass through valve 15 into separator 16. Separator 16 is depicted as a cyclone separator but can be any desired liquid-solid separator. On separation, the sand and other solid wastes pass through valve 17 to a waste disposal means. The liquids pass from separator 16 through line 18 into distillation tower 19 where the light, low-boiling solvent is distilled from the mixture. The solvent is then recycled through line 20 to solvent storage 12. The bituminous bottoms are then removed to storage tank 1. From storage, the bituminous materials are transported to market, etc.

Addition of Hydrocarbon Diluent

W.H. Price; U.S. Patent 2,965,557; December 20, 1960; assigned to Cities Service Research and Development Company describes a process by which crude oil and silt may be separated from bituminous sands with essentially no loss of crude oil with waste sand.

According to the process, crude oil and silt may be separated from bituminous sands by mixing the bituminous sand with a small amount of hydrocarbon diluent and introducing the mixture into a separation zone in which a lower fluidized layer of sand and an upper liquid layer of oil and silt are formed. Additional hydrocarbon diluent is introduced into the lower layer of sand to aid in the separation of the original mixture into these upper and lower layers and each of the layers is separately removed from the separation zone.

Referring to Figure 3.10, bituminous sand is introduced into a feed hopper 11 as indicated by an arrow 12. The bituminous sands treated according to the process are bituminous sands which include crude oil and silt in addition to the coarser sand particles.

Prior to introducing bituminous sand to a separation zone it is generally preferable to first mix the sand with liquid hydrocarbon diluent in order to obtain a slurry which is easily transferable to the separation zone. Such mixing may be done in any suitable manner such as by passing the tar sand from the feed hopper 11 into a mixing tank 14 by a conventional screw conveyor 15 driven by a motor 16.

In order to avoid unnecessary loss of valuable vaporous hydrocarbons the mixing tank 14 is preferably closed. In order to still further reduce the amount of hydrocarbon vapors escaping via the feed hopper and mixing tank, a relatively small amount of seal oil is preferably

FIGURE 3.10: TAR SAND SEPARATION PROCESS EMPLOYING HYDROCARBON DILUENT

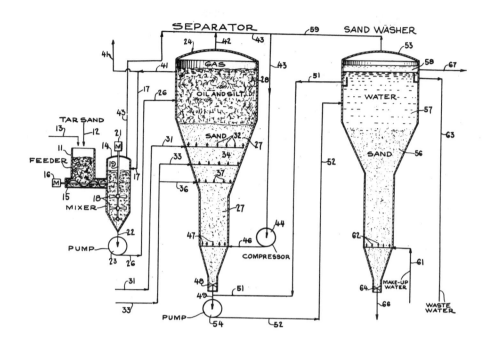

Source: W.H. Price; U.S. Patent 2,965,557; December 20, 1960

introduced with the sand feed as indicated by an arrow 13. Introduction of seal oil into the feed hopper with the sand feed prevents the escape of any substantial amounts of hydrocarbon vapors from the mixing tank or feed hopper. Such seal oil may be used in any desired amounts but relatively small quantities such as between about 1 and about 5 volume percent of total feed usually suffice to prevent escape of hydrocarbon vapors. Suitable seal oils may cover a wide variety of hydrocarbon oils, but oils of intermediate weight such as No.2 furnace oil are preferred.

The hydrocarbon diluent with which the sand is preferably mixed to form a slurry prior to introduction into the separation zone is introduced into the mixing tank 14 through a conduit 17. The hydrocarbon diluent thus introduced may, if desired, be fresh diluent such as that described below but for convenience is preferably a recycle stream comprising a portion of the mixture of crude oil, hydrocarbon diluent and silt withdrawn from the separation zone as a product of the process as described below.

The recycle stream of hydrocarbon oil and silt introduced into the mixing tank 14 through conduit 17 is thoroughly mixed with the tar and by suitable means such as mixing paddles 18 carried on a shaft 19 and driven by a motor 21. A slurry of tar sand and diluent is withdrawn from the lower portion of the mixing tank 14 through a conduit 22 and passed by a pump 23 to a separator 24 via a conduit 26. In the separator 24 the slurry of tar sand and diluent separates to form a lower fluidized layer or bed 27 of sand and an upper liquid layer 28 of oil and silt. Liquid hydrocarbon diluent is introduced into the separator 24 through conduits 31, 33 and 36 and is injected into the sand bed 27 at a plurality of points as by suitable sets of nozzles 32, 34 and 37.

The hydrocarbon diluent injected into the sand bed 27 through conduits 31, 33 and 36 aids in separating oil and silt from the sand and also serves to fluidize the sand bed. A mixture of this diluent together with the crude oil and silt separated from the sand forms the upper layer of oil and silt 28 while sand which is substantially free of crude oil forms the lower fluidized layer or bed 27.

The sand bed 27 is a conventional bed of fluidized solids and has physical characteristics which are generally similar to those of beds of fluidized solids used in other processes such as catalytic cracking, fluid coking, etc. The fluid characteristics of the bed 27 are not substantially altered by the use of a liquid fluidizing medium rather than the more conventional gaseous fluidizing medium. The liquid fluidizing medium may be passed upwardly through the bed 27 with any suitable apparent velocity such as between about 2 and about 10 ft./sec.

The hydrocarbon diluent with which the bituminous sand is contacted in the separation zone should have a specific gravity substantially less than 1.0 and preferably has a gravity between about 55° and about 65° API. Suitable diluents are, for instance, those having boiling point ranges between about 100° and about 400° F.

Oil and silt is removed from the separator 24 through a conduit 41. From the conduit 41 a portion of the oil and silt passes to the mixing tank 14 through the conduit 17 as described above in order to slurry the incoming tar sand feed while the remainder is removed from the process through conduit 41 as a product of the process. The portion of the oil and silt removed through conduit 41 may be treated in any suitable manner for the recovery of valuable commercial products therefrom. For instance the oil and silt mixture may be treated directly as by fluid coking or some or all of the silt may be separated from the oil by suitable means, such as settling tanks prior to treating the oil by suitable processes such as coking, visbreaking, hydrogenation, hydro or catalytic cracking, reforming, etc.

The mixture of oil and silt removed through the conduit 41 may be subjected to further treatment as desired to produce commercial products. Gaseous hydrocarbons present in the crude oil or diluent rise to the top of the separator 24 and may be removed through a conduit 42. Likewise, vaporous hydrocarbons which accumulate in the mixing tank 14 are removed through a conduit 43.

In order to further aid in fluidizing the sand layer as well as to insure more complete separation of hydrocarbons from sand, gaseous material is preferably injected into the lower portion of the sand layer in the separation zone. Gas injected in this manner may comprise any suitable gaseous material such as nitrogen, hydrogen, helium, etc. from an appropriate source, but preferably comprises normally gaseous hydrocarbons such as those removed from the upper portions of the separation zone and mixing tank through conduits 42 and 43. Such gas, in addition to aiding in fluidizing the layer of sand, also serves to at least partially strip the sand of entrained hydrocarbons.

While contact with hydrocarbon diluent as described above is usually sufficient to remove substantially all crude oil from the sand, such diluent itself frequently becomes entrained with or adsorbed on the sand at least to some extent and at least a portion of such entrained or adsorbed diluent may be removed by stripping with suitable gaseous material as just described. The gases in the conduits 42 and 43 are, therefore, passed through the conduit 43 to a compressor 44 and from the compressor 44 are passed through a conduit 46 into the lower portion of the separator 24 where they are injected into the lower portion of the sand bed 27 by suitable means such as nozzles 47.

The gases thus injected into the lower portion of the sand bed through the nozzles 47 serve to at least partially strip the sand of any entrained or adsorbed hydrocarbons and also assist in fluidizing the sand bed. Relatively clean stripped sand is removed from the separator 24 through a valve 48 and a conduit 49.

Although the sand withdrawn from the lower layer of the separation zone through conduit 49 is substantially free of crude oil, such sand, even though it has been stripped as described above, contains small amounts of hydrocarbon diluent which it is usually desirable to recover. Also, in the event stripping gas is not employed, such sand will, of course, contain somewhat greater amounts of hydrocarbon diluent. Such hydrocarbon diluent is preferably recovered by passing the withdrawn sand to a sand washing zone in which it is contacted with water to form in the washing zone a lower fluidized layer of sand, an intermediate layer of water and an upper liquid layer of hydrocarbons which usually consist essentially of hydrocarbon diluent carried from the separation zone with the sand as described above. Sand withdrawn from the separation zone is conveniently transported to the washing zone in the form of a slurry. Such a slurry is preferably obtained by mixing the sand in conduit 49 with water supplied through a conduit 51. The resulting slurry of sand and water is passed through a conduit 52 to a sand washer 53 by a pump 54.

In the sand washer 53 the slurry of sand and water separates into a lower fluidized bed or layer of sand 56, an intermediate layer 57 of water and an upper liquid layer 58 of hydrocarbon liquid. The sand bed 56, like the sand bed 27, is a conventional fluidized solids bed and is preferably fluidized by means of water injected into the bed.

A stream of recycled water is withdrawn from the water layer and passed through conduit 51 to form the slurry of sand and water as described above. Any hydrocarbon vapors which accumulate in the sand washer 53 are removed through a conduit 59 and passed through the conduit 43 for use in stripping sand in the separator 24 as described above. Fresh makeup water is preferably introduced to the sand washer 53 through a conduit 61 and injected into the lower portion of the sand bed 56 through nozzles 62 in order to fluidize the sand bed and also to aid in stripping hydrocarbons from the sand. Excess water is removed from the sand washer through a conduit 63 while clean sand substantially free of hydrocarbon material is removed through a valve 64 and a conduit 66. Hydrocarbon liquid which has been separated from the sand in the sand washer is removed from the hydrocarbon layer 58 through a conduit 67 for use in any suitable manner.

Example: An Alberta tar sand having the properties shown in the table on the following page is fed to the feed hopper 14 at the rate 100,000 barrels per day (b.p.d.).

Composition and Properties of Bituminous Sand Feed

Composition of bituminous sand:

Water, vol. percent	2.1
Mineral matter, vol. percent	82.8
Crude oil, vol. percent	15.1

Density, lb./ft.^{3} 125

Composition of crude oil:

Carbon, vol. percent	83.3
Hydrogen, vol. percent	10.4
Sulfur, vol. percent	4.7
Nitrogen, vol. percent	0.4
Oxygen, vol. percent	1.2
Carbon/hydrogen ratio	8.0
Specific gravity at 77°F.	1.007

Sieve analysis of mineral matter after ignition
retained on:

50 mesh, wt. percent	18.3
80 mesh, wt. percent	49.9
100 mesh, wt. percent	13.3
200 mesh, wt. percent	11.0
Passing 200 mesh, wt. percent	7.5

No. 2 furnace oil is also added to the feed hopper as seal oil. Gasoline having a gravity of 59° API is added to the separator 24 through conduit 31 and nozzles 32 at the rate of 130,000 b.p.d. as hydrocarbon diluent. Hydrocarbon diluent consisting of gasoline having a gravity of 60° API and a boiling range of 125° to 350°F. is also added to the separator 24 through conduit 33 and nozzles 34 at the rate of 100,000 b.p.d. and through conduits 33 and 36 and nozzles 37 at the rate of 70,000 b.p.d. Liquid hydrocarbons withdrawn from the upper hydrocarbon layer of the sand washer 53 have a gravity of 60° API.

In a continuation of the above work W.H. Price; U.S. Patent 3,070,541; December 25, 1962; assigned to Cities Service Research and Development Company has found that it is desirable to remove some or all of the silt prior to passing the tar sand mixture to the processing unit. Thus, for instance, if the mixture is to be passed to a coking unit removal of a majority of the silt before passing the mixture to the coker will substantially lessen the load on the coking unit and will also make a larger proportion of the coke produced available for supplying heat or for other purposes.

In the process, a mixture containing crude oil and silt separated from bituminous sand in a sand separation zone and preferably containing liquid hydrocarbon diluent is passed to a first silt settling zone wherein it is allowed to settle to form a lower layer of silt, crude oil and hydrocarbon diluent and an upper layer of hydrocarbon diluent and crude oil. The upper layer is withdrawn from the first silt settling zone and preferably passed to a fluid coking unit for conversion of crude oil into liquid hydrocarbon products and coke while the lower layer containing silt is withdrawn from the first silt settling zone and passed to a second silt settling zone. Additional hydrocarbon diluent is introduced into the second silt settling zone, preferably together with the silt, and the resulting mixture is allowed to settle to form a lower layer of silt substantially free of crude oil and an upper layer of hydrocarbon diluent substantially free of silt. Hydrocarbon diluent is preferably withdrawn from this upper layer and recycled as the original hydrocarbon diluent contained in the mixture of silt and crude oil passed to the first silt settling zone. Silt is withdrawn from the second silt settling zone and passed to a silt washing zone to remove the remainder of the hydrocarbon diluent therefrom.

In the silt washing zone the silt is contacted with water to form a lower layer containing silt and substantially free of hydrocarbon diluent, an intermediate layer of water and an upper layer of hydrocarbon diluent. Silt is withdrawn from the lower layer of the silt washing zone and discarded while water is withdrawn from the intermediate layer and hydrocarbon diluent is withdrawn from the upper layer of the silt washing zone and recycled with the hydrocarbon diluent from the second silt settling zone. A portion of the liquid hydrocarbon product from the fluid coking zone is passed to the second silt settling zone as fresh hydrocarbon diluent, while the remainder of the liquid product from the fluid coking zone may be used in any suitable manner. Likewise the coke formed in the coking zone may be disposed of in any suitable manner.

J.D. Frame, J.D. Haney and E.W. White; U.S. Patent 3,041,267; June 26, 1962; assigned to Cities Service Research and Development Company describe a process which mixes the tar sand with a hydrocarbon diluent in sufficient amount to form a pumpable slurry. This is accomplished by utilizing the diluent in a volume ratio of tar (bitumen) to diluent of from 1:2 to 1:5. The tar sand slurry after gentle mixing to insure substantially complete solution of the tar or bitumen in the diluent and recycled oil, is delivered to the first stage in a two step separating and disengaging treatment.

In the first stage where separation and disengagement of tar and diluent from sand is accomplished, the sand diluent mixture is eased gently into a water wash tank that includes at the inlet end an inclined surface. The sand, in the presence of water moves at a slow rate, less than the rate of gravitational free flow down the inclined or sloping surface during which movement a substantial portion of the diluent tar mixture is disengaged and separated from the sand particles. As the sand moves down the sloped surface it assumes a natural angle of repose at which time, and while in movement, the sand is gently fluffed or fluidized by water. The fluidization of the sand is conducted in such a manner as to continuously move the sand away from the area of the bottom of the inclined surface along the bottom of the wash tank to a sand outlet. In this fluidized zone the second stage of the disengagement and separation of hydrocarbons from sand is accomplished.

The gentle fluffing of the sand in this stage effects a substantially complete disengagement of hydrocarbons (diluent tar mix) from the sand particles. After disengagement a hydrocarbon water mixture is withdrawn from the water wash tank and delivered to conventional separatory means with separated water being recycled to the wash tank. The recovered oil product after separation is processed according to conventional hydrocarbon processes such as hydrocracking, visbreaking or similar processing techniques.

Use of Propane

R.C. West; U.S. Patent 3,131,141; April 28, 1964; assigned to Jersey Production Research Company describes a process for the recovery of oil from tar sands utilizing a process which eliminates the use of water, thereby eliminating the problems of sludge separation, oil-water emulsions. An integrated operation is utilized employing a hydrocarbon fraction in the gas oil boiling range and a light hydrocarbon such as propane and butane, where by a particular technique the bitumen is recovered and the gas oil and light hydrocarbon efficiently recovered.

Referring to Figure 3.11, bituminous sands at atmospheric temperatures are introduced into heating zone 1 by means of feed line 2. In zone 1 the sands are heated to a temperature preferably in the range from 100° to 140°F., such as about 120°F. These sands are then introduced into the upper area of a first countercurrent treating zone 4 by means of line 3. In essence, countercurrent treating zone 4 comprises a bituminous sand solvent contactor maintained at a pressure sufficient to keep hydrocarbons in the liquid phase. A relatively heavy solvent which comprises a conventional light gas oil is introduced into the lower end of zone 4 by means of line 5. Any suitable contacting or distributing means may be employed in zone 4.

FIGURE 3.11:   NONAQUEOUS PROCESS EMPLOYING PROPANE

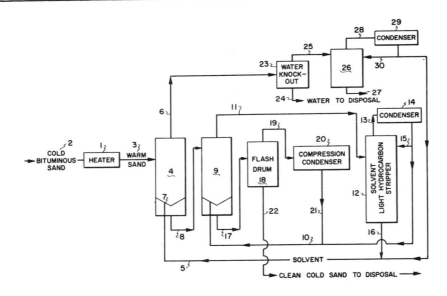

Source: R.C. West; U.S. Patent 3,131,141; April 28, 1964

The solvent is preferably a gas oil boiling in the range from about 400° to 700°F., preferably in the range from 425° to 600°F. The API gravity is in the range from about 28° to 35°, preferably about 32° API, while the Saybolt viscosity at 100°F. is in the range from 60 to 100 seconds, preferably about 80 seconds.

A bitumen gas oil solution is removed from the top of zone 4 by means of line 6 and handled as hereinafter described. A sand-gas oil mix falls through a screen or separating element 7 and is withdrawn from the bottom of zone 4 by means of line 8. In the operation, the crushed sand is moved forward by a rock pump, screw conveyor, or any suitable means.

This sand-gas oil mix is introduced into the top area of a second countercurrent treating zone 9 by means of line 8. In this zone, the sand is contacted with a light hydrocarbon solvent so as to produce clean sand. A light hydrocarbon solvent such as a liquefied normally gaseous hydrocarbon as, for example, liquid propane or butane is introduced into the bottom of zone 9 by means of line 10. Zone 9 is maintained at a sufficient pressure to keep the liquefied normally gaseous hydrocarbons in the liquid phase. The light gas oil and the light hydrocarbon solvent is removed overhead from zone 9 by means of line 11 and introduced into a light hydrocarbon stripping zone 12. In this zone, the light hydrocarbon, as for example propane, is removed overhead by means of line 13, passed through condenser 14 and recycled to zone 9 by means of line 10. The light gas oil free of propane is removed from the bottom of zone 12 by means of line 16 and recycled to zone 4 by means of line 5.

The sand and light hydrocarbon solvent is removed from the bottom of zone 9 by means of line 17 and passed at a reduced pressure into flash drum 18. Under these conditions, the light hydrocarbon, as for example propane, flashes from the sand and is removed overhead from flash drum 18 by means of line 19. This stream is passed into compression condenser 20 where the propane is liquefied and recycled to the system by means of line 21. Clean sand is withdrawn from flash drum 18 by means of line 22 and withdrawn from the system and subsequently handled as desired.

The bitumen and solvent removed by means of line 6 overhead from initial zone 4 is passed to a water knockout drum 23 where connate water separates and is removed from the system by means of line 24. The solvent plus the bitumen is removed from knock-out drum 23 by means of line 25 and passed to a solvent or light gas oil stripper 26. In this zone, the bitumen is removed as a bottom stream by means of line 27 and further handled as desired, as for example by cracking, coking and the like. The light gas oil solvent is removed overhead by means of line 28, passed through condensing zone 29 and recycled to the system by means of line 5. A portion of this stream may be recycled to zone 26 by means of line 30.

Solvent Extraction

A process described by C.M. Gable, E.A. Duncan, Jr. and E.R. Freitas; U.S. Patent 3,475,318; October 28, 1969; assigned to Shell Oil Company involves extracting tar low in asphaltenes from a tar sand that contains asphaltenes by treating tar sand with a saturated hydrocarbon solvent having from 5 to 9 carbon atoms per molecule and steam stripping the solvent-containing sand after the solvent-tar liquid has been drained off. Steam stripping preferably is accomplished in two stages, the first stage effected by passing steam into a solvent-containing sand bed until just prior to steam breakthrough and the second stage effected by countercurrent contact between a moving bed of sand and a flowing stream of steam.

The process has the obvious advantages of providing deasphalting and extraction in one step which eliminates or greatly simplifies a subsequent flash distilling step in which undesired asphaltenes are removed. This process also has the advantages of not forming water-tar emulsions as found in the recovery of tar by water addition. Large quantities of solvent are not required as in the slurrying operations and only a single solvent is used for product extraction, thereby essentially eliminating the problems arising with complex solvent systems. For example, solvent recovery by steaming is a relatively simple operation and provides a means for substantially complete solvent removal.

Example 1: A tar sand containing 6.2% weight tar having an asphaltene content of about 31% by weight basis tar was extracted with n-heptane, a nonaromatic solvent. The tar sand was placed on a filter, thereby forming a bed initially 9.5 inches deep. A pressure drop of 7.5 psi was maintained across the bed by means of applied vacuum. When extracted in two stages with n-heptane at a solvent to original tar ratio of 4.2 per stage, a tar recovery of 65% was obtained. A similar two-stage extraction with benzene gave a 97% tar recovery. The difference in recovery indicates that 33% of the tar remained on the sand after the n-heptane extraction, in good agreement with the 31% asphaltene content of the tar.

Example 2: In separate experiments with extracted tar, insolubles were determined at several solvent to tar ratios in several heptane-toluene solvent mixtures.

Solvent, percent weight			
Toluene	n-Heptane	Solvent/Tar	Insolubles
10	90	4/1	25.5
19.5	80.5	4/1	19.8
36	64	4/1	9.8
49	51	4/1	2.0
10	90	20/1	29
36	64	20/1	17

From these data it follows that by suitable selection of solvent composition, any desired rejection of asphaltenes may be obtained.

W.E. Savage and H.A. Cheney; U.S. Patent 3,553,099; January 5, 1971; assigned to Shell Oil Company describe a process for recovering tar from tar sand by a solvent extraction method.

The process is initiated by subjecting tar sand to solvent extraction in an expanded, or mobile, bed within an extraction zone. Preferably, the tar sand is ground and premixed with solvent before being introduced into extraction zone; and in the extraction zone, it is maintained as an expanded or mobile bed by an upwardly moving stream of solvent. The term mobile bed is intended to mean a bed of solid particles in an upwardly moving liquid stream wherein the combined effect of moving liquid and buoyancy cause the particles to be supported primarily by the liquid instead of being supported by resting on each other.

A liquid hydrocarbon phase consisting of tar dissolved in solvent is removed from the mobile bed through a passageway that starts within the bed, passes laterally from it, and terminates above the upper level of the bed. It has been found that a mobile particle bed acts as a self-cleaning filter which removes substantially all of the fines from a liquid stream.

The liquid stream removed from the mobile bed in the extraction zone may be subjected to a final particle separation before it is fractionated to remove solvent from the tar product, but the removal of the small amount of entrained fines from the product stream is a feasible process step in the process because the small amount of entrained fines does not require treating large amounts of solids. For example, the fines may be removed readily by subjecting the liquid stream to centrifugal separation in apparatus such as a hydroclone, or even filtration may be employed because the small solids content of the large volume liquid stream does not result in rapidly clogging filters.

As a specific example of the process, a cement mixer is employed as a low energy first-stage mixing device. Ground tar sand and toluene containing some dissolved tar are charged to the mixer. Enough liquid is charged to the low energy mixer to produce a flowable slurry of tar sand in toluene and the slurry is passed into an expanded bed of tar sand in an upwardly flowing solvent stream. Fresh toluene is added at a rate of 0.25 gallon per pound of tar and the upwardly flowing liquid stream is divided between the portion that recirculates to the low energy mixer and the product portion that is withdrawn first laterally and then vertically so that it is removed from the mobile bed laterally and withdrawn from above the upper level of the bed.

The product stream consists of a tar-solvent liquid containing about 0.1 pound of fines per gallon of liquid. This stream is subjected to final fines removal by centrifugal separation in a series of hydroclones, it is washed with water and the resultant hydrocarbon stream is fractionated conventionally into a tar fraction and a solvent fraction, the latter being returned to the extraction zone as fresh solvent and the former being recovered as the product from the process.

From the lower portion of the mobile bed in the extraction zone a mixture of sand and hydrocarbon phase is withdrawn and introduced into the center portion of an elutriation zone wherein a mobile bed of solid particles is maintained in an upwardly flowing liquid stream. The elutriation zone is charged at a lower portion with 0.1 gallon of water per pound of sand, the water containing enough sodium hydroxide to produce a 0.3 molar solution.

A mixed phase system is withdrawn from the upper portion of the elutriation zone and passed to a phase separation zone wherein hydrocarbon phase is withdrawn from the lower portion. Fines are entrained in both the hydrocarbon phase and in the water phase, but the distribution of fines is much heavier in the water phase due to preferential wetting. The hydrocarbon phase is returned to the extraction zone at an intermediate point and the water phase is returned to the lower portion of the elutriation zone. A mixed water and sand phase is withdrawn from the bottom of the elutriation zone and separated into water and sand phases, the former being recirculated to the elutriation zone and the latter being discarded.

The underflow from the hydroclone centrifugal separators consists of a small liquid stream densely loaded with fines particles and it, too, is returned to the extraction zone. Examination of the sand indicates that 99.7 percent of the total solids charged are recovered in the sand phase and it contains 0.6 percent total hydrocarbon and only 0.1 percent solvent. Examination of the hydrocarbon phase indicates that 95 percent of the tar in the tar sand is recovered as product.

Sonic Energy

In a process described by T.J. Bulat, J.R. Logan and P.F. Kusy; U.S. Patent 3,017,342; January 16, 1962; assigned to The Bendix Corporation oil bearing media is immersed in a body of solvent for the oil. The solvent is sonically activated, advantageously to cavitate the liquid solvent, for rapid separation of the oil from the media. The media is then removed to a second body of liquid where any oil and solvent remaining with the media is substantially separated therefrom. The second liquid is advantageously a nonsolvent for the oil and solvent and has a specific gravity different from the oil and solvent and they will be separated by gravity.

Residing in the same container, one of these liquids, either the solvent or the second liquid, will float on the other. Advantageously, the solvent has the lower specific gravity whereby it will float on the second body of liquid and the media may be moved, as by being dropped, through both bodies of liquid.

The combination of a solvent floating on a nonsolvent, the whole being sonically activated, has several advantageous results. The crude oil contains a wide range of fractions united in solution and is "soluble" in light petroleum fractions such for example as kerosene, benzene, fuel oils and others, and both the oil and these solvents are insoluble in and lighter in weight than certain other liquids such, for example, as water. The oil bearing media is moved first through the solvent and then the nonsolvent; the latter being heavier provides the immediate advantage that gravity may be utilized to move the oil bearing media through the liquids.

The media may simply be dropped into the solvent and allowed to free fall through the solvent and nonsolvent. The oil will be dissolved in the solvent so that as the particles of media move into the nonsolvent layer they carry with them not oil but only a coating of solvent. The solvent layer will contain some dissolved oil but is substantially a single substance which can be removed from the media particles by a sonic action, control of the acidity of the nonsolvent liquid and other simple expedients. Once removed from the media particles, the solvent floats upward through the nonsolvent to rejoin the body of solvent floating above.

Referring to Figure 3.12, crushed oil sand at 10 is conveyed to a premixer 11 where fresh solvent from storage container 12 is added to the oil sand and the whole mixed as by mechanical agitation. Sonic energy to be applied in a next step is capable of complete deagglomeration of the crushed oil sand but the premixing step is preferably employed for initial deagglomeration for which the sonic action is not required.

Advantageously the sonic separation step is conducted in a column of liquid through which the oil sand solvent slurry is allowed to free fall. Such a column of liquid is shown in the separating tower 13 which has a plurality of sonic transducers 14 attached in sonic wave transmitting relation to its side walls whereby sonic waves will be transmitted to the liquid when the transducers are energized. The liquid column comprises an upper column 15 of the solvent number two furnace oil 15, and a lower column 16 of water. Sonic energy transmitted to the liquid causes the solvent and water to emulsify at their interface providing a layer of emulsion 17 between them.

FIGURE 3.12: USE OF SONIC ENERGY IN OIL SEPARATION PROCESS

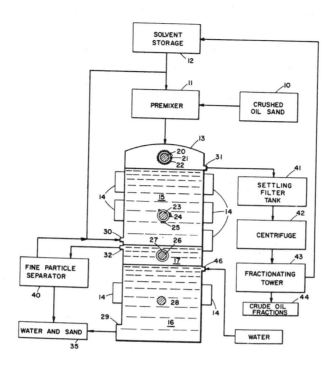

Source: T.J. Bulat, J.R. Logan and P.F. Kusy; U.S. Patent 3,017,342; January 16, 1962

Slurry from the premixer 11 is introduced into the separating tower 13 at its upper end and is allowed to fall down through the liquid. Four grains of sand are shown to illustrate the oil removal action as the sand falls through the tower 13. The upper sand grain 20, before it enters the liquid column, is surrounded by a water film 21 which in turn is surrounded by a layer 22 of crude oil together with solvent added in the premixing stage.

A lower sand grain 23 in the solvent column 15 and subjected to sonic action retains its insoluble water film 24 but its crude oil layer 25 is almost all dissolved by the solvent. A third sand grain 26, having reached the emulsion layer 17, retains its water film 27 but no crude oil layer remains. The lowest grain 28 is simply a clean sand grain in the water column. The sand is collected at the bottom of the tower 13 and removed by way of an outlet 29 out of the tower to a place 35.

Use of the tower 13 makes continuous processing convenient. A fresh supply of solvent is insured by flowing solvent from container 12 to an inlet 30 in tower 13 near the bottom of the solvent column 15. The flow of solvent is counter to the sand movement, and, together with the dissolved crude oil, is drawn from the tower at an overflow outlet 31. Many of the fine sand and clay particles which would settle down through the tower very slowly, are caught and held in suspension in the emulsion layer 17. These are drawn from the tower at a tap 32 and transported with emulsion to a fine particle separator 40. Separator 40 may comprise any convenient means such as a centrifuge or sonic separator for separating the sand and water, which are sent to the discharge point 35, from the solvent and any dissolved crude oil which are returned to the tower through inlet 30. The solution of crude oil and solvent is removed from the tower through overflow outlet 31 and is introduced to a settling and filter tank 41 to remove leaves, wood chips and like matter introduced into the system with the oil sand together with much of any fine sand or clay not caused by the emulsion layer 17. Any fine, solid mineral particles remaining are then removed by passing the solvent and crude oil from the tank 41 to a centrifuge 42. From the centrifuge 42 the crude oil and solvent are sent to a fractionating tower 43 where the solvent fraction is recovered and sent back to the storage container 12. Other fractions are sent to storage container 44. Water to replace that removed at outlet 29 with the sand is added through an inlet 46.

The oil separation is greatly accelerated by sonic activation of the solvent and this is especially true when the degree of activation is sufficient to cause cavitation in the solvent. The transducers may comprise any apparatus by which sonic energy can be applied to the solvent. The transducers 14 comprise magnetostrictive units electrically energized by alternating current at their resonant frequency which may or may not be in an audible range. Advantageously, however, the transducers are energized by alternating current whose frequency is near ten thousand cycles per second. The frequency of commercially available 10 kc. rotary generators is very satisfactory and such generators are advantageously employed.

If the water in column 16 is slightly acidic the removal from the sand of any oil or solvent still adhering to the sand particles will be facilitated and this oil is removed and will float upward to rejoin the column 15. On the other hand, it will aid in settling the sand particles through the emulsion layer 17 if this layer is basic. Accordingly the pH of the water and solvent may be controlled by additives to meet the conditions and to accomodate changing conditions in the oil sands without need to modify the mechanical arrangement of the tower and the height of the liquid columns.

The height of the water column is not critical since its purpose is to facilitate separation of the sand and solvent without drag-out of solvent. The height of the solvent column must be great enough so that the oil sands are subjected to sonic activity for a long enough period to effect separation of the crude oil from the sand. It has been found entirely possible to effect the separation in seconds and fractions of seconds with reasonable amounts of sonic power.

In related work J.R. Logan; U.S. Patent 2,973,312; February 28, 1961; assigned to The Bendix Corporation also describes the use of sonic energy to activate the solvent and sand solution.

Solvent Addition with High Energy Shear Treatment

A process described by E.L. Claridge, G. Edwards and J.T. Smith; U.S. Patent 3,553,098; January 5, 1971; assigned to Shell Oil Company is based on preparing tar sand to have certain critical physical characteristics and then subjecting each particle of the tar sand to a high energy shearing treatment in an aqueous phase where a critical amount of kinetic energy is expended on each particle of tar sand. When these critical relationships are employed, there is substantially complete recovery of tar and solvent as a gravitationally separated hydrocarbon phase; and substantially all of the liquid losses in the discarded sand fraction involve the inexpensive and readily replaced aqueous phase.

The process is initiated by preparing tar sand to be in a specific predetermined condition by mixing it with a solvent and, if necessary, adjusting the temperature of the mixture. The objective of this first step in the process is to produce a hydrocarbon phase, which includes the tar and the solvent, having a maximum viscosity of two poises and preferably a viscosity of less than one poise. Such a hydrocarbon phase can be prepared by employing a light hydrocarbon solvent such as gasoline, which will produce a hydrocarbon phase when mixed with the tar that has the required viscosity at ambient temperature.

When heat energy is available, the hydrocarbon phase at proper viscosity may be produced with a heavier solvent such as gas oil if the mixture is heated to at least 50°C. The preferred mode of operation will depend upon the conditions that prevail. If heat energy is available, reducing viscosity through temperature elevation may be preferred because a less volatile solvent can be employed; but if processing is at a mine site where heat is not available inexpensively, a lighter hydrocarbon, which reduces the viscosity of the resultant hydrocarbon phase without heat, is preferred. Mixing of tar sand and hydrocarbon solvent is accomplished in a low energy mixer such as a muller or rotary drum. Mixing of hydrocarbon and tar sand may be in the presence of water or other material to aid in handling. For example, added water may be included in the hydrocarbon-sand mixture to produce a slurry for transporting the mixture to the next step in the process.

The mixture of hydrocarbon solvent and sand, with or without added water, is subjected to treatment that produces a predetermined amount of shearing on each particle of sand. This treatment involves introducing each particle of sand into a flowing aqueous stream in such manner that there is sufficient difference in velocity between the sand and the aqueous stream to produce a Reynolds number in the system including a sand particle and the surrounding water of at least 150. This portion of the process should not be confused with stirring or mixing because the criteria are quite different. This portion of the process requires that the sand and water have greatly different relative velocities so that a rapid acceleration of each sand particle is effected to produce strong shear forces at the surface of the sand particles.

Flow may be quite smooth, for example, when the sand-solvent mixture is introduced into the throat of a Venturi in which there is rapid flow of water. Stirring in its usual sense is not indicated because in ordinary stirring both the solid phase and the liquid phase might be at high velocity, and acceleration of the solid particles by the liquid phase might be quite small.

In the sense of accelerating a sand particle in an aqueous phase, the Reynolds number found to be critical is a special case of the Reynolds number limited to the system including the sand particle and the surrounding aqueous phase without regard to the conduits in which the system is contained. The dimensionless group known as the Reynolds number usually relates the diameter of the conduit, the density of the liquid medium, the viscosity of the liquid medium, and the linear flow rate of the liquid medium in feet, pounds, and seconds as dimensions to determine the degree of turbulence in the system.

In the special system under consideration, the diameter involved is the diameter of the sand particle, and the linear flow rate involved is the difference between the velocity of the sand particle and the velocity of the surrounding aqueous phase. In such a limited system, the change from laminar to turbulent flow occurs at particle Reynolds numbers between 2 and 5 rather than at the usual Reynolds numbers between 2,000 and 4,000 when measuring turbulence in fluid flowing through a cylindrical pipe.

The tar separated as set forth above remains tacky and is capable of recontaminating the sand, particularly any sand grains which were originally tar-wetted on any part of their surface. To avoid recontamination, it has been found that an adequate volume of aqueous phase must be present. Recontamination is substantially avoided if the volume ratio of water to the initial sand charge, exclusive of solvent, is maintained at at least four and preferably ten. In other words, a minimum of four volumes of water must be employed for each volume of sand measured before solvent is added to it; and when such volumetric proportions are observed, it has been found that tar recovery is excellent, usually involving more than 90 percent and frequently more than 99 percent of the tar in the original sand. A concomitant effect is that solvent loss to the tailings fraction is negligible.

The aqueous phase may be ordinary water, sea water, effluent from water treating plants, or water from other sources; but it is preferably fresh water having the pH adjusted to 8 or higher. Although water with a pH in excess of 8 is not essential for effecting the separation of tar from sand, water with high pH is beneficial in reducing interfacial tension between the liquid phase and the solid phase so that tar-wetted fine sand grains separate more readily from the hydrocarbon phase and are more easily recovered with the tailings fraction. Since it is more difficult to achieve high-shear conditions with small sand grains (fines) than with large ones, and the net density of grains with adherent tar and hydrocarbon solvent relative to water tends to be lower for fine grains than for coarse grains, separation of tar from large grains is usually readily achieved even at pH values below 8.

For fine grains, the removal of tar, while not adding greatly to total tar recovery, may add substantially to the recovery of fine sand in the tailings. This of course also greatly reduces the contamination of recovered tar by fine sand. Therefore, the high pH water is not required so much to promote the recovery of tar as to promote the inclusion in the tailings of the fine sand fraction as clean sand. High pH water thus reduces the load on subsequent separation equipment which is required to remove suspended fines from the hydrocarbon phase and the aqueous phase.

Screen Separation

In a process described by E.W. White; U.S. Patent 3,068,167; December 11, 1962; assigned to Cities Service Research and Development Company hydrocarbon oil is recovered from bituminous sand by the process which includes the steps of mixing the sand with liquid hydrocarbon diluent to form a slurry, passing the slurry through a first separating screen to thereby separate a first portion of sand particles too large to pass through the openings of the screen and containing entrained hydrocarbon liquid; passing the remainder of the slurry through a second separating screen having smaller openings than the first screen to separate from the slurry a second portion of sand particles too large to pass through the openings of the second screen containing entrained hydrocarbon liquid, separately mixing each of the thus separated portions of sand with water to form slurries of water, hydrocarbons liquid and sand, and treating the last mentioned slurries for removal of hydrocarbon liquid. Referring to Figure 3.13, sand is introduced into a mixing vessel 11 as indicated by an arrow 12. In the mixing vessel 11, the tar sand introduced as indicated by the arrow 12 is thoroughly mixed with hydrocarbon diluent introduced through a conduit 13 and recycle oil introduced through a conduit 14 by suitable means such as conventional mixing paddles 16 carried on a shaft 17 and rotated by a motor 18. Any suitable amount of diluent may be used in forming the slurry in the mixing vessel 11 but between about 1 and about 5 barrels of diluent per barrel of crude oil is preferably employed. Such hydrocarbon diluent should have a specific gravity substantially less than 1.0 and preferably has a gravity between about 20 and about 65 degrees API.

FIGURE 3.13:   SCREEN SEPARATION OF TAR SAND

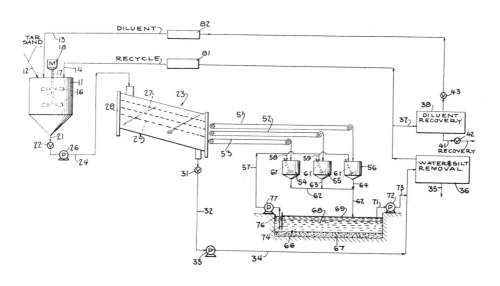

Source: E.W. White; U.S. Patent 3,068,167; December 11, 1962

Slurry formed in the mixing vessel 11 is withdrawn through a conduit 21 and valve 22 and passed to a screen separation vessel 23 containing two or more screens such as 27, 28 and 29 having successively smaller openings. A portion of the solid material passing through the screen 27 will thus be retained on the screen 28 while a portion of the material passing through the screen 28 will be retained on the screen 29, etc. The screens 27, 28 and 29 are preferably oscillated to facilitate passage of the slurry and to prevent bridging or plugging by retained sand. Solids particles sufficiently small to pass through all of the screens in the screen separation vessel 23 as well as most of the liquid contained in the slurry introduced through the conduit 24 pass through all of the screens and may be withdrawn from the vessel 23 through a valve 31 and conduit 32.

It is preferred that the last separating screen through which the slurry passes have openings sufficiently large so that most of the silt passes through with the hydrocarbon liquid. This material may then be passed via a pump 33 and conduit 34 to suitable purifying equipment shown as a water and silt removal system. The silt and water removal system 36 may take any suitable form such as one or more conventional settling tanks, electrostatic separating equipment, etc. Water and silt removed by the system 36 may be withdrawn through a conduit 35. From the water and silt removal equipment 36 a portion of the purified hydrocarbon oil passes through the conduit 14 to the mixing vessel 11 as recycle oil while the remainder of the purified oil from the water and silt removal equipment passes through the conduit 14 and a conduit 37 to diluent recovery equipment 38. The diluent recovery equipment may take any suitable form such as conventional distillation towers and serves to separate hydrocarbon diluent from crude oil recovered from the tar sand. Crude oil product may be withdrawn through a conduit 41 and a valve 42 while diluent may be withdrawn through a valve 43 and conduit 13 for use in forming the original slurry.

The portions of sand separated from the slurry by the screens 27, 28 and 29 are removed from the screens and passed by suitable means such as conveyor belts 51, 52 and 53 to suitable mixing vessels such as 54, 55 and 56. Each of these portions of sand has a different size range of particles due to the different sized openings in the screens 27, 28 and 29. Each of portions of sand also contains entrained hydrocarbon liquid and small amounts of water and silt. It should be noted, however, that the vast majority of the silt present in the original bituminous sand passes through all of the screens 27, 28 and 29 and is withdrawn with the hydrocarbon liquid through the valve 31. It should also be noted that the amount of hydrocarbon oil entrained with the sand removed on the screens, while significant from an economic standpoint, represents only a small portion of the oil present such as up to about 0.5 percent. Further, this small amount of crude oil is diluted with recycle oil and diluent as described above.

In the mixing vessels 54, 55 and 56 the separate portions of sand containing entrained hydrocarbon oil are thoroughly mixed with suitable quantities of water introduced through conduits 57, 58 and 59 to form slurries of sand, water and hydrocarbon oil. Any suitable mixing apparatus may be employed such as conventional stirring rods 61. By separately slurrying the portions of sand removed by the various separating screens as described above it is possible to vary the slurrying conditions for each batch of sand so as to insure sufficient slurrying without unnecessary waste of water or of the power required for mixing. In order to insure complete mixing and thereby insure complete removal of entrained hydrocarbons from the sand particles it is desirable that all of the sand be suspended in the water during the mixing operation. To achieve this it is necessary that the upward velocities in the mixing chamber exceed the terminal settling velocity of the individual sand particles.

Since relatively larger sand particles require substantially higher upward mixing velocities than do relatively smaller sand particles, it is obvious that the minimum amount of mixing which would suffice to slurry a relatively fine sand will not suffice to satisfactorily slurry a coarser sand. By separately mixing the individual portions of sand in accordance with the process it is possible to slurry each portion under conditions of minimum mixing power and water consumption to assure sufficient slurrying while avoiding wasted power such as would be the case if the relatively fine sand particles and relatively coarser sand particles are slurried together. This is especially true if the sizes of the openings in the separating screens are so chosen that the majority of sand is separated following initial separation of the relatively coarser sand particles which require relatively more mixing power for proper slurrying with water. The relatively finer particles separated on the remaining screens such as 28 and 29 may then be slurried with a minimum amount of power appropriate to the size ranges of particles in these respective portions of sand.

The slurries of water, sand and entrained hydrocarbon oil formed in the mixing vessels 54, 55 and 56 are then treated for removal of hydrocarbon oil therefrom in any suitable manner. As shown in Figure 3.13 these slurries may be withdrawn through conduits 62, 63 and 64 respectively and passed to a settling pond 66 in which the slurries are allowed to settle to form a lower layer 67 of sand, an intermediate layer 68 of water and an upper layer 69 of hydrocarbon oil. Separate settling ponds for each of the slurries may, of course, be used. The sand may then be removed at intervals by suitable means such as a conventional drag line while the hydrocarbon oil may be removed from the surface of the pond through a conduit 71 and passed via a pump 72 and conduit 73 to the conduit 34 and thence to the water and silt removal equipment 36 described above. The pond 66 is preferably provided with a baffle such as 74 which serves to prevent entry of hydrocarbon oil into the portion of the pond from which water is withdrawn as through a conduit 76 and pump 77 for passage through conduit 57 to the mixing vessels 54, 55 and 56. The following example illustrates the process.

Example: An Alberta tar sand having the properties shown below is fed to the mixing vessel 11 at the rate of 71,760 tons per day.

Composition and Properties of Bituminous Sand Feed

Crude oil, weight percent	9.6
Water, weight percent	4.1
Solids, weight percent	86.3
Density, lbs./ft.^{3}	120

Sieve Analysis of Solids

Retained on 80 mesh, weight percent	22.8
Retained on 100 mesh, weight percent	43.7
Retained on 150 mesh, weight percent	13.9
Passing 150 mesh, weight percent	19.6

Hydrocarbon diluent having a gravity of 25° API is introduced into the mixing vessel 11 through the conduit 13 at the rate of 73,640 barrels per day (b.p.d.) at a temperature of 181° F. Recycle oil is supplied to the mixing vessel 11 through the conduit 14 at the rate of 157,300 b.p.d. at a temperature of 181°F. Slurry is withdrawn from the mixing vessel 11 and passed through the conduit 24 to the separation vessel 23 at a temperature of 150°F.

In the vessel 23 the separating screens 27, 28 and 29 have openings of 80 mesh, 100 mesh and 150 mesh respectively. Material retained on the screen 27 is passed via the conveyor belt 51 to the mixing vessel 56 in the following proportions.

	Tons per Day
Solids too large to pass through 80 mesh screen	13,390
Hydrocarbon oil	115
Silt	30
Water	425

Likewise material retained on the screen 28 is passed by the conveyor belt 52 to the mixing vessel 55 as follows:

	Tons per Day
Solids too large to pass through 100 mesh screen	25,650
Hydrocarbon oil	230
Silt	65
Water	1,840

Similarly material retained on the screen 29 is passed via the conveyor belt 53 to the mixing vessel 54 as follows:

	Tons per Day
Solids too large to pass through 150 mesh screen	8,170
Hydrocarbon oil	90
Silt	25
Water	565

In the mixing vessels 54, 55 and 56 the material carried from the screens by the conveyor belts is slurried with a proper amount of water under optimum conditions for thorough mixing in order to separate and drain hydrocarbon oil from the solids particles. In this respect water is introduced to the mixing vessels as follows:

	Tons per Day
Mixing vessel 56	1,200
Mixing vessel 55	2,720
Mixing vessel 54	980

It is one of the advantages of the process that the solids materials to be slurried in the mixing vessels 54, 55 and 56 are of different size ranges. Thus the solids to be slurried in the mixing vessel 56 are almost entirely solids too large to pass through an 80 mesh screen while the solids to be slurried in the mixing vessel 55 comprise mostly solids capable of passing through an 80 mesh screen but not capable of passing through a 100 mesh screen. Likewise the solids to be slurried in the mixing vessel 54 are almost entirely those solids which passed through the 100 mesh screen but were unable to pass through the 150 mesh screen. It is obvious that the smaller solids particles present in the mixing vessels 54 and 55 will not require the same mixing conditions as the relatively larger particles present in the mixing vessel 56. The savings in energy required for mixing slurries in these mixing vessels may be appreciated when it is considered that the terminal settling velocity of the solids particles present in the mixing vessel 54 is only about 1.0 foot per second while the terminal settling velocity of the solids present in the mixing vessel 55 is about 1.8 feet per second and the terminal settling velocity of the solids present in the mixing vessel 56 is about 2.0 feet per second. It is thus apparent that considerably less agitation is necessary to properly slurry the solids in the mixing vessels 54 and 55 than would be needed if the relatively larger particles were present in these vessels.

Freezing Technique Employing Propylene

M.A. Bergougnou and T. Kalina; U.S. Patent 3,114,694; December 17, 1963; assigned to Esso Research and Engineering Company describe a technique for reducing the tar sands to a relatively low temperature in a manner to freeze the bitumen and water in the sands. The mixture is then readily fractured by grinding and the smaller and lighter bitumen particles are separated. An efficient operation is utilized for cooling the tar sands to the required low temperature, –50° to –60°F. The process involves cooling the sands by direct contact with boiling propylene. One source of make-up propylene is available from the off-gas from a fluid coker associated with the recovery of oil from tar sands.

Referring to Figure 3.14, mined tar sands are introduced into ball mill 2 by means of conveyor 1. These tar sands are ball milled to lumps 1" in diameter in order to facilitate the freezing. Generally, the diameter of the lumps will vary from 1/2" to 1 1/2".

FIGURE 3.14: RECOVERY PROCESS EMPLOYING PROPYLENE AS COOLANT

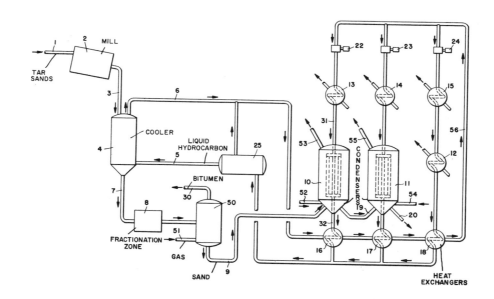

Source: M.A. Bergougnou and T. Kalina; U.S. Patent 3,114,694; December 17, 1963

Tar Sands Separation Processes

The crushed tar sands are withdrawn from ball mill 2 by means of line 3 and introduced into tar sand cooler zone 4. Sand cooler zone 4 may comprise one or more stages. In the sand cooler zone 4, the sands are contacted with, for example, cold propylene liquid. In the upper area of cooler 5, the sands countercurrently contact vaporous propylene which has boiled off from the liquid propylene in the lower area of the cooler. This propylene liquid preferably comprises relatively pure propylene, but may contain other hydrocarbons. The liquid is at a temperature of about –54°F. which is its normal boiling point at atmospheric pressure. The liquid propylene is introduced into zone 4 by means of line 5 and is withdrawn overhead from zone 4 as a vapor by means of line 6.

The cooled sands at a temperature of about –54° F. are withdrawn from the bottom of zone 4 by means of line 7 and are separated. A preferred method is to introduce the sand into a fractionating zone 8 where the bitumen-sand agglomerates are fractionated. The mixture is then introduced into an elutriation zone 50 which may comprise a cylindrical tower wherein upflowing gases are introduced by means of line 51. These upflowing gases carry out the smaller and lighter bitumen particles by means of line 30 where the same may be further processed for the recovery of the bitumen.

The bitumen agglomerates removed overhead by means of line 30 may be solvent treated in order to recover the bitumen or may be thermally treated as, for example, in a fluid coker. The fluid coker may comprise a fluid coking operation such as described in U.S. Patent 2,881,130.

The clean cold sand is withdrawn from separation zone 50 by means of line 9 and introduced into a fluid bed condenser 10. The temperature of the sand at this point is about –44°F. The sand, after exchanging heat with propylene vapors in fluid bed condenser 10, is withdrawn by means of line 19 and introduced into a second fluid bed condenser 11. Here the sand, at a somewhat higher temperature than in zone 10, exchanges heat with propylene vapors and is withdrawn from the system by means of line 20 and handled as desired.

Fluidization of the sand in zones 10 and 11 is secured preferably by means of propylene vapor which is introduced into zone 10 by means of line 52 and withdrawn by means of line 53. Fluidizing propylene is introduced into zone 11 by means of line 54 and is withdrawn by means of line 55. Furthermore, the propylene vapors withdrawn by means of lines 53 and 55 are handled to segregate entrained sand which is removed from the bottom of the respective zones. The propylene withdrawn by means of lines 53 and 55 is condensed, cooled, and recycled to the system.

The propylene withdrawn overhead from zone 4 by means of line 6 is passed successively through heat exchangers 16, 17 and 18 and is withdrawn from heat exchanger 18 by means of line 56. In the final stage 12, all the propylene not condensed in the fluid bed condensers is condensed with cooling water as illustrated. Clean sand from separation zone 50 is introduced into fluid bed condenser 10 by means of line 9 and withdrawn by means of line 19. Propylene vapor is used to fluidize the sands instead of the air or steam normally used for fluidizing solids. This is done so that the propylene vapor left in the sand pores in the separation zone will not be diluted and, therefore, can be recovered from the spent sand by water displacement. The propylene fluidizing gas system required for each fluid bed is not shown.

226

A portion of the propylene vapor to be condensed is passed by means of line 56 through compressor 22 wherein the same is compressed to about 3.3 atmospheres, at which point it can be condensed in fluid bed condenser 10 at about -10°F. Prior to introducing the vapors into exchanger 10, the same are passed through heat exchanger 11 where water is introduced at a temperature of about 40°F.

An additional portion of the propylene vapor is compressed in compressor 23 to 6 atmospheres. This stream is then passed through heat exchanger 14 wherein it is heat exchanged with water at about 40°F. The cold propylene is then passed into heat exchanger 11 where it condenses at a temperature of about -25°F. The remainder of the propylene is compressed in compressor 24 to about 8.5 atmospheres and then passed in heat exchange through heat exchangers 15 and 12 where the propylene contacts water at about 40°F. Under these conditions, the propylene condenses.

The condensed propylene from heat exchangers 10, 11 and 14 are passed and heat exchanged with vapors in heat exchangers 16, 17 and 18 respectively. The liquid propylene is then passed into storage tank 27 and introduced into zone 4 by means of line 5. Thus, the liquid propane secured as described has a temperature of approximately 0°F. and is passed to a flash drum 25 where it is flashed to about 1 atmosphere. Part of the liquid vaporizes, resulting in autorefrigeration to a normal boiling point of -54°F. The liquid is then ready to be reused in cooling zone 4.

Overall, the operation comprises a cold method where efficient heat transfer between the respective streams is secured, utilizing a plurality of fluid bed condensers in conjunction with a plurality of heat exchange units where condensate from the respective condensers is in heat exchange with the boiling propylene utilized to cool the incoming fresh sands.

Centrifugal Separation

J.L. Tiedje, J.A. Bichard and R.M. Butler; U.S. Patent 3,161,581; December 15, 1964; assigned to Esso Research and Engineering Company describe an anhydrous separation technique, using a continuous solid bowl centrifuge. In essence, the operation comprises mixing the tar sands with a quantity of a suitable solvent and then introducing the mixture at an intermediate point in the centrifuge. Gravitational forces remove the hydrocarbons outwardly toward the wide end of the bowl and the sand is moved by a screw conveyor up the incline toward the narrow end. Solvent introduced at the narrow end gives the sand a countercurrent wash and an efficient recovery of the oil from the sand is secured.

OTHER PROCESSES

In Situ Process Employing Gamma Radiation

S.L. Ruskin; U.S. Patent 2,906,680; September 29, 1959; assigned to Union Carbide Corporation has found that electronic and ionic influences exerted by gamma radiation profoundly affected petroleum and reservoir gases leading to the formation of products of reaction of petroleum and gaseous hydrocarbons. The carrying out of these reactions in the oil-bearing natural compositions in the earth by gamma radiation in the range of 100 million R.

to 400 million R. not only promotes the formation of these valuable hydrocarbon products but markedly increases the flow of petroleum from the rock compositions. Thus a sample of steel gray oil-bearing rock, having the appearance of dry concrete and extremely hard in composition, from which earth formation no petroleum could be made to flow, after irradiation with 100 million R. changed in color to a brownish shade and readily crumbled in the hand under moderate pressure, releasing the trapped oil which could be taken up with absorbent paper.

To carry out the procedure, one encases a source of gamma radiation in a specially constructed canister so arranged that the radiation source is completely shielded. The dimensions of the canister are such as not to exceed the dimensions of the average oil well pipe. The radiation source is permanently fixed in the canister bottom while the shielding cylinder around the canister is readily separable from the canister. Thus the radiation source may be lowered into the well for the desired period and then reshielded before removal. The source and canister are housed within a lead cylinder so that the movements of the canister and source are at no time exposed to possible contact.

Referring to Figure 3.15, the part intended to be lowered into the well includes a canister or cylindrical casing 2 in each end of which is secured a block 4 of lead or other shielding material. Between the lead blocks is a source 6 of gamma radiation, such as cobalt 60. In the upper lead block is secured a staple 8 by which a chain or cable can be secured to the canister.

FIGURE 3.15:   IN SITU IRRADIATION PROCESS

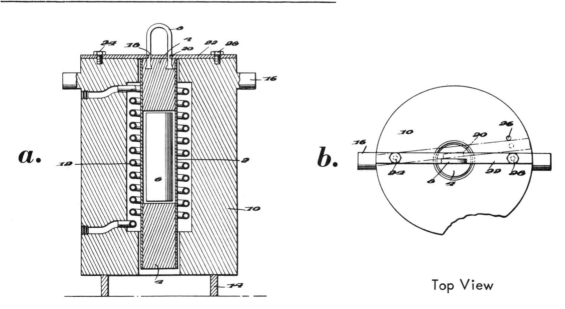

Cross-Section of Shielded Radiation Source

Source: S.L. Ruskin; U.S. Patent 2,906,680; September 29, 1959

The canister occupies the center of a lead cylinder 10. With this cylinder may be a coil 12 for passage of a regulating fluid. This block can rest on a well pipe 14 so as to allow the canister to be lowered into and pulled out of the well without exposing the operator to the radioactive material. The cylinder 10 can be handled by projection 16. Staple 8 has notches 18 in its legs, into which can engage parts 20 of a lever 22 pivoted at 24 on the top of the cylinder 10, and swingable between the solid and broken line positions shown in Figure 3.15b, being limited in the latter position by stop 26. In this latter position, canister 2 is free to move downward, but cannot move upward because lever 22 still overlies it. In the solid line position, in which lever 22 can be releasably held by removable bolt 28, parts 20 engaged in notches 18 support the canister within the shielding cylinder 10.

To further promote the effects of the irradiation of the oil-bearing strata, one may cause an intermediate chemical reaction to occur as a result of the irradiation with 100 million R. to 400 million R. whereby the products of the chemical reaction affect the flow of petroleum and/or the composition of the oil-bearing rock, shale or sands. By irradiation with 100 million R. to 400 million R. in the presence of glycerol, the glycerol is converted to acrolein, glyceraldehyde, glyceric acid and further breakdown products. This leads to a softening of the silicate structure of the oil-bearing rock, shale or sand and an aggregation of the petroleum molecules facilitating the flow of petroleum in strata having nonproducing oil wells. Thus when a limestone core from a nonproducing oil well is immersed in glycerol and irradiated with 100 million R. to 400 million R. or more, the white or gray color of the limestone darkens perceptibly. The limestone tends to disintegrate and soften and is more easily fractured. When Athabasca sand is so treated, the petroleum separates from the sand and discolors the conversion products of the glycerol. Agitation of the sands promotes the separation of the petroleum.

Example 1: A light colored 8 inch core from an oil well that has ceased producing oil was immersed in glycerol and irradiated with 200 million R. The core darkened in color and developed a strong odor of petroleum. The compression test gave the following results:

Cores	No. 1 light, control	No. 2 dark, 200 million R.
Capping material	Sulphur	Sulphur
Height after capping	2.437	2.437
Diameter (in.)	2.437	2.437
H/O	1	1
Correction factor	.85	.85
Area (in.)	4.66	4.66
Total load	7,260	5,820
P.s.i.	1,558	1,250
Corrected p.s.i.	1,325	1,064

The glycerol became syrupy and the presence of acrolein and glyceraldehyde could be readily detected. The glycerol also appeared to have polymerized.

Example 2: A three inch limestone core was irradiated with 100 million R. while immersed in water. The core darkened in color and became granular with an increased odor of petroleum.

Example 3: A 3 inch limestone core was irradiated with 100 million R. in the presence of an atmosphere of acetylene. A marked increase in darkening and odor of petroleum developed. The core could be readily crushed by the hand at the edges.

Substituted Nitrobenzenes in Water Flooding

D.G. Feuerbacher and T.E. Sample, Jr.; U.S. Patent 3,554,286; January 12, 1971; assigned to Texaco Inc. describe a process for the recovery of hydrocarbons from subterranean hydrocarbon-bearing formations by the treatment of the formation with an aqueous medium containing a base and a substituted nitrobenzene.

It has been found that when an aqueous medium containing a base, e.g. an alkali metal hydroxide, and a substituted nitrobenzene, such as o-nitroanisole, is contacted with a hydrocarbon-bearing formation, mobility of the hydrocarbons from the matrix occurs together with the formation of an oil-in-water emulsion, thereby enhancing the recovery of the hydrocarbons. It has also been found that a nonionic emulsifying agent may be incorporated in the aqueous medium so as to facilitate the formation of an oil-in-water emulsion. Furthermore, the use of a solubilizing agent in aqueous medium may in addition be preferred to improve the solubility of the substituted nitrobenzene.

The method can be utilized as an improved water flood where the aqueous medium, described above, is employed as the flooding agent. Alternately, the method may be utilized by the injection into a subterranean hydrocarbon-bearing formation via an injection well of a slug of the aqueous medium containing a base and a substituted nitrobenzene, and then injecting a drive agent, e.g. H_2O as water or steam, so as to drive the slug toward a producing well, from which the hydrocarbon is produced.

As example of the process, test runs were made in which an aqueous medium composed of a 0.1N aqueous solution of sodium hydroxide, and containing 500 ppm of the o-nitroanisole (ONA) was passed through a pack of 50 to 60 mesh glass beads containing a heavy crude (11° API) at an oil saturation of approximately 32 percent. Initially, three pore volumes of the displacing medium were passed through the pack during which time the displaced oil and effluent displacing medium were collected and the amount of displaced or extracted oil determined. The flood was then continued until either no more oil was displaced or until a total of twenty pore volumes of the displacing medium (including the first three) had been passed through the pack.

The following table shows that improved oil recovery was obtained by the method and that the presence of the substituted nitrobenzene, o-nitroanisole (ONA), resulted in about fifteen times more recovery than that obtained using the sodium hydroxide solution in the absence of a substituted nitrobenzene. Furthermore, the use of a sodium hydroxide aqueous solution containing either nitrobenzene or anisole did not show improved oil recovery.

In addition, other substituted nitrobenzenes that demonstrated improved oil recovery over that obtained using a sodium hydroxide aqueous solution included o-nitrophenol and nitrated mixed (m,p) cresols. The latter agent is a mixture of mono-, di-, and trinitrated meta- and para-cresols. In runs which were performed where a nonionic surfactant was incorporated into the solution containing sodium hydroxide and o-nitroanisole, an additional improvement in recovery was noted.

The results also demonstrate that a solubilizing agent such as isopropyl alcohol, can be used in combination with the substituted nitrobenzene such as o-nitrotoluene (ONT) to increase the solubility of the substituted nitrobenzene and thereby increase oil recovery. The tests demonstrated that the preferred location of the substitute relative to the nitro group is in the ortho position.

Additive	Substituted nitrobenzene conc. (p.p.m.)	Oil recovered (grams)[1]	Total oil recovered (grams)	Total, percent recovery
(1) Dist. water		None	None	0
(2) 0.1 N aqueous NaOH		0.19	0.24	3.1
(3) Nitrobenzene	500	0.08	0.08	0.9
(4) Anisole	2,000	0.11	0.11	1.6
(5) ONA	500	0.48	3.04	42.6
(6) N-95 [2]	5,000	None	None	0
(7) ONA [3] plus N-95	([4])	1.33	4.14	44.0
(8) ONA [4] plus N-95	([4])	1.18	3.74	49.6
(9) ONT plus 5% isopropanol	2,000	0.25	3.22	41.6
(10) o-Nitrophenol	2,000	0.46	0.56	6.7
(11) Nitrated mixed (m,p) cresols	2,000	0.54	0.70	8.0

[1] After 3 pore volumes through pack.
[2] Jefferson Chemical Co. Surfonic N-95.
[3] 5,000 p.p.m. o-nitroanisole (ONA) plus 1,000 p.p.m. N-95 as an emulsion.
[4] Saturated.
[5] Repeat of above run.
NOTE.—In Runs 3 through 11, the additives were contained in 0.1 N aqueous NaOH.

An injection well was drilled into a subterranean hydrocarbon-bearing formation through which a slug of the aqueous medium containing the base and the substituted nitrobenzene as described above was injected into the formation. The slug is then followed by a subsequently injected aqueous drive agent, e.g. water. The size of the slug injected may vary within relatively wide limits, and will depend on a number of conditions, including the thickness of the formation, its characteristics, and the conditions for the subsequent injection of the aqueous drive medium. The aqueous drive agent may be H_2O in the form of either water or steam, the temperature of which may range up to 500° F.

In the passage of the aqueous medium through the subterranean hydrocarbon-bearing formation, hydrocarbons are desorbed from the formation, forming an oil-in-water emulsion which is then produced at production wells. Separation of the hydrocarbons from the emulsion is accomplished by one of several known emulsion breaking techniques.

pH-Sensitive Aqueous Surfactant Solutions

A process described by H.L. Greenwald; U.S. Patent 3,108,059; October 22, 1963; assigned to Rohm & Haas Company involves recovery of oil by the use of an aqueous surfactant solution which causes an oil-water emulsion to be produced. The emulsion is readily broken so that the surfactant can be efficiently recovered in a single phase and re-used and the oils economically obtained.

The process makes possible high recovery of all components by controllably changing the hydrophile-lipophile balance of a surfactant during the process. The controlled change of this balance is brought about by the use of pH-sensitive emulsifiers. The oil is either emulsified under alkaline conditions and the emulsion later broken by adding acid to make the solution acidic, or emulsified under acid conditions and broken by adding alkali to make the solution alkaline. In actual practice, it may be desirable in some cases to effect a closer control of the acidity or alkalinity of the treated solution in order to maximize the recovery of surfactant. This variation of pH effectively controls emulsion stability and the concentration of the surface-active agent in each phase.

In the oil recovery process the mined oil-bearing formations are treated in a reservoir such as an open pit. The steps comprise agitating portions of the mined formations with an alkaline aqueous solution of a pH-sensitive surfactant to emulsify the oil in the mixed formations, the surfactant being selected from the class consisting of:

(a) the ethylene oxide adducts of a range of amines represented by the formula $C_{11-24}H_{23-49}NH_2$ where the number of ethylene oxide units is from 5 to 50 per amine;

(b) $C_{11-24}H_{23-49}NH(C_2H_4O)_nSO_4Na$, where $n = 3$ to 50; and

(c)

$$R-N \big< {(C_2H_4O)_xH \atop (C_2H_4O)_yH}$$

in which R is a dehydroabietyl group and $x + y = 15$ to 50,

allowing the solids to settle, and subsequently breaking the emulsion by addition of an acidic substance so as to make the oil-water system acidic and thereby concentrate the surfactant in a bulk phase where it is available for further use, while concentrating the oil in another phase.

TAR SANDS RETORTING AND REFINING PROCESSES

RETORTING AND COKING

Simultaneous Separation and Cracking

V. Haensel; U.S. Patent 2,733,193; January 31, 1956; assigned to Universal Oil Products Company describes a continuous fluidized method for carrying out simultaneously the separation and cracking of oil from oil-bearing sands. The process is accomplished by contacting the oil sands material with heated reactivated catalyst particles and recirculated heated oil sand particles, which in turn are separated and returned in a controlled operation.

The method for effecting the separation and catalytic cracking of oil, from oil containing sands, comprises, introducing the oil sands in particulated form to a distillation and cracking zone together with a heated stream of particles consisting primarily of subdivided catalytic material, effecting a fluidized contacting between the oil sands and the heated catalyst-containing particle stream within this cracking zone, discharging resulting hydrocarbon vapors from the upper portion of the distillation and cracking zone and withdrawing contacting solid material from the lower end.

The process continues by passing the withdrawn and contacted particles, with a coke deposition thereon, to a burning and classification zone, introducing an oxygen-containing stream into the latter zone and effecting a burning of at least a major portion of the carbonaceous deposit from both the catalyst and sand particles while fluidizing and passing the oxygen-containing stream through the particles in a manner effecting a classification thereof into an upper fluidized bed of primarily catalyst particles and a lower fluidized bed of primarily sand particles.

The resulting combustion gases are removed from the upper portion of the burning and classification zone while discharging a continuous stream of sand particles into the lower portion of the zone, and continuously withdrawing hot catalyst particles from the upper fluidized bed in the burning and classification zone and returning them to the distillation and cracking zone, together with fresh oil sand particles.

By effecting the simultaneous processing steps within both the cracking zone and the burning and classification zone, a relatively compact unit is provided and a minimum of transfer lines is necessitated to carry out the continuous fluidized operation. In other words, only two major contacting zones are utilized, with the separation and cracking of oil vapors being effected in a single confined conversion zone, and reactivation and heating together with the elutriation and classification of particles being effected within a single confined regenerating and classification. The latter zone being operated to effect substantially distinct fluidized beds of catalyst and sand particles and is equipped with separate draw off means, so that selected quantities of catalyst or sand may be discharged or withdrawn from the chamber and selectively returned to the conversion zone.

Preferably a catalyst having a density and particle size substantially different from that of the sand particles in the oil and tar sands is utilized, such that the classification of particles within the reactivation and separating zone effects the maintenance of two distinct layers or beds within the lower portion of that zone. The cracking catalyst may be any of the known types of catalyst such as silica-alumina, silica-magnesia, silica-zirconia, or a natural catalyst such as Superfiltrol, with the catalyst particles being maintained in a finely divided state so that they readily fluidize and maintain a light fluidizable characteristic.

Internal Combustion Retorting

F.J. Sanders; U.S. Patent 3,130,132; April 21, 1964; assigned to The Standard Oil Co. describes a process which involves a retorting method for recovering oil from oil-bearing minerals so that the oil may be effectively removed from the solids and, furthermore, to avoid subjecting the product oil vapors to severe refluxing conditions with consequent overheating and loss in yield.

The process also provides a retorting apparatus of compact and simple design adaptable to the continuous passage of oil-bearing solids downward through the vessel, thereby attaining a high throughput unit capacity. The process for recovering oil from oil-bearing minerals is made self-supporting in heat requirements for retortation by utilizing direct internal combustion of part of the hydrocarbons present on such solids without appreciably affecting the potential yield of valuable liquid and vapor oil products.

Referring to Figure 4.1, the reference numeral 1 refers generally to an elongated upright retorting vessel comprising a metal shell 2 suitably insulated with a refractory lining 3. A charge hopper 4 of any suitable construction is disposed at the top of the retort and is so adapted as to maintain a continuous feed of solid material into the top of the retorting vessel 1.

The upper portion 5 of the retorting vessel 1 is substantially cylindrical in shape with the wall diverging outwardly in a downward direction to a maximum diameter for the vessel somewhat below the combustion zone of the unit so as to diminish the tendency of bridging or agglomeration of the particles within the combustion zone. The lower portion 6 of the retorting vessel 1 forms a frustum of a cone and converges into a central opening 7 in which is disposed a suitable valve means 8. The rate of flow of solids through the retort will, of course, be controlled by regulating the discharge of spent solids from valve 8.

A series of conduits enter the retorting vessel 1 at various levels as shown, extending horizontally across the unit. These conduits may be supported in any suitable manner within the retort, such as being directly supported from the walls of the retort. At the uppermost level is the oxygen-containing gas conduit 9.

FIGURE 4.1: RETORT PROCESS

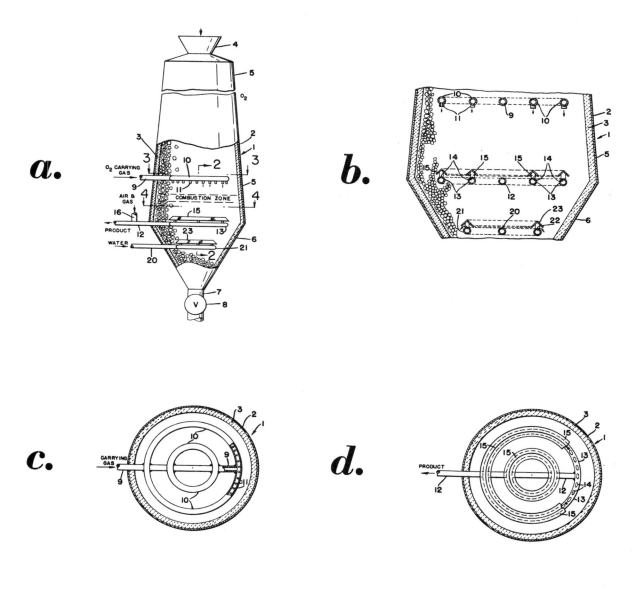

(a)   Overview of Apparatus

(b)   View Along Line 2—2 of Figure 4.1a

(c)   Section Along Line 3—3 of Figure 4.1a

(d)   Section Along Line 4—4 of Figure 4.1a

Source: F.J. Sanders; U.S. Patent 3,130,132; April 21, 1964

In order to achieve a uniform distribution of gas within the retort, conduit 9 is adapted with communicating circular tubes 10 which are arranged in a common horizontal plane with conduit 9 and are provided with openings 11 to supply gas in a downward direction. At a level lower in the retort is the product outlet conduit 12 adapted with communicating circular tubes 13. The topside of tubes 13 have slotted openings 14 to effect the removal of combustion gases and products from the retort.

Depending upon the size of the retorting vessel, conduits 9 and 12 each may be adapted with more or less than the two communicating circular tubes shown. It is only important that the structural arrangement associated with conduits 9 and 12 will provide for a uniform distribution of oxygen-containing gas from conduit 9 to the combustion zone and the even removal of products from the retort to the product outlet conduit 12.

Deflectors 15, which may conveniently be an angle bar positioned as an inverted V, is mounted above each of the tubes 13 and overlying the tubes 13 sufficiently to provide an angle of repose for the solids immediately above tubes 13 to prevent the entrainment of granular solid particles in the gases removed from the unit. Deflectors 15 may be mounted on tubes 13 in any suitable manner, such as by welding directly to tubes 13, or if desired, deflectors 15 may be supported directly from the walls of the retort.

The level of conduit 9 in the retort is not critical but its position will be determined by the relationship that must be observed between the height of the retort bed over conduit 9 to the distance in the retort between conduits 9 and 12. For a fixed distance between the levels of conduits 9 and 12 the pressure drop from conduit 9 to conduit 12 will be inversely proportional to approximately the square of the distance from conduit 9 to the top of the retort.

It therefore becomes obvious that in order to have the gases which are supplied through conduit 9 flowing substantially downward in the retort toward conduit 12, it is necessary to maintain the height of the retort above conduit 9 several times the distance between the levels of conduits 9 and 12. Consequently, in order to supply sufficient air in a downward direction within the retort for the effective removal of products by conduit 12 without the need for excessive pressures on the gas in conduit 9, it is desired to have the distance between conduits 9 and 12 to the height of the retort above conduit 9 maintained in a ratio of at least 1:4 and preferably 1:5 to 1:6.

For example, if the retort height is to be 30 ft., conduit 9 would be located at a level 22 ft. from the top of the retort and conduit 12 would be located 26 ft. from the top of the retort so that the height above conduit 9 to the distance between conduit 9 and conduit 12 would be in the ratio of 5.5 to 1. Of course, a ratio of these distances less than 1:4 can be used if for other reasons it is desired to have a retort of relatively short over-all length if a corresponding adjustment of pressure on the oxygen-carrying gas supplied through conduit 9 is made.

Conduit 20 is positioned in the lower portion 6 of the retorting vessel 1. Conduit 20 supplies a cooling medium to the retort and is adapted with communicating circular tube 21 having openings 22 so as to introduce the cooling medium uniformly to this level in the retort. Deflector 23 is provided in the manner shown to protect the openings 22 from being clogged by solids.

236

The operation of the retort is described in particular reference to the processing of tar sands. At the start of the operation, let it be assumed that the retorting vessel 1 has been filled from hopper 4 by gravity flow with tar sands crushed to a suitable particle size and that star valve 8 is closed. Hopper 4 contains an additional supply of crushed tar sands particles so that once valve 8 is opened the particles will pass continuously downward in an uninterrupted column.

The size of the tar sands particles is not critical, but it is preferred that the particles will pass a 2 inch mesh sieve while being substantially free of silt and fines which might be entrained in the product gases and vapors leaving the retort. It may be desirable in initially starting the operation of the unit to fill the lower portion 6 of retorting vessel 1 with sand such as flint shot Ottawa ranging from 20 to 50 mesh in particle size, and filling the balance of the unit with the tar sands particles.

The retorting operation is started by igniting the hydrocarbons present on a horizontal strata of tar sands particles extending across the unit immediately above the level of conduit 9. To accomplish this, a mixture of a combustible gas and air may be temporarily injected through conduit 12 from conduit 16 and burned within the retort to heat the hydrocarbons to a temperature above their ignition temperature, which is approximately 500° to 600°F. When the combustion process is under way, the supply of gas is stopped while the supply of air is continued through conduit 12 to support combustion.

As an alternate method of initiating the combustion process, an air gas burner may be temporarily placed within the retort just above conduit 12 to again heat the hydrocarbons across this level of the retort to a temperature above their ignition temperature. When the combustion process is under way, the air gas burner may then be removed from the side of the retort so as not to later interfere with the sustained operation of the process and air is temporarily supplied through conduit 12 to support combustion.

The combustion zone thus created is permitted to move upward a short distance from the original ignition level. It is most desirable that the combustion zone attains uniform depth across the bed as well as uniform temperatures. Thermal indicators well-known to the art may be positioned within the retorting vessel to observe the conditions of the combustion zone so it will be possible to adjust air flow rates as required to reach desired conditions within the unit.

When the combustion zone reaches a level at least one-half the distance between the level of conduit 12 and the level of conduit 9 and has built up a uniform temperature across the bed in the range of 650° to 1100°F., the temporary supply of air through conduit 12 is stopped and a supply of air is introduced through conduit 9. This supply of air may be preheated if desired.

During the initial ignition period, the products of combustion move upward in the retort and are cooled by the unheated particles above the combustion zone. In this comparatively brief period of time, a small band of oil contained on the particles above is displaced by such gas flow; and when the reverse flow of air from conduit 9 reaches this area, these liquid products, together with products of combustion, flow downward in the retort toward product outlet conduit 12, and the combustion process continues with relatively even temperatures throughout the combustion zone. After the flow of air has been reversed, the temperature in the combustion zone is continued in the range of 650° to 1100°F. for sustained operation. At temperatures below 650°F. the viscous oil present on the tar sands is not effectively removed from the mineral particles. At temperatures substantially greater than 1100°F. the combustion reaction progresses too vigorously and the oil burns in place, giving off substantially all combustion gases with very little yields of valuable oil products.

Valve 8 is now opened and the rate of discharge of residual solids from the retort is regulated so as to maintain the level of the combustion zone constant for the continued operation of the unit, and the rate of feed of fresh particles to restoring vessel 1 from hopper 4 is equal to the rate of discharge.

It is desirable that no more oxygen be introduced by way of conduit 9 than will be consumed in the reactions at the combustion zone. In this manner, no further combustion of the oil products can occur while these products pass downward in the retort toward conduit 12. Therefore, it will be obvious that when using air as the oxygen-containing gas that if the rate of air supplied through conduit 9 to attain the desired temperature level in the combustion zone is inadequate to effectively force the oil products and the combustion products to flow downwardly in the retort, then some extra noncombustible gas such as nitrogen must be added with the air to cause such a result.

The heat from the combustion zone is sufficient to educt the hydrocarbons from the oil-bearing solids immediately above the combustion zone as vapors and liquid. The actual distribution of product between the vapor and liquid states will depend in great part on the temperature level maintained in the combustion zone. The products are forced across the combustion zone and pass downwardly in the retort through the residual solids to the open areas found around tubes 13 due to deflectors 15.

The liquid and vapor oil products entering these open areas are readily collected in tubes 13 by means of slots 14, together with the gaseous combustion products and steam which is rising from the lower portion of the retort. The products so entering tubes 13 are withdrawn from the retorting vessel by means of conduit 12 into a recovery system forming no part of this process where they are to be cooled, condensed, and put in storage. The products, while passing through the residual solids below the combustion zone, do not cool or reunite to the solids in any appreciable degree since these solids are still hot from leaving the combustion zone. A slight vacuum of approximately 100 to 300 mm. may be placed on conduit 12 if desired to facilitate the removal of the products and combustion gases therethrough to the recovery system.

The residual solids flowing below conduit 12 are cooled by the introduction of water through conduit 20 and tube 22. The water is converted to steam on the hot solids which forms a seal against vapor leakage into outlet pipe 7. Some of the steam produced rises upwardly in the retort to be collected in tubes 13 and is quite helpful in stripping the descending solids of residual oil products and forcing these residual products upwardly in the retort to where they are also collected by tubes 13 and removed from the retort by means of conduit 12.

H.F. Tse; U.S. Patent 3,518,181; June 30, 1970; assigned to Sun Oil Company describes an improvement in pyrolytic methods of treating bituminous tar sands. Specifically, the process comprises preheating the tar sands to between 200° and 380°F. and feeding the preheated sands, while within this temperature range, into the pyrolytic treating zone. It has been found that tar sands, when heated above about 200°F., flow readily and are easily handled and transported but that when heated above 380°F. the sands become viscous again and tend to reagglomerate. The process can be applied to thermal cracking, catalytic cracking and coking among others.

Recycle of Hot Decoked Feed Solids

C.M. Fitch; U.S. Patent 3,267,019; August 16, 1966; assigned to Signal Oil and Gas Co. describes a process which includes the recycling of hot decoked feed solids to a point, prior to the still or retorting zone, where the recycle solids contact and are mixed with fresh feed sand or shale, initiate cracking and materially assist in the particle size reduction. In such initial mixing zone, the feed solids can also be ground, pulverized, etc., to free-flowing particles, preferably of substantially the same particle size as the recycle solids.

The recycle solids prevent balling up or clogging of pulverizing equipment in the mixing zone due to plasticized feed. Such recycling of the decoked solids to an initial mixing (and, preferably, particle size reducing) zone provides improved heat transfer efficiency and results in improved recovery of oil in the subsequent still, holding or retorting zone, and at a relatively low temperature. Large quantities of fluidizing gases are not needed, so that recovery of the oil is simplified.

As one particular example of the process, tar sand in up to steam shovel sized chunks is passed through a pulverizer in which it is intimately mixed with hot decoked sand having a temperature of about 1200°F. The weight ratio of the recycled sand to the fresh feed sand is about 5.7:1. The hot recycle sand heats the feed sand to about 950°F. in the pulverizer, aids in the breakdown of large lumps of the feed in the pulverizer and also initiates cracking of the oil in the feed.

The pulverized particulate hot mixture is then dropped directly from the pulverizer into a rotary retort and is passed through for a 7 minute retorting time at 950°F., the hot mixture being tumbled or cascaded approximately 8.75 times per minute. Hydrocarbons vaporize and are stripped from the mixture by means of countercurrently flowing purge gas, preferably superheated steam, although recycled retort gas or any hydrocarbon gas can be used. The purge gas-vaporized hydrocarbon effluent mixture passes to a hydrocarbon recovery unit, the purge gas, when a hydrocarbon purge gas is used, being recycled back to the retort for repassage through it countercurrent to the solids flow, and the hydrocarbons, including oil and gas, being recovered and passed to storage, to a product pipeline, etc.

The stripped solids mixture passes from the retort to a rotary coke burner in which the residual hydrocarbons are burned, heating the solids sufficiently (to 1200°F.) so that they can be utilized as hot recycle solids, that is, so they can be passed back to the pulverizer unit. Some of the hot decoked solids are discarded, after they pass through an air preheater. The air heated thereby is used in the coke burner. In discarding the hot solids, such solids go into a unit where they are directly contacted with water to generate steam. The steam is used to provide pneumatic conveying of the excess solids out of the system and into a waste area.

Compacted Tar Sands

P.E. Chaney, R.W. Ince and C.M. Mason; U.S. Patent 3,487,002; December 30, 1969; assigned to Sun Oil Company describe a method of recovering oil from mined tar sands which involves forming compacted tar sands pieces by special conditioning treatment that provides low internal permeability and then retorting in fixed bed form. The conditioning treatment can involve rolling of preformed pellets, compaction in a mold or pressure extrusion. Substantial collapsing of the bed during retorting is avoided.

The improvement provided by the process in the retorting of bituminous sands is achieved by virtue of the manner by which the bituminous sands are prepared for retorting, and the manner of handling the material during the retorting operation. The conditioning treatment can be carried out in several ways, but in all cases the tar sands are compacted in a manner such that air or gas is squeezed out of the pores and the internal permeability of the tar sands material is reduced to within the range of 0 to 2,000 millidarcies. The tar sands pieces so compacted can then be retorted in fixed bed form, and the pieces will substantially retain their shapes during retorting so that collapsing of the bed is avoided.

The process involves first forming the bituminous sands into pellets or chunks having sizes which are more or less uniform in all dimensions and which are mainly in the range of 1/4 to 6 inches, more preferably 1 to 4 inches. The pellets then undergo treatment in a conditioning step that is essential for imparting to the pellets weight-supporting characteristics necessary for effecting the retorting step successfully. This conditioning step involves subjecting the pellets to a rolling action that effects a continuous gentle deformation, whereby the sand grains within each pellet become more densely packed and the pellets assume a smoother and glossier appearance than they had before rolling.

This rolling action causes a marked decrease in the permeability of the individual pellets. After the pellets have been rolled sufficiently, they are then capable of forming a bed which can be subjected to retorting conditions without exhibiting any substantial tendency to collapse. During the retorting the pellets retain their shapes and do not tend to stick together appreciably. By passing sufficient gas heated to above 700°F., preferably to within the range of 900° to 1500°F., through the bed, typically 80% by weight of the bituminous material can be driven out and recovered as oil. The rest of the bitumen or heavy oil is converted to normally gaseous hydrocarbons and carbonaceous material which remains as a residue in the pellets.

The following example is an illustration of the process as applied to a batch of Athabasca tar sands having a bitumen content of about 12% by weight. The tar sands were first extruded by means of an ordinary meat grinder and cut into pieces having dimensions mainly in the range of 1/4 to 1/2 inch. A minor amount of smaller particles was present in the pelleted material. The surfaces of the pellets at this stage appeared dry and rough.

This material was placed in a drum which was inclined with its axis at an angle of about 45° from horizontal. The drum was rotated on its axis at a speed of about 60 rpm for 20 minutes. This subjected the pellets to a continuous rolling action, whereby they became more compacted internally and took on a smooth and glossy or oily appearance.

During the rolling the smaller particles disappeared due to melding with the larger particles. Tests on two random samples prior to rolling and two other random samples after the rolling showed the following permeabilities.

	Permeability, millidarcies
Before rolling	20,400; 19,000
After rolling	272; 907

These results show that the rolling action markedly decreased the permeabilities of the pellets. The rolled pellets in amount of 53 pounds were then placed in a retort which was a vertical section of pipe of 10 inch i.d. to form a bed 18 inches high. Means were provided for passing hot retorting gas upwardly through the pipe and then through a condenser.

Nitrogen was used as the retorting gas and it was heated externally before entering the bottom of the retort. The rate of nitrogen flow, corrected to standard conditions, was 35 cubic feet per minute. Means were also provided for measuring inlet and outlet temperatures of the bed and also the pressure drop through the bed during the run. The operation was started with the entire bed at ambient temperature, and the following readings were taken as the run proceeded.

Time, min.	Temperature, ° F.		ΔP across bed, inches of water
	Upstream	Downstream	
Start	52	52	0.5
20	350	90	1.4
40	400	160	3.3
62	650	330	4.2
90	920	750	5.1
120	1,100	900	5.1

The run was stopped after 2 hours from start, as substantially complete retorting had then been effected. The yield of liquid hydrocarbon product obtained was about 85% by weight on the bitumen in the tar sands charged. This oil product had the properties shown below. For comparison the properties of raw tar obtained by solvent extraction from the original tar sands are included.

	Raw tar	Retort oil
Gravity, ° A.P.I.	7	14
Viscosity, cp. at 75° F.	>50,000	140
Viscosity, cp. at 155° F.	800	12
Pour point, ° F.	90	−10
Conradson carbon, wt. percent	13	4
Sulfur, wt. percent	4.7	3.7

The pressure drop data given for the run above show that there is some increase in pressure drop through the bed during retorting but that this amounts to only a few inches of water. From this it is apparent that tar sands which have been conditioned by rolling according to the process can be successfully retorted without the necessity of providing compressors to circulate the retorting gas.

The low pressure drop that occurs permits fans or blowers to be used to effect the gas circulation, and hence the operation can be conducted with less expense than would be entailed if the step of rolling the pellets prior to retorting were omitted.

In another modification of the process, the mined tar sands can be placed in a mold of any suitable shape and compacted by mechanical application of pressure of at least 25 psig. For example, a cylinder having a piston for application of pressure, means for introducing batches of mined tar sands and means for removing the compacted cylindrical mass can be used to prepare pellets having a minimum width in the range of 1/4 to 6 inches suitable for retorting. It has been found that application of pressure to a tar sand mass in this manner will readily reduce its permeability to essentially zero when the pressure is raised sufficiently, e.g., to 200 psig or higher. The resulting compacted pellets have excellent characteristics for retorting.

Compaction and Retorting

J.D. Bennett; U.S. Patent 3,623,972; November 30, 1971; assigned to Sun Oil Company describes a retort system for retorting bituminous materials which includes a horizontally moving bed of such materials which are compacted and then perforated prior to entry into the retort. Such perforating provides vertical flow channels through the compacted bed of material to permit a controlled distribution of heat and burning within the retorting apparatus.

The retorting apparatus is comprised of two zones, the first being a retorting zone for educting volatile hydrocarbon materials from the horizontal bed. The second zone, into which the bed passes after reduction of the hydrocarbons, comprises a burning zone which burns the remaining coke within the materials. Heat from such burning operation is transferred to the retort zone for providing retort heat. A heat exchanger also utilizes heat from the educted hydrocarbons for heating the burning zone.

Referring to Figure 4.2, an apparatus is shown for forming vertical flow paths through a bed of bituminous sand material to be retorted. Bituminous materials which are mined from the earth are placed on top of the conveyor 12. The conveyor has side members 14 which form a trough for holding the materials in place on the conveyor. The conveyor is constructed in hinged sections to permit movement of the bottom and side members over a pulley.

The materials are moved on the conveyor until they are aligned with a compacting and perforating device 16 which is positioned above the conveyor. The compacting and perforating device 16 is comprised of a body platen 20 having downwardly extending perforating members 18 which are formed in the shape of a truncated cone. Upon lowering the compacting and perforating device 16 onto the conveyor, the lower face of the platen 20 engages the materials on the conveyor and compacts these materials into the conveyor trough formed by the conveyor 12 and sidewalls 14.

The platen is sized to be received on the conveyor between the sidewalls so that the top of the compacted material is below the top of the sidewall members 14 in the conveyor. The perforators 18 are arranged to be aligned with openings 22 in the conveyor. During the perforating operation the platen is lowered onto the material being carried by the conveyor. The material is thus compacted between the platen and the conveyor trough.

FIGURE 4.2: HORIZONTAL BED PROCESS FOR TAR SAND RETORTING

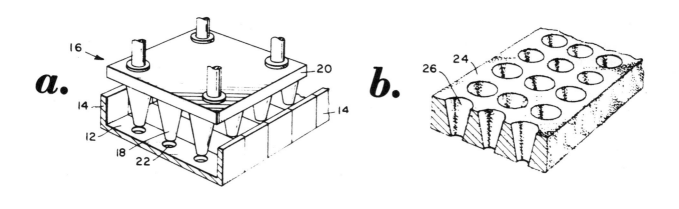

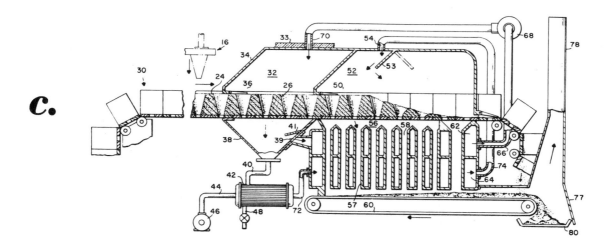

(a)   Compacting Apparatus

(b)   Horizontal Bed of Compacted Material

(c)   Retorting System

Source: J.D. Bennett; U.S. Patent 3,623,972; November 30, 1971

The perforators form holes or conically shaped openings through the compacted material to provide communication between the top and bottom sides of the compacted bed of materials on the conveyor. The shape of the perforating members causes the tar sands to be laterally displaced and compacted upon entry of the conically shaped members into the material.

Compacting of the material about the opening provides a strong structure which will retain its shape and thereby maintain an opening while the material is being moved through the retorting process. Figure 4.2b shows a cutaway view of a portion of such material as it appears after the compacting and perforating operation. The bed of materials 24 has conically shaped openings 26 formed therein with the large portion of the cone at the top of the bed and the small portion of the truncated cone at the bottom of the bed. The openings are spaced in the bed to provide an approximately equal thickness of material in all directions for purposes to be hereinafter described. The thickness of the bed, and size and spacing of the openings will be determined by the rate of movement of the bituminous materials through the retorting system.

The compacted material forming the bed together with the conical perforations create a bed of material which is characterized by a substantially greater strength than the unconsolidated materials which are originally placed on the conveyor belt. The conical openings provide a strong unsupported sidewall portion which is designed to maintain its form throughout the retorting operation, while being subjected to movement of the conveyor and movement of gaseous fluids therethrough during the retorting and burning operations.

Such openings provide a means for passing gaseous fluids through the beds and at the same time expose a maximum amount of cross-sectional area of the bed to such gases, leaving an equal volume of such materials unexposed between the opening to effect a uniform exposure of such materials to the atmosphere within the retorting zones. By maintaining a proper feed of materials through the retorting system, such materials are uniformly treated and therefore a maximum amount of hydrocarbons may be educted together with a maximum amount of thermal energy which is derived from the materials during passage through the burning zone.

Referring to Figure 4.2c, a conveyor 30 is shown for moving a continuous bed or briquet 24 of bituminous materials into a retorting apparatus. While the conveyor 30 is shown passing over pulleys at the ends of the retorting mechanism, additional pulleys are provided for diverting the conveyor outwardly around the retorting mechanism to produce a continuous conveying system. The apparatus includes a first retorting zone 32, provided with a housing 34 enclosing the zone. Insulating materials such as at 33 are used throughout the construction of the retort system to maximize the utilization of heat energy generated in the system.

A swinging door seal 36 rides lightly along the top surface of the bed of material to provide a sealed enclosure to the interior of the retort zone. The door seal is sized to swing downwardly between the sidewall members 14 on the conveyor. A pipe 70 communicates with the top of the housing 34. Hot gases are forced through pipe 70 into the retort zone to bring the zone 32 to an approximate temperature range of from 1000° to 1300°F. Such heated gases move about and through the bed of materials to raise the temperature of such materials to a retorting temperature of approximately 750° to 900°F.

Such heated gases pass through the openings 26 in the material and openings 22 in the conveyor into a funnel shaped enclosure 38 positioned below the conveyor beneath the retort zone. Enclosure 38 has an opening 39 in its sidewall to permit passage of such hot gases from the enclosure. The enclosure 38 also provides a means for catching educted hydrocarbons which are driven from the bed of material during heating in the retort zone.

A cover 41 prevents educted hydrocarbons from entering the opening 39. The funnel shaped housing terminates in an outlet conduit 40 at the lower end thereof. The conduit 40 provides means for moving the educted hydrocarbon fluids into a heat exchanger 42. The heat exchanger 42 may be of any known type where heat is conducted through tubular members from one medium to another. In this case the heat exchanger provides a means for transferring heat energy in the educted hydrocarbons to a gas, such as fresh air, being blown through conduit 44 by means of blower 46. The hydrocarbon materials are thus cooled and leave the heat exchanger through the conduit 48. The educted hydrocarbons enter the exchanger from conduit 40 at approximately from 200° to 600°F. Air entering the heat exchanger through conduit 44 will absorb some of this heat energy, before exiting the heat exchanger through conduit 72.

The moving bed of bituminous materials leaves the retort zone 32 and moves through a swinging door seal 50 into a second, burning zone 52. Heated air is supplied to the burning zone 52 by means of a pipe 54, which communicates with the top of the burning zone. A defuser 53 is positioned below the opening of pipe 54 into the burning zone. The defuser provides a means for regulating the distribution of hot gases within the burning zone. The heated air entering the burning zone causes the fixed carbon or coke within the sand to be burned.

The coke serves as a bonding material to hold the sand in its compacted and perforated shape. As the coke burns, the face of the exposed material becomes unconsolidated to the extent that the burned face sluffs off and drops by gravity through the openings in the conveyor. The openings in the material are thereby enlarged as the burning takes place until the material has substantially completely burned. The velocity and turbulence of hot gas moving through the openings 26 in the material will carry the material out the openings 22 in the conveyor. Means may be provided at the end of the conveyor for sweeping any remaining sand from the conveyor before the conveyor exits the retort.

A heat exchange chamber 56 is formed below the conveyor belt, beneath the burning zone. The heat exchange chamber is provided with baffles 57 which form vertical channels 58 interconnecting the upper and lower portions of the chamber. The channels 58 provide a means for the unconsolidated sand to fall to the bottom of the chamber, where they collect on a conveyor belt 60 for removing spent sand to the exterior of the retort system. Upper and lower transverse flow ducts 62, 64 respectively, are formed within the baffles 57 positioned within the heat exchange chamber.

The flow ducts establish a means for transferring heat energy from the burned sand to gases passing within the ducts 62 and 64. Additional baffles or surface area may be provided in the chamber 56 to facilitate such heat exchange. The upper duct 62 is connected at its left end, as viewed in Figure 4.2c, with the opening 39 in the funnel shaped enclosure 38 beneath the retort zone. The opposite end of the duct 62 is connected by means of a conduit 66 with a blower 68 for moving gaseous fluids between the duct 62 and the pipe 70 communicating with the top of the retort zone 32.

The flow path just described creates a continuous circulation of gases within the retort zone. The movement of such gases through duct 62 adds heat energy to the gases, and thereby maintains the temperature within the retort zone at a level which will insure retorting of the volatile constituents from the bituminous material.

Such temperature may, for example, be in the range of 1000° to 1300°F. In the event that fogging occurs in the enclosure 38, a defogging device may be placed in the entry to duct 62 to prevent the fog from getting into the heat exchanger and forming coke deposits.

The lower transverse duct 64 within the heat exchange chamber communicates at its left end with a conduit 72 leading from the heat exchange device 42. The lower duct provides a means for passing gaseous fluids which emit from the heat exchanger 42 through the heat exchange chamber 56 for supplying additional heat energy to such gaseous fluids. The lower duct 64 connects at its other end with conduit 74, which in turn communicates with conduit 54 and the upper end of the burning zone within the retort system.

Gases entering the burning zone through conduit 54 may have an approximate temperature range of from 500° to 1000°F. Such heated gas flowing into the burning zone maintains the burning zone at a temperature which will insure burning of the coke or fixed carbon residue within the bituminous materials. The burning of such coke or fixed carbon materials provides additional heat to gaseous fluid flow through the heat exchange chamber to maintain temperatures within the retorting system. The burning coke may raise the temperature in the burning zone to an approximate range of from 1300° to 1700°F.

The hot gases which are moved into the upper end of the burning zone by means of the blower 46, pass downwardly through the burning sands, the conveyor, and outwardly through the vertical flow paths 58 within the chamber 56. Such gases then continue along the path taken by the spent material conveyor belt into a plenum 77 at the end of such conveyor, where they are permitted to escape through a flue gas chimney 78.

Additional blowers other than those shown may be provided throughout the system to provide for necessary heat transfer. It is anticipated that a substantial amount of the heat energy will have been removed from such escaping gases so that the temperature of the gas escaping through chimney 78 will be very low and contain relatively few unburned hydrocarbon elements. A transversely moving conveyor 80 at the bottom of the plenum 77 receives sand from conveyor 60 for removal to a disposal site.

Summarizing the operation just described, mined bituminous tar sand materials are loaded on a conveyor 30 where they are compacted and perforated by means of an apparatus as shown in Figure 4.2a for performing this operation. Such perforated and compacted material is then moved into a first sealed retort zone 32 where heated gases are passed downwardly through openings 26 within the material to heat the material and permit the flow of volatile hydrocarbon fluid into the funnel shaped enclosure 38 below the retort zone.

Next, the retorted bituminous materials are passed into a burning zone 52 where the remaining fixed carbon or coke is burned. While such coke is burning, a gaseous fluid is passed through the burning zone to move the heat energy evolving therefrom into a heat exchange chamber 56 below the conveyor 30.

A pair of transverse heat exchange ducts 62, 64 within the chamber 56 move gaseous fluids through the chamber to remove the heat energy from the burning zone gas for: (1) heating the circulating fluid through the retort zone; and (2) supplying additional heat to the burning zone.

As the coke is burned from the bituminous material in zone 52, the sands containing such coke become unconsolidated and are permitted to drop through the openings 22 within the conveyor belt and vertical channels 58 within the chamber 56 onto a spent material conveyor belt 60, which removes such unconsolidated sands from the retort zone to the disposal conveyor 80.

Slurry Process

H.V. Rees; U.S. Patent 2,793,104; May 21, 1957 and U.S. Patent 2,885,275; May 5, 1959; both assigned to Texaco Development Corporation describes a process for the generation of a mixture of carbon monoxide and hydrogen suitable as a source of gaseous fuel or as a source of feed gas for the synthesis of hydrocarbons from oil-bearing minerals. In the process, the oil-bearing mineral in particle form is mixed with a liquid which may be converted to vapor form on heating. The suspension is passed under conditions of turbulent flow into a tubular heating zone where it is heated to a temperature at least sufficient to convert all of the suspending liquid to vapor.

Part or all of the resulting residual solid may be separated from the resulting vapors. Liquid condensed from the vapors may be used in the preparation of the slurry. The residual solid may be separated and discarded, or where combustible matter is still associated with the solid, used for fuel or for the generation of carbon oxides and hydrogen. If desired, the dispersion of residual solid may be passed directly to a combustion zone or gas generator without separation. Residual unvaporized oil or carbonaceous solid associated with the mineral residue is useful for the production of a mixture of carbon monoxide and hydrogen which may be used as fuel gas or as a source of feed gas for the synthesis of hydrocarbons.

Important advantages result from the method of recovering hydrocarbon oil from minerals in accordance with the process. As a dispersion or slurry, the oil-bearing mineral is readily transported and subjected to elevated pressures. Since the slurry may be handled in a manner analogous to handling of a liquid, troublesome lock hoppers and similar devices which are normally required for handling solid materials are eliminated and replaced simply by the slurry preparation equipment and pumps. The slurry may be made up some distance from the processing site and transported thereto by a pipeline. The quantity of material fed to the process may be accurately metered as a slurry of relatively constant controlled composition.

Referring to Figure 4.3, tar sand is mixed with water in a mixer 2 to form a slurry. The water and sand are heated to a temperature sufficient to insure ready mixing. Emulsifying agents or wetting agents may be used to facilitate mixing. The slurry is passed by pump 3 through line 4 to a heating coil 6 disposed in furnace 7. In the furnace, the slurry is heated to a temperature sufficient to vaporize all of the water.

The resulting mixture of vapors and residual sand is discharged into a cyclone separator. Residual sand is withdrawn through line 10 for disposal. The steam and hydrocarbon vapors are discharged from the separator through line 11. In a typical operation, the slurry is passed into the heating coil at a pressure of 400 pounds per square inch gauge and the temperature at the outlet of the heating coil is 1000°F. The hydrocarbon vapors and steam discharged from the separator through line 11 are passed to a reaction zone 12 where they are reacted with oxygen to produce a mixture of carbon monoxide and hydrogen.

FIGURE 4.3: SLURRY PROCESS

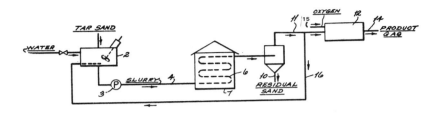

Source: H.V. Rees; U.S. Patent 2,793,104; May 21, 1957

Commercial oxygen containing in excess of 95% by volume is preferred. The oxygen is admitted to the reaction zone 12 through line 15. Product gas is discharged from the reaction zone through line 14 for use as fuel gas or feed gas for the synthesis of hydrocarbons   A portion of the vapor stream from line 11 may be passed through line 16 to the mixer 2. These heated vapors supply heat in the mixer, aiding in the formation of a fluid dispersion of tar sand and water.

In a typical operation, oxygen concentrate containing in excess of 95% oxygen by volume is supplied to the reactor 12. Reactor 12 is operated at a temperature within the range of from about 2000° to 2600°F. The reaction zone contains a substantially unobstructed reaction space so designed that the ratio of the internal surface of the reaction zone to the surface of a sphere of the same volume is less than 1.5.

Retorting and Coking Process with Hot Sand Recycle

C.H.O. Berg; U.S. Patent 2,905,595; September 22, 1959; assigned to Union Oil Company of California describes a tar sand treating process in which a recycled stream of hot sand is utilized to heat the heavy hydrocarbon materials in the bituminous sand to produce a coked sand and to produce a coker gasoline and gas oil which are directly useable as feed stocks to existing refinery processes.

Referring to Figure 4.4 the three essential elements of the apparatus of this process include coking kiln 10, coked sand furnace 12, and coker distillate fractionating column 14. Sisquoc tar sand is introduced at a rate of 10,000 tons per day by means of conveyor 16 into the upper or sand inlet end of rotary coking kiln 10. Simultaneously recycle sand removed from the bottom of coked sand furnace 12 through line 18 is combined and introduced at a rate of 20,000 tons per day and at a temperature of 1445°F. The coking kiln 10 is approximately 16 feet in diameter, 90 feet long, is rotated at a rate of about 3 rpm, and has a total slope of about 3.2 feet.

FIGURE 4.4:   TAR SAND DISTILLATION PROCESS

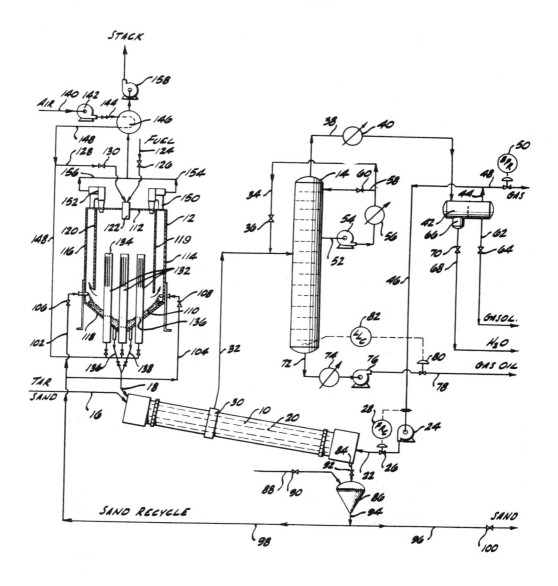

Source: C.H.O. Berg; U.S. Patent 2,905,595; September 22, 1959

It is provided with a plurality of longitudinal baffles of flights 20 by means of which the sand is mixed forming a uniform mixture at about 900°F. The sand mixture progresses downwardly through coking kiln 10 which provides a residence time of approximately 1 hour. A stripping gas comprising the coked noncondensable gas product is introduced into the bottom of coking kiln 10 by means of line 22 under the influence of blower 24 at a rate of 2,490 Mscf/day (1 Mscf = 1,000 standard cubic feet) controlled by valve 26 under the influence of flow recorder controller 28. The stripping gas sweeps the coker distillate upwardly through the kiln and it is removed from disengager 30 by means of line 32 at a temperature of 900°F.

This total coker distillate is combined with 9,180 barrels per day of 200°F. quench oil flowing through line 34 controlled by valve 36 and the mixture is introduced at 500°F. into coker distillate fractionation column 14.

The overhead vapor is removed from column 14 through line 38 and is cooled and partly condensed at 100°F. in cooler 40. The mixed overhead phases are introduced into vapor liquid separator 42 wherein the noncondensable gases which are in vapor form at 100°F. and approximately atmospheric pressure are removed at a rate of 5,980 Mscf/day per line 44. Of this produced coker gas approximately half is passed through line 46 by means of blower 24 previously described and is introduced as a stripping gas into the bottom of coking kiln 10. The remainder is removed through line 48 at a rate controlled by back pressure regulator 50. This gas may be used for fuel as subsequently described in the coked sand furnace 12.

A side cut is removed from column 14 above the coker distillate inlet through line 52 at a temperature of about 400°F. This material is pumped by means of pump 54 at a rate of 43,880 barrels per day through side cut cooler 56 where it is cooled to 200°F. This cooled stream includes the 9,180 barrels of quench oil referred to previously, and the remainder is introduced through line 58 at a rate of 34,700 barrels per day controlled by valve 60 as a reflux into the top of column 14.

The coker gasoline is removed from separator 42 through line 62 at a rate of 853 barrels per day controlled by valve 64 actuated by means of a conventional liquid level controller. Water is removed from trap 66 through line 68 at a rate of about 570 barrels per day as controlled by valve 70 actuated by a conventional differential liquid level controller.

From the bottom of distillation column 14 is removed the heavy or gas oil fraction of the total coker product and which boils above about 400°F. This material flows through line 72 through bottoms cooler 74 at a rate of 5,360 barrels per day. It is pumped by pump 76 through line 78 at the rate given controlled by valve 80 which in turn is actuated by liquid level controller 82. The coker gas oil thus produced constitutes a feed stock for a catalytic desulfurization unit to produce a low sulfur cracking stock.

The coked sand product is removed from the bottom of coking kiln 10 through line 84 at the rate of 28,806 tons per day. This material is either intermittently or continuously introduced into coked sand induction zone 86. A conveyance gas under pressure is introduced thereinto through line 88 at a rate controlled by valve 90. With the solids inlet sealed by element 92, which may constitute either a solids feeder or a valve adapted to seal line 84 against a counterflow of gas, the conveyance gas depressures through line 94 and through line 96 and 98 concurrently with an elongated gas permeable moving mass of coked sand. The gas flow is controlled at a rate sufficient to overcome opposing forces of gravity and friction acting on the sand so as to permit solids movement.

Through line 96 controlled by valve 100 a flow of coked sand is produced from the process at a rate of 8,756 tons per day. Through line 98, which later divides into a plurality of parallel lines 102 and 104, each in turn controlled respectively by valves 106 and 108 which serve to restrict the discharge of solids from the outlet of lines 102 and 104, a sand recycle flowing at a rate of 20,150 tons per day is introduced into a plurality of points along each side near the bottom of coked sand furnace 12 forming a moving bed 110 there.

By restricting the discharge of solids from the outlet of lines 96, 102 and 104 without causing any substantial restriction on the discharge of gas therefrom, the sand is caused to move through the lines in the form of a nonfluidized dense or compact continuous moving mass of solids. The quantity of gas required to convey the solids is roughly less than 10% of that required to convey the same solids at the same rate as a gas lift suspension in a conventional pneumatic conveyor, and the conveyor conduit is approximately 80% samller in diameter.

Coked sand furnace 12 is shown in Figure 4.4 as it appears in vertical cross-section. It is actually an elongated furnace having a flat or curving top 112, flat parallel sides 114 and 116 and a trough shaped bottom 118. The slope of the trough is about 45° or any slope sufficient to cause downward flow of the solids there. Extending longitudinally along each side of the furnace and spaced apart are bridge walls 119 and 120 extending downwardly from roof 112 to a point just above the sand inlets and forming flue gas removal flues.

The coked sand furnace is 20 feet wide, 36 feet high, 100 feet long, and is provided with a series of ten surface combustion gas burners 122 disposed in a row along the top. Fuel gas is introduced through line 124 at a rate of 1,300 Mscf/day controlled by valve 126 together with air flowing through line 128 at a rate of 37,700 Mscf/day controlled by valve 130. The combustion of this fuel supplies approximately 35% of the heat required in the process, the remaining 65% being generated within furnace 12 through combustion of the coke deposited on the coked sand. The fuel and air rates are controlled to produce coke free sand at the desired rate and temperature.

Disposed in three parallel rows along the length of furnace 12 and extending upwardly through trough shaped bottom 118 are gas lift tubes or zones 132. These tubes are 10 inch nominal iron pipe size conduits approximately 35 feet high disposed vertically in three rows each containing about 65 tubes, being spaced apart about 1.5 feet. The upper part of each of these lines is provided around its periphery with six slots 134 each 10 feet long and 2 inches wide. Provided around the periphery of each of these tubes at a point just above the trough shaped bottom of the kiln are apertures 136.

Moving bed of coked sand 110 flows downwardly and enters these apertures, the sand is suspended in an upwardly flowing stream of preheated 1000°F. combustion air to form a sand suspension. The lift gas velocity is about 25 feet per second in the lift lines. The suspension velocity is decreased in the slotted portion of the combustion tubes and the gas and sand move radially outward through the slots and the sand falls by gravity back onto moving bed 110. The recirculation rate of the sand through the combustion tubes 132 may be varied at a rate sufficient to adequately reduce the coke content of the sand.

In the process of this example this recycle rate was controlled at a value of about 27 to 1, that is, with a coked sand feed rate of 20,150 tons per day, the internal sand recirculation rate was 540,000 tons per day. The hot spent sand is withdrawn from the bottom at points along the bottom of the furnace section through lines 136 and 138 and passes through line 18 into coking kiln 10. Combustion air is introduced at 116,000 Mscf/day through line 140 via blower 142 and through line 144 to preheater 146; then heated from 80° to 1000°F. and passes through line 148 at 78,300 Mscf/day into the bottom of vertical sand combustion tubes 132. Here they suspend and burn the coke from the coked sand grains. The flue gas produced by sand combustion and by fuel combustion in burners 122 passes downwardly therethrough under the lower edge of bridge walls 118 and 120 and then upwardly between these bridge walls and the outer walls of the furnace. Here part of the suspended sand grains are separated and the gas passes through a plurality of dust collectors 150 and 152 disposed along the edge of the top of furnace 12. Here the dust is separated from the flue gases and is returned to the furnace and the dust free flue gas passes through lines 154 and 156 through air preheater 146. Herein the gases are cooled from 1445°F. and discharged by means of blower 158 to the atmosphere at a temperature of 550°F.

The furnace is constructed of mild steel and has 6 inches of internal insulation. The gas lift tubes exposed to 1000°F. gas and sand are fabricated of type 314 stainless steel containing 25% chromium, 20% nickel and 2.5% silicon. The raw tar sand used as a raw material in the above example analyzed 1% water, 12.1% hydrocarbon material and 86.9% silica sand by weight. The product obtained in the process includes a total condensable coker distillate amounting to 72.8% of the hydrocarbon contained in the raw tar sand feed and the average gravity thereof is 19.1°API if the coker gasoline and the coker gas oil are combined. The coke production is 18.3% of the hydrocarbon fed and approximately 70% of this is burned to supply heat to the process. The gas production is 8.9% by weight of the hydrocarbon content of the raw tar sand fed to the process.

The process as described above successfully treats hydrocarbon saturated sands to produce a coker distillate hydrocarbon without the use of aqueous phases or flotation reagents. It is characterized by producing directly a distillate product rather than a heavy residual oil which often is heavier than water and thus difficult to treat in aqueous systems. Frequently the raw tar sand contains a hydrocarbon phase containing substantial quantities of hydrocarbon derivatives of sulfur. In some cases the hydrocarbon phase will analyze between 4 and 6% by weight of sulfur. In the combined tar sand retorting and hydrocarbon coking process a substantial desulfurization is effected with the production of hydrogen sulfide in the gas phase and a coker distillate containing less than about 3% by weight of sulfur.

Coking a Mixture of Tar Sand and Froth Product

I. Steinmetz; U.S. Patent 3,466,240; September 9, 1969; assigned to Great Canadian Oil Sands Limited, Canada has found that bitumen extracted from tar sands by the hot water process can be mixed with fresh tar sands and used as a feed for direct coking. The proportion of added bitumen in the feed can be adjusted so that regardless of the proportion of bitumen in the fresh sands, the mixed feed will always contain the same amount of cokable material.

This process has several advantages over direct retorting alone. Firstly, a coker feed comprising a mixture of bitumen and sands has a lower mineral content than a feed consisting of only tar sands. This allows a more efficient utilization of heat since a great deal less siliceous and mineral material need be heated compared to that of a feed of only tar sands. Secondly the mixed feed gives improved combustion characteristics in a moving bed type of operation where it is essential that enough coke is generated to heat the sands so that they can be recycled hot back into the reaction zone. In short, by adjusting the proportions of bitumen and tar sands in the mixed feed of this process, the advantages of both an extraction process and a direct retorting process may be maximized and disadvantages minimized. The process is particularly advantageous in that it allows for a uniform coker feed regardless of the composition of the tar sand.

For example, with a high tar sand, the amount of bitumen in the feed mixtures could be reduced while with a low tar content sand, the bitumen content could be increased making possible a constant composition retort feed. The particular process used in the coking step is not critical.

Fluid Coking Processes

In a process described by D.E. Blaser; U.S. Patent 3,261,775; July 19, 1966; assigned to Esso Research and Engineering Company a feed extracted from tar sands and containing bitumen, solids and water is preheated and then is introduced into the top of a tower. The feed is then contacted countercurrently with flue gas and much of the water is stripped out of the feed. The resulting mixture is then passed to a conventional fluid coker which consists of a reactor and burner; within the burner may be two or three stages of cyclone separators.

The remaining water is vaporized out of the feed and much of the coke formed during the coking step is burned off the sand within the burner; the remaining coke serves to coat the solids. The diplegs of the cyclones within the burner empty into the burner itself or outside the burner. All or part of the fines may be rejected; rejected fines are disposed of by conventional means. The reactor cyclone diplegs discharge to the reactor stripper. In this manner most of the fine materials are carried to the burner.

Since fluid coking requires a fairly constant particle size, the efficiency of a fluid coker designed to process these bitumens would be greatly enhanced by providing these methods for separation of fine material. The solids and the remaining coke are transported to a second high temperature burner, where all the coke is burned and the sand is heated. The hot sand is now transferred to a steam-water drum. Contacting of the hot sand and water releases about 15 to 45 psig of steam; this large amount of energy is recovered and may be used for any desired purpose. The sand is then removed in the form of a sand-water slurry.

The flue gas from the second, high temperature burner is passed to the first stage burner thereby combining the flue gases. The combined gases are then passed through one or more stages of cyclones where dust and fine coke is recovered. The flue gas may then be channeled through a waste gas turbine, driving an air blower which supplies air for both the first and second burner. From the turbine the hot flue gas passes to the lower portion of the tower where it serves to impart some heat to the feed and also strip out most of the water. Water is injected into the second stage burner to absorb the heat of combustion of the coke by forming steam and also provide additional heat carrier in the flue gas for stripping. Water may also be added to the first stage burner for the same reason.

Referring to Figure 4.5, the reference numeral 9 indicates a line through which feed containing bitumen mixed with clay, water, air and sand is introduced into heater or heat exchanger 10. The feed is an extract of tar sand or bituminous sand and contains about 30 to 45% H_2O, 6 to 12% of solids and the balance of approximately 40 to 60% bitumen. The extracted oil contains between 10 to 50 volume percent of air. The feed is preheated to a temperature of 100° to 250°F. and is then introduced into the upper portion of tower 11 by means of line 10'. Tower 11 may be any one of a variety of towers and is shown as a shed tower.

FIGURE 4.5: FLUID COKING PROCESS

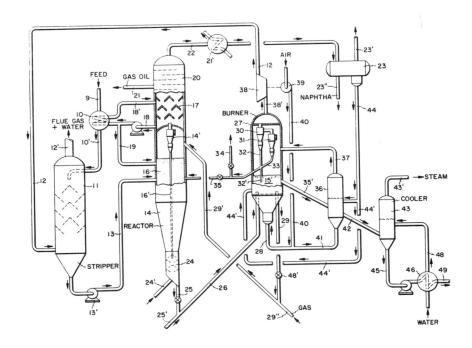

Source: D.E. Blaser; U.S. Patent 3,261,775; July 19, 1966

Burner or flue gases at a temperature of 1000° to 1200°F. are introduced into the bottom region of shed tower 11 through line 12. The feed and heated gas are contacted counter-currently and the gas serves to evaporate and remove most of the water which is found within the bitumen-containing feed. Temperature within the tower is about 200° to 250°F. The bitumen, sand, clay and remaining water are removed from the bottom of tower 11 through line 13. Flue gas and steam pass overhead through valved outlet line 12' from tower 11. This mixture in line 13 is passed through pump 13' and then is introduced into the reactor 14 of a fluid coker unit. The coker unit consists of reactor 14 and burner 27.

Reactor 14 is maintained at a temperature between 800° and 1200°F. and preferably at about 950°F. Pressure may be maintained between 0 to 30 psig and preferably at about 10 to 15 pounds per square inch gauge. Superficial gas velocity in reactor 14 may be between 0.5 and 4 feet per second and the fluid bed depth should be kept at 30 to 70 feet.

Coke particle size may vary between 60 and 1,000 microns, mostly between 20 and 300 microns. The fluidized bed 16 is maintained as such by the upflowing hydrocarbon gases and vapors formed by the coking of the bitumen in the feed and by steam added to the stripping section 24 in reactor 14 through line 24'. The steam acts to strip out volatile hydrocarbons from the solid particles therein.

When using finely divided coke of about 20 and 300 microns and at a superficial gas velocity as above mentioned the density of the fluidized bed 16 will be about 40 pounds per cubic foot, but may vary between about 15 and 60 pounds per cubic foot, depending on the gas velocity selected and the particular particle size range.

The bitumen is distributed on the solid mineral particles, including sand, and is cracked and vaporizes and coke is deposited on the solid particles in the bed 16. Vapor products leave the bed 16 and pass through one or more cyclone separators 14' at which time most of the entrained coke is removed and returned to stripper 24 through dipleg 16'. Vapors from reactor 14 pass up through scrubber 17 at which time remaining coke dust and clay are scrubbed out and products are cooled and heavy ends condensed to form a slurry. The slurry is removed through line 18 and a portion recycled back to bed 16 through line 19. Another portion of the slurry is passed through heat exchanger 10 via line 18' and returned as cooled liquid to scrubber 17 as reflux.

The vapor continues on upward to fractionator 20 and is fractionated. Gas oil is removed through line 21; overhead products are removed through line 22 and directed to separator 23 after passing through condenser 21'; naphtha is removed from separator 23 through line 23". Water is removed from the bottom of separator 23 and passed to the burner 36 through line 44; C_6 gaseous hydrocarbons are removed through line 23'. Any remaining water in the bitumen feed is vaporized within the reactor 14. The water in the separator is recovered from the steam and tar sands. It is at a temperature of 70° to 230°F. when removed from separator 23.

Coke is deposited on the sand and clay particles and upon coke particles in the reactor 14 during the coking step in reactor 14. The coke-containing particles pass down the reactor 14 into stripping zone 24. After this the particles flow down standpipe 25, are mixed with steam introduced through line 25' and then flow up through riser 26 into the fluid bed burner 27.

The burner 27 may be maintained at a temperature between 800° and 1400°F., but preferably at a temperature of 1100° to 1200°F. is utilized. Pressure may vary between 0 and 30 pounds per square inch gauge, with about 11 psig being preferred. Superficial gas velocity in burner 27 should be between 1 to 3 ft./sec. and the depth of bed 15' is best maintained between 10 to 20 feet. Additional air to effect combustion is added to the bottom of the burner through line 28. Hot coke and sand-clay particles are withdrawn from bed 15' and returned to reactor 14 through standpipe 29, slide valve 48', and riser 29' to supply heat of coking in reactor 14. Steam is introduced into riser 29' via line 29". Flue gases are discharged to the stack 38' after passing through cyclones 30 and 31 arranged in series in burner 27. These flue gases will be subsequently discussed in greater detail.

Cyclones 30 and 31 are used to separate fine particles from gases in which they are entrained and these fine particles may be returned directly to the bed 15' through dipleg 32'. However, this may be undesirable in some cases since fluid coking requires a fairly constant particle size and small particles should be removed from the circulating coke. Therefore, diplegs 32 and 33 of cyclones 30 and 31 preferably discharge outside of the burner vessel 27. The fines from one or both of the diplegs 32 and 33 may be discarded from the system through line 34, or all or part of the fines may be transferred to reactor 14 through line 35.

In the same fashion dipleg 16' of cyclone 14' may discharge outside of reactor 14. Within burner 27 about 5 to 100% of the coke, depending upon feed, Conradson carbon residue, water in the feed and unit operating conditions, is burned. The remaining coke, sand and clay are transferred by means of line 35' to a high temperature second burner 36 which is of the fluid bed variety. There is an advantage of not burning all the coke in the first burner as the coke serves to coat the sand and prevent much of the erosion which high speed sand particles would cause. The second burner 36 may be maintained at a temperature of 1000° to 1700°F., preferably at about 1400°F.

The solids holdup in reactor 14 may be between about 50 and 1,000 tons. The solids holdup in first burner 27 may be between about 15 and 500 tons. The solids holdup in second burner 36 may be between about 2 and 100 tons.

The flue gases from burner 36 in an amount between about 10×10^3 and 6×10^6 scf/hr. are removed overhead through line 37 and enter burner 27 above dense bed 15'. The flue gases in line 37 are at a temperature between about 1100° and 1500°F. Here, the combined flue gases from burners 27 and 36 pass through cyclone separators 30 and 31 so that dust and fine coke particles are removed. The flue gases then pass through waste gas turbine 38. The turbine drives air blower 39 and this supplies the air for burners 27 and 36. Air is directed through line 40 and is then directed into the bottom of the burners 27 and 36 through lines 28 and 41, respectively. The waste gas turbine drive air blower may be replaced with a conventional air compressor equivalent.

The combined flue gases from burners 36 and 27 and from turbine 38 at a temperature between about 1000° and 1200°F. are passed through line 12 and enter into the lower region of shed tower 11. About 60×10^3 to 33×10^6 scf/hr. of hot gases pass through line 12. Within shed tower 11 the flue gas is passed countercurrently to the bitumen-containing feed. Consequently the hot flue gas serves to preheat the bitumen feed and most important of all remove much of the water from the feed. In fact, as much as 5 to 100% of the water is removed from the feed in this tower 11. It should be noted that the flue gases prior to their entry into shed tower 11 carry a quantity of water as a heat carrier; the source of this water shall be discussed subsequently.

Returning to burner 36, the sand and clay within this burner are burned clean of carbon. The sand itself is heated to a temperature of about 1200° to 1500°F. It is transferred by means of standpipe 42 to steam-water drum 43. In steam-water drum 43 the hot sand directly contacts the water introduced through line 48 and generates approximately 20 to 50 psig of steam which is removed overhead through line 43'. The drum 43 is at a temperature between about 212° and 350°F. The steam may be utilized for any one of a great variety of purposes. Distinct possibilities include a source of heat for buildings. One use for the steam would be as a source of process steam for the fluid coker via line 24' or via line 29".

The water removed from the separator 23 through line 44, which may be between 2,000 and 100×10^6 gallons per hour, is injected into high temperature burner 36. This water serves to absorb the heat of combustion from the coke to form steam and to reduce the temperature of the combustion gases in burner 36. The steam is entrained in the flue gas and this provides additional heat carrier in the flue gas for stripping purposes in tower 11. The hot solids are removed from the bottom of drum 43 as a water slurry through line 45 and are pumped through indirect heat exchanger 46 used to preheat water passing through line 48 into drum 43 to form the steam in steam drum 43. The cooled solids slurry is discarded from the process through line 49. In a specific example of this process, the following conditions were utilized.

Coker 14:

Coking temperature, °F.	950
Pressure coker, psig	6
Feed rate of bitumen, w./w./hr.	0.5
Solids holdup, tons	1,000
Bed depth, feet	60
Superficial fluidization gas velocity, f./s.	3

Burner 27:

Amount of gas passing through line 12, scf/hr.	26×10^6
Burner temperature, °F.	1125
Pressure, psig	8
Solids holdup, tons	500
Coke circulation rate, lbs./lb. feed	20
Superficial fluidization gas velocity, f./s.	3
Bed depth burner, feet	10

Burner 36:

Amount of gas passing through line 37, scf/hr.	5×10^6
Temperature, °F.	1500
Solids holdup, tons	100
Pressure, psig	8

Separator 23:

Waters, gallons per hour	60×10^3

Steam Drum 43:

Temperature, °F.	200

The table below indicates the composition of the bitumen-containing crude extract feed which is used in the example.

	Percent
H_2O	45
Solids	10
Bitumen	45

(continued)

	Percent
Solid material was of the following size:	
Less than 100 mesh	15
100 to 200 mesh	15
200 to 325 mesh	9
Through 325	61

About 10,000 bpd of Athabasca bitumen-containing crude extract are preheated to a temperature of about 200°F. and are then introduced into tower 11 through line 10'. Flue gases at a temperature of about 1150°F. are introduced into the lower region of tower 11 through line 12. The tower 11 is maintained at a temperature of about 200° to 250°F.

The crude extract and gases are contacted countercurrently in tower 11 and about 60% of the water in the crude extract is thereby removed or stripped from the crude extract. The crude extract from which 60% of the water has been removed is then removed from the bottom region of tower 11 and passed through line 13. It is propelled by means of pump 13' and then introduced into reactor 14. Reactor 14 is maintained at a temperature of 950°F. and a pressure of 6 psig.

Within the reactor vaporous products pass through cyclone 14'. The vapors contain entrained solids which are separated in the cyclone system and passed through dipleg 16' to be returned to bed 16. The vapors pass up through scrubber 17 and subsequently to fractionator 20. About 57.1 volume percent of bitumen feed is drawn off through line 21 as 430°F./1015°F. gas oil.

Products boiling below about 430°F. pass through line 22 and into separator 23. About 13.6 volume percent naphtha on bitumen feed of hydrocarbon are withdrawn through line 23". About 8.2 weight percent on bitumen feed of gaseous C_6 and below hydrocarbons are withdrawn through line 23'. About 33,000 gal./hr. of water are withdrawn through line 44 and passed into secondary burner 36.

Burner 27 is maintained at a temperature of 1125°F. and a pressure of 8 psig. Gaseous material, with entrained solid particles, pass through cyclones 30 and 31. Solid material is removed through diplegs 32 and 33 which discharge outside of burner 27. In this fashion about 3,000 tons per day of solid material is recovered. All or part of this material is rejected. The portion which may be retained is returned to reactor 14 through line 35. In this manner about 1,500 tons per day of material are removed through line 34' and about 1,500 tons of material are removed through line 35 and passed to reactor 14.

Approximately 90% of the coke is burned in burner 27; the remaining coke and solid particles pass into burner 36 through line 35. Here the remaining coke is completely burned at a temperature of 1500°F. Water in the amount of about 400 pounds per hour from separator 23 is injected into burner 36 through line 44. This water in the form of steam becomes entrained in the flue gas which leaves burner 36 through line 37 and enters burner 27. Here the flue gases from the two burners are combined. The gases pass through cyclones 31 and 30, through turbine 38 and then out through the stack 38' into line 12. The gases pass through line 12 and are introduced into tower 11 where they are utilized for stripping additional feed. The remaining solids, which have been heated to a temperature of about 1500°F. are removed through a standpipe 42 and are passed into steam water drum 43. The contacting of the hot solids and the water produce about 30 psig of steam. Solid products in the form of a water slurry are withdrawn through line 45. Steam is drawn off through line 43'. The slurry amounts to about 660 tons per day and represents about 30% of the total solids which were found in the original feed.

In related work J.W. Brown; U.S. Patent 3,278,412; October 11, 1966; assigned to Esso Research and Engineering Company describes a modified system of fluid coking in which viscous crude petroleum oil is separated and cracked from a mixture with sand, clay and water.

According to the process a tar sand which may be an Athabasca tar sand is subjected to a froth flotation. That is to say, hot water is mixed with the tar sand; several phases are formed including an aqueous phase, a sand phase, and a froth. The froth forms because gas is liberated from the bitumen, the gas being predominantly ethane, methane and trapped air. The froth may contain up to 40 volume percent of gas. The water phase and the sand phase are withdrawn and discarded.

This froth is then subjected to a fluid coking process to remove oil and water and to form coke and lower boiling hydrocarbons from the oil within the froth. Extraneous hot gas or fuel may be added to the burner of the coking unit and this combined with the low coking temperature utilized prevents the coke from being entirely burned to provide heat for the coking process.

The lighter overhead hydrocarbon products are separated from the heavier products and removed or may further be put to use. The heavier, 900°F. + fraction, is subjected to conventional process such as fluid coking in which gas and liquid product are produced along with a high value coke. However, the heavier fraction may be subjected to other processes such as visbreaking, for example.

The solids, including sand and other mineral matter such as clay, are coated with coke in the first stage, low severity or low temperature coking reactor during the coking step, and the coated solids are then trapped within the coking reactor. By trapped it is meant that the coke coating serves as a glue. Therefore, the smaller solids become stuck to larger particles and this serves to keep the smaller solids within the reactor rather than allowing them to escape through the stack. This is particularly true of very fine solid material within the 1 to 5 micron range; the cohesive force of the coke tends to keep them stuck to larger particles and, therefore, they tend to remain within the coking unit. As much as 50% of the coke formed during coking is maintained on the solids.

Fines from the cyclones and some of the coarser solids of the low temperature burner are regenerated in a fluid bed and used as cracking catalyst in the reactor. The clay in these particles becomes activated and acts as a cracking catalyst. Some of the stack solids from the high temperature burner may also be used. The net carbon or coke coated solids are removed from the burner of the fluid coker and are introduced into a high temperature burner. Because of the high temperature in this burner, and the fact that all the coke is burned, the coke coating is burned to CO_2 thereby producing a large amount of heat. This heat in the form of hot gas is passed into a boiler where it may be utilized for the production of steam.

Alternately, part of this hot gas may be passed through the coker burner to supply heat. The extreme heat causes some of the sand and clay to become sintered, that is to say agglomerated in large masses which are, therefore, easier to remove than smaller pieces. Alternately, the solids may be removed as slag where ash melting point is low. Solid particles are removed from the high temperature burner and introduced into a cooler. The heat liberated during this cooling process is captured in a boiler and may be used for production of steam.

In the case of a froth from an Athabasca sand, the protective coke covering on the solid particles eliminates problems of erosion of apparatus and entrainment of fine solid particles, which would otherwise be encountered if all the carbon were burned off the solids in a conventional fluid coker burner. The principle of operation of the burner is that at least 5%, and preferably 50% of coke is maintained on the solids to produce a protective covering during burning in the burner. If necessary, in cases where the heat load is unusually high in the reactor, supplementary fuel such as torch oil is burned in the burner in preference to the coke covering to maintain this protective coating.

In a process described by M.F. Nathan, G.T. Skaperdas and G.C. Grubb; U.S. Patent 3,320,152; May 16, 1967; assigned to Pullman Incorporated tar sands agglomerates are introduced into a feed preparation zone and mixed with relatively hot particulate material obtained from a reaction zone. The feed preparation zone is maintained under temperature conditions to convert the agglomerates and particulate material into a fluidizable mixture suitable for introduction as feed material into a fluid coking zone and at a pressure suitable for introducing agglomerates into the feed preparation zone.

Mixing in the feed preparation zone is preferably carried out in a fixed bed agitated by suitable method and means to insure adequate intermixing of the agglomerates and hot particulate material. The relatively hot particulate material can be obtained at a suitable elevated temperature, which is preferably between about 400° and 1400°F., from a hydrocarbon conversion zone, e.g., the coking zone, or from a heat generation zone employed in the process.

The ratio of relatively hot particulate material to agglomerates feed is preferably maintained between about 0.5:1 and 2.5:1 in order to regulate the temperature of the bed in the feed preparation zone at the desired level. Hot particulate material, such as sand, is a preferred hot contact material, since it serves as a fluidization promoting diluent for the sand-oil mixtures contained in the agglomerates feed as well as a heating medium to reduce the viscosity of the heavy hydrocarbons in the feed.

The temperature in the feed preparation zone is generally maintained at a level which is sufficiently high to cause reduction in the viscosity and expel water from the agglomerates feed such that the agglomerates are triturated, and yet, preferably, below the level at which any substantial percentage of the entering hydrocarbon material is converted to gaseous material which is not condensable under atmospheric pressure conditions, e.g., dry gas.

It is important to minimize dry gas production at this point in order to minimize the cost of recovering hydrocarbon materials leaving the feeder as vapor. For these purposes, the preferred temperature range in the feed preparation zone is maintained between about 250° to 600°F., and most preferably, between 275° and 450°F.

260

The feed preparation zone is preferably maintained under essentially atmospheric pressure and most preferably under a subatmospheric pressure to prevent loss of gaseous material at the location where agglomerates are introduced. It has been found that agglomerates feed can be converted into a fluidizable mixture employing relatively hot particulate material as the contact agent employing an agglomerates residence time in the feed preparation zone preferably between 1 and 10 minutes.

The fluidizable mixture produced in the first zone by the action of the relatively hot contact material mixed with the agglomerates feed is withdrawn from the feed preparation zone into a pressure developing zone for passage into a hydrocarbon conversion zone. The conversion zone preferably constitutes a coking zone containing a dense bed of fluidized solids material operating at an elevated temperature and pressure substantially above the conditions in the feed preparation zone.

Preferably, the feed preparation zone is situated at an elevation above that of the thermal coking zone such that the fluidizable mixture can be passed to the upper portion of a standpipe communicating between such zones for passage by gravity into the fluidized bed of the thermal coking zone. Suitable agitation means is provided preferably within the standpipe in order to prevent bridging of the standpipe.

The hydrocarbon conversion zone employed to convert the hydrocarbon material contained in the fluidizable mixture of tar sands and particulate material produced in the feed preparation zone comprises a fluidized bed of particulate material maintained under thermal coking conditions. In the coking zone, heavy oil adhering to the solid particles undergoes pyrolysis, evolving lighter hydrocarbon vapors and leaving carbonaceous residue denoted as coke on the solids.

Temperatures between about 850° and 1100°F. and pressures between about atmospheric and 40 psig are preferable. Particulate material bearing coke at the surface is passed from the coking zone into a heat generation zone in which coke is burned thereby raising the temperature of the particulate material to an elevated level. Heated particulate material at a temperature preferably about 200° to 300°F. above the temperature in the conversion zone and in the range from about 1050° and 1400°F. is passed from the heat generation zone into the coking zone to supply heat required for the coking operation.

Removal of Suspended Material by Filtration

In a process described by D.S. Pasternack; U.S. Patent 3,365,384; Jan. 23, 1968; assigned to Canadian Patents and Development Limited, Canada the high viscosity residue of water washed dehydrated tar sands is subjected to controlled thermal-cracking at atmospheric pressure or under vacuum. This is followed by filtration of the hot residual oil through a filter at a suitable temperature to prevent congealing of the residual oil and permit rapid and complete filtration. Desirably the filter temperature is low enough so that additional thermal-cracking does not take place in the pores of the filter, e.g., less than about 650°F. The filtration may be carried out either under vacuum or under pressure. Preferably the feed material is subjected to controlled thermal-cracking at atmospheric pressure (or under a slight vacuum provided that excessive frothing does not occur), with simultaneous removal of the hydrocarbon vapors and gases which are produced, until an adequate amount of thermal-cracking has occurred. An adequate amount of thermal-cracking has occurred when the hot residual oil will filter rapidly and completely by conventional means through a hot filtering medium and still provide a low ash filtrate. Generally some advantage in separating the solids is obtained when distillate formation is within the range 20 to 60% by weight of the pure oil in the feed. This corresponds to free carbon formation of from about 0.2 to 3.0 weight percent based on pure oil in the feed. The following examples illustrate the process.

Example 1: Dehydrated Athabasca oil sands oil (obtained by a warm water washing method) was heated slowly at atmospheric pressure from 650° to 775°F. in a period of about 3.5 hrs. until about 40 weight percent of distillate was obtained. The hot residual oil was then filtered rapidly and completely by passing under a vacuum of 27 inches, through a hot filtering medium composed of a No. 1 Whatman filter paper on a Buechner funnel suitably preheated and kept hot during the filtration.

The temperature of the filter medium was about 600°F. The solids in the filter cake consisted of 78% clay and 22% free carbon, and were oil wet. A low ash filtrate, with an ash content of about 0.11 weight percent was obtained. (Coke produced from this filtrate by heating in a Ramsbottom furnace at 1020°F. for 20 minutes had an ash content of about 0.28%.)

Example 2: The same dehydrated Athabasca oil sands oil was heated comparatively rapidly at atmospheric pressure from 650° to 820°F. in a period of about 40 minutes until about 40 weight percent of distillate was obtained. The hot residual oil was then filtered rapidly and completely similarly to Example 1. The solids in the filter cake consisted of 85% clay and 15% free carbon, and were oil wet. A low ash filtrate, with an ash content of about 0.12 weight percent was obtained. (Coke produced from this filtrate by heating in a Ramsbottom furnace at 1020°F. for 20 minutes had an ash content of about 0.45%.) Examples of preferred variants of the process (using a diluent) are as follows.

Example 3: The warm unfiltered residual oil from Example 1 was diluted with about two to three volumes of warm diluent (the diluent was the portion of the distillate from the thermal-cracking with a boiling range from 325° to 525°F.) The diluted residual was filtered rapidly and completely while under a vacuum of 27 inches, through a filtering medium composed of a No. 1 Whatman filter paper on a Buechner funnel, giving retention of all suspended solids (including the precipitated material).

The filter temperature was about 250°F. The diluent-free filter cake consisted of 15% clay, 4% free carbon, and 81% diluent insoluble material. Upon removal of the diluent by distillation, the extract showed an ash content of about 0.011 weight percent. (Coke produced from this extract by heating in a Ramsbottom furnace at 1020°F. for 20 minutes had an ash content of about 0.07%.

Example 4: The warm unfiltered residual oil from Example 2 was diluted with about two to three volumes of warm diluent. The diluent was the portion of the distillate from the thermal-cracking with a boiling range from 325° to 525°F. Rapid and complete filtration was obtained using a vacuum of 27 inches, through a filtering medium composed of a No. 1 Whatman filter paper on a Buechner funnel, giving retention of all suspended solids (including precipitated material).

The filter temperature was about 250°F. The diluent-free filter cake consisted of 20% clay, 4% free carbon, and 76% diluent insoluble material. Upon removal of the diluent by distillation, the extract showed an ash content of about 0.016 weight percent. (Coke produced from this extract by heating in a Ramsbottom furnace at 1020°F. for 20 minutes had an ash content of about 0.11%.

HYDROGENATION

Hydrofining Process

J. Eng and W.R. Guggisberg; U.S. Patent 3,480,540; November 25, 1969; assigned to Esso Research and Engineering Company describe a hydrofining process which provides adequate desulfurization, denitrogenation and saturation of olefins for a blend of fractions derived from bitumen in a single unit employing the same conditions and catalyst for all. It has been found that when the bitumen fractions are blended in certain quantities and processed at certain hydrofining conditions, the fractions are each upgraded in the desired manner.

Generally, the process comprises separating the relatively solids-free bitumen into an overhead virgin fraction and a bottoms fraction, cracking the bottoms fraction, blending the virgin and cracked fractions, hydrofining the blend and recovering desired product fractions.

Referring to Figure 4.6, the bitumen derived from tar sands is fed by line 1 to distillation tower 2. Suitable bitumens have distillation characteristics such that 50% of the material is distilled at a temperature in the range of 800° to 1100°F. The bitumens contain 1.5 to 6 weight percent sulfur, 0.1 to 1.0 weight percent nitrogen, 100 to 500 ppm metals, less than 5% inorganic solids and water and they have pour points in the range of 20° to 110°F. In tower 2 the bitumen is separated into a virgin overhead fraction having an end point of 500° to 1000°F., preferably below 700°F. and a bottoms fraction boiling below 500° to 1000°F., preferably above 700°F.

The virgin fraction is passed by line 3 to hydrofining reactor 4 without any further treatment. The bottoms is passed by line 5 to a conversion unit, preferably a fluid coker 6 or a visbreaker. The conversion unit can be any suitable type of thermal-cracking or depolymerization reactor including a delayed coker, a fluid coker, a visbreaker or a hydrovisbreaker. If desired, cracking processes involving inert solids, catalysts, hydrogen and steam can be used although conventional thermal-cracking processes are deemed more suitable for cracking the heavy bitumen bottoms.

In the case of fluid coking the coking zone is usually maintained at a temperature of about 800° to 950°F. Typical fluid coking processes, thermal-cracking processes and visbreaking processes are described in Hydrocarbon Processing, September 1966, volume 45, No. 9, pp. 191 to 194. Cracking severity can be controlled in accordance with the type of products desired. Coke is removed from the coker by line 7. A gas and light ends fraction is removed from the coker by line 8. A cracked fraction boiling in the range of C_5 to 1100°F., preferably 70° to 925°F., is passed by line 9 to line 3 where it is blended with the virgin fraction. The blend is hydrofined in reactor 4. Any suitable hydrofining reactor can be used. Conventional hydrofining catalysts can be used.

FIGURE 4.6: PROCESS FOR HYDROFINING BITUMEN

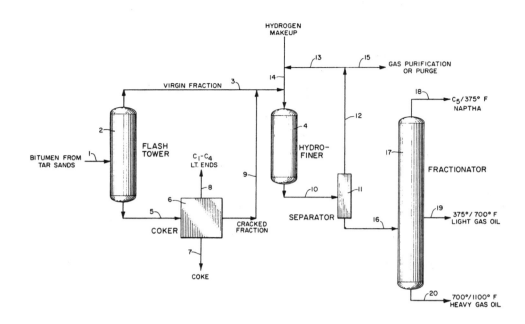

Source: J. Eng and W.R. Guggisberg; U.S. Patent 3,480,540; November 25, 1969

The preferred catalyst is one containing 2 to 5 weight percent cobalt oxide, 10 to 25 weight percent molybdenum oxide and the balance silica stabilized alumina. Oxide catalysts are preferably sulfided in any conventional manner prior to use or in situ.

The reaction conditions in reactor 4 depend in part on the characteristics of the components of the blended feed and on the type of products desired. In general the reaction temperature is about 500° to 850°F., preferably 600° to 800°F.; the reaction pressure is about 400 to 2,000 psig., preferably 500 to 1,200 psig and the fresh feed rate is 0.2 to 3.0 v./v./hr. The hydrogen containing treat gas contains 60 to 100% hydrogen and it is supplied at the rate of 500 to 2,000 scf/bbl. Under these conditions hydrodesulfurization, hydrodenitrogenation and saturation of olefins and polyaromatics are the dominant reactions.

Reaction products are removed by line 10 and passed to separator 11. A gas fraction containing hydrogen, H_2S and ammonia is passed overhead by line 12. All or part of the gas is recycled to the reactor by lines 13 and 14. Make up hydrogen is supplied by line 14. Part of the gas can be purged from the system or sent to purification by line 15. Hydrofined oil is passed by line 16 to distillation tower 17. In a preferred example, three fractions are recovered. A C_5 to 375°F. gasoline fraction is recovered by line 18. A light gas oil fraction boiling in the range of 375° to 700°F. is recovered by line 19. A heavy gas oil fraction boiling in the range of 700° to 1100°F. is recovered by line 20.

The fractionation in zone 17 can be arranged in any suitable manner depending upon the number and type of products desired.

Example: Hydrofining of blended bitumen fractions is demonstrated by the following data. A blend of coker distillates and virgin distillates simulating a tar sand bitumen distillate blend was prepared. The blend contained 37 volume percent virgin gas oil from a tar sand bitumen and 63 volume percent of petroleum derived materials having characteristics similar to distillates derived from tar sands. The properties of the components of the blend are shown in Table 1 below. The simulated distillate blend and its fractions have the inspections shown in Table 2 below. 12,000 g. of the total distillate blend was hydrofined in a reactor in the presence of a sulfided cobalt molybdate on silica stabilized alumina catalyst.

The catalyst contained 3.5 weight percent cobalt oxide, 12.1 weight percent molybdenum oxide, 2.0 weight percent silica and the balance was alumina. The pressure was 800 psig; the space velocity was 1.0 and the hydrogen rate was 2,000 scf/bbl. The data in Table 3 shows the results for hydrofining temperatures of 650°, 700° and 750°F. The data show that the bromine No. and the sulfur content of the total feed have been reduced to satisfactory values. Sulfur has been reduced from about 2 to 0.3% or less depending on the reaction temperature.

TABLE 1:   COMPONENTS IN SIMULATED ATHABASCA TAR SAND DISTILLATE BLEND[1]

	LV percent in Blend	Boiling Range, ° F.	Gravity API	Sulphur, Wt. percent	Nitrogen, Wt. percent	Bromine No.
Naphtha:						
Coker	14	C₅/350	62.9	0.36	0.006	73
Virgin	1	C₅/380	63.6	0.06	[2] 1	1
Light Gas Oil:						
Coker	12	355/680	24.0	1.43	0.046	32
Virgin	20	400/650	36.1	0.80	0.010	3
Heavy Gas Oil:						
Coker	16	650/1,000	23.3	2.50	0.520	
Virgin	37	650/1,000	15.4	3.00	0.118	8

[1] The heavy virgin gas oil was produced from Athabasca Tar Sand bitumen. Other components from topping and delayed coking unit when processing sour blend crude.
[2] Parts per million.

TABLE 2:   INSPECTIONS ON THE SIMULATED TAR SAND DISTILLATE BLEND AND ITS FRACTIONS

		Fractions		
	Total Blend	Naph-tha	Light Gas Oil	Heavy Gal O s
LV, Percent on Blend	100	16.8	34.7	48.1
ASTM Dist. Range, ° F	C₅/1,000 Nominal	126/378	420/620	692/911 (95% pt)
API Gravity	28.3	58.5	32.5	16.5
Bromine Number	20.5	65.9	15.9	12.2
Sulphur, Wt. Percent	1.97	0.36	1.17	2.82
Total Nitrogen, p.p.m	1,030	25	350	2,300
Basic Nitrogen, p.p.m	291	25	139	533
Mercaptan Number	28.8	66.4	19.2	8.0

TABLE 3: HYDROFINING SIMULATED TAR SAND DISTILLATE BLEND

	Treat Temperature, °F.								
	650			700			750		
Total Liquid Product:									
Bromine Number	2.1			2.1			2.5		
Sulfur, Wt. Percent	0.29			0.10			0.03		
	Fraction [1]								
	Naph.	Lt. G.O.	Hvy. G.O.	Naph.	Lt. G.O.	Hvy. G.O.	Naph.	Lt. G.O.	Hvy. G.O
LV Percent on Total Prod	17	39	44	18	39	43	21	43	36
API Gravity	58.9	33.9	22.2	59.4	34.1	22.9	58.5	33.4	23.8
Bromine Number	0.3	1.3	3.5	0.3	1.5	3.3	0.6	2.2	4.4
Sulfur, Weight Percent	[2]16	0.10	0.55	[2]17	0.05	0.19	[2]16	0.01	0.04
Total N, p.p.m.	15	225	1,350	6	134	1,170	7	66	168
Basic N, p.p.m.	15	130	288	6	90	217	6	52	60
Mercaptan Number	0.2	0.2	0.6	0.1	0.1	0.2	0.2	0.1	0.2

[1] 15/5 distillation to nominal C₅/380, 380/650 and 650° F.+ vapor temperature fractions.
[2] Parts per million.

The product naphtha fraction has a bromine No. of less than 1.0 which is desirable for gasoline components. The nitrogen and sulfur content of the naphtha is low enough for subsequent reforming and/or incorporation into mogas without sweetening. Light gas oils are often used as domestic heating oils and the light gas oil products are low enough in sulfur content for this use. The heavy gas oil product has a sulfur content of 0.5% or less making it suitable for use as industrial fuel oil in areas where sulfur contents must be very low.

A process described by E.T. Layng; U.S. Patent 3,151,054; September 29, 1964; assigned to Hydrocarbon Research, Inc. is directed to the thermal hydrogenation of tar sands to convert the fines to a settled condition whereby a silt free product can be produced.

The refining process includes the steps of passing the tar sand substantially in the liquid phase through a reaction zone in the presence of a hydrogen-containing gas under temperature in the range of 700° to 950°F. and hydrogen partial pressure in the range of 200 to 1,000 psig and space velocity to provide a residence time in the order of one-half hour to about one and one-half hours whereby the silt becomes free settling and settling the effluent to remove a substantially silt free liquid and an ash containing residue.

Hydrogenated Thermal Tar as Hydrogen Donor-Diluent

A process described by J. Stewart, S.C. Fulton and A.W. Langer, Jr.; U.S. Patent 2,772,209; November 27, 1956; assigned to Esso Research and Engineering Company involves the use of an inexpensive hydrogen donor-diluent, such as a partially hydrogenated thermal tar obtained from catalytic cracking operations on hydrocarbon fractions such as petroleum gas oils in the recovery of oil from tar sands.

In the process it is preferred to use a donor-diluent having a boiling range within the limits roughly of about 500° to 700°F. The lower boiling material makes it easier to strip the oil from the sand in later stages of the process. However, diluents boiling above 700° and up to about 900°F. may be used in many cases without difficulty. The diluent is preferably used in sufficient proportions to form a liquid or pumpable slurry with the sand. For this purpose, with high grade sands, the diluent should have a weight ratio of up to about 5 to 1, based on the tar content of the sand.

For sands of low bitumen or oil content, even larger proportions may be needed, up to about 10 to 1 on the same basis. Using 5 to 10 parts of donor-diluent by weight for each part of tar or bitumen, the transferable hydrogen in the donor-diluent need not be very high. Hydrogenation to the extent of about 200 to 600 scf of hydrogen per barrel of diluent is quite adequate.

In the process, sand is broken up and mixed with the donor-diluent in proportions suitable for forming a mobile slurry. The slurry is pumped through a fired coil and into a soaking and settling zone where the mixture is heated to a temperature within the range of about 700° to 1000°F., preferably between 750° and 900°F. The material is held for a period sufficient to obtain good extraction, sufficient agitation being applied to accomplish this result. The usual residence time is from about 10 minutes to 120 minutes. The process is preferably carried out under moderate pressure, e.g., up to 500 psig, a pressure of about 200 psig being very satisfactory. However, the pressure need be no greater than is necessary to prevent loss of volatile ingredients.

The sand settles gradually to the bottom, as its oil content is extracted, and an oil phase forms at the top. The rate of sand settling and the completeness of oil extraction varies in part with the viscosity of the slurry and in part with the degree of agitation. The latter should be so controlled as to obtain maximum extraction of oil, consistent with good throughput. If the average residence time of the sand is within the limits described above and the sand slurry is free-flowing, extraction will be reasonably complete. With a residence time of 1 hour, for example, and a ratio of diluent to bitumen of 4:1, using a temperature of at least 750°F., and a diluent of boiling range about 500° to 700°F., 95% or more of the bitumen may be extracted.

As shown in Figure 4.7, oil sand is broken into small lumps or particles of a maximum size of 1 inch or less, preferably not over 1/4 inch in average diameter. The subdivided bituminous sand is fed to a slurry tank 11 through a line 13. There it is mixed by any conventional means with a liquid donor-diluent fraction supplied through a line 15, to form a slurry, preferably a free-flowing or pumpable slurry.

The slurry leaves tank 11 through a line 17 and passes to a heating coil 19 and into a soaking and settling tank 21. Additional heat may be applied to or in tank 21 by conventional means if desired. In any case, the temperature of the slurry in the settler is brought up to at least 700° and not more than 1000°F., preferably between 750° and 900°F.

Agitation by a propeller or stirrer or the equivalent is maintained in the tank 21 so that the sand settles slowly to the bottom with a residence time between about 10 and 120 minutes, as previously described. Oil moves to the top of the tank 21 and is drawn off through a line 23 to fractionator 25. The sand is taken out at the bottom through a line 27 to a receiver, shown as a fluid solids stripper vessel 29. Here a stripping fluid, preferably steam, though an inert gas may be used, is introduced through one or more lines 31 to fluidize the sand and to strip its residual oil content. The spent sand may be withdrawn through a line 33, preferably to a heat exchanger to make use of its sensible heat. The oil is fractionated in fractionater 25 to obtain desired products such as gas through line 35, gasoline through line 37, light gas oil through line 39, a diluent-donor base material through line 41

FIGURE 4.7:   SLURRY PROCESS EMPLOYING HYDROGENATED THERMAL TAR AS DONOR-DILUENT

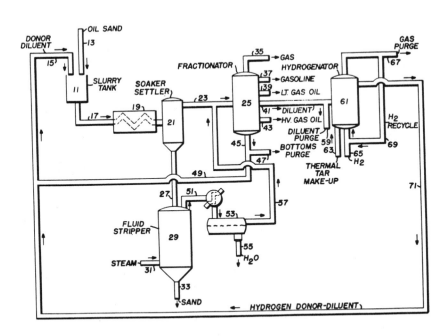

Source: J.Stewart, S.C. Fulton and A.W. Langer, Jr.; U.S. Patent 2,772,209; Nov. 27, 1956

(preferably boiling between 500° or 550° and about 700°F.) and a heavy gas oil through line 43. Bottoms are withdrawn through a line 45, from which part may be purged through line 47. The remainder, or all if desired, may be recycled to the diluent line 15 through line 49.

The stripped products from stripper vessel 29 go through line 51 to a condenser 53 where the steam is condensed and removed through a line 55. The oil products then go through line 57 to join the feed to the fractionator described above.

In order to control the quality of the diluent, part of it may be purged from line 41 through line 59. The remainder is taken to a hydrogenator 61. Here makeup thermal tar may be added, to keep the condensed ring aromatics content high, through a line 63. This is preferably a tar from catalytic cracking of petroleum (gas oil), with the same general boiling range, i.e., above 500° and below 900°F. Gaseous hydrogen is added, from any suitable source such as hydroformer through line 65.

As noted above, hydrogen requirements may vary between about 50 and 1,000 scf/bbl. of diluent, more or less, depending upon the ratio of diluent to bitumen, as well as upon other factors such as pressure and temperature in the soaker.

Gas may be purged overhead through line 67, but preferably much or most of it is recycled through line 69. Hydrogenation is carried out in a conventional manner. The partially hydrogenated donor-diluent material is then recycled through line 71 to join line 15 into the slurry tank 11. From here the process is repeated.

In related work J. Stewart, S.C. Fulton and A.W. Langer, Jr.; U.S. Patent 2,847,306; August 12, 1958; assigned to Esso Research and Engineering Company describe the application of the above hydrogenated thermal tar donor-diluent process to the recovery of oil from shale.

Jet Fuels

A process described by M.C. Kirk, Jr.; U.S. Patent 3,594,307; July 20, 1971; assigned to Sun Oil Company involves producing a jet fuel having a luminometer number of at least 75. The process involves contacting a charge comprising jet fuel range distillate from coked (thermally cracked) tar sands bitumen (such as that separated from Athabasca tar sands by the hot water process) or a straight run kerosene charge, or a catalytic gas oil charge, acyclic C_9 to C_{18} olefin charge (or a mixture of at least two such charges) with hydrogen in the presence of a hydrogenation catalyst formed from at least one member selected from the group consisting of nickel, cobalt, iron, molybdenum and tungsten and related oxides and sulfides on an inert porous carrier.

This is carried out at a temperature of 500° to 785°F., a pressure of 350 to 2,000 psig, a liquid hourly space velocity of 0.5 to 10.0 and a hydrogen circulation rate of 0 to 20,000 standard cubic feet per barrel of the charge. The resultant product is contacted with hydrogen in the presence of a catalyst which comprises a metal selected from the group consisting of nickel, cobalt, tungsten, Ru, Rh, Re, Os and the noble metal hydrogenation catalysts (Pt and Pd), the catalyst being supported on a porous support (e.g., alumina, kieselguhr) at a temperature of 450° to 775°F., at a pressure of 500 to 3,000 psig, a liquid hourly space velocity of 0.1 to 10.0 and a hydrogen circulation rate of 0 to 20,000 scf/bbl. of the product of the first stage, the combination of conditions being selected to produce a jet fuel having an ASTM smoke point of at least 32± 3. The following example illustrates the process.

A straight run kerosene meeting the specifications for JP-5 and having the properties listed in the table below, under the heading charge, and containing 12.4% aromatics, was hydrodesulfurized in the presence of a sulfided catalyst comprising cobalt and molybdenum oxides on alumina (which catalyst was commercially available under the trade name Aero HDS-2). The hydrodesulfurization was conducted at 750 psig and 600°F. at a liquid hourly space velocity of 2 and a hydrogen recycle of 5,000 scf/bbl. of charge.

The hydrodesulfurized product was then charged to a second hydrogenation stage wherein the catalyst was Ni on kieselguhr. The second stage hydrogenation was conducted at 500°F. and at 500 psig, at a liquid hourly space velocity of 0.75 with a hydrogen recycle of 10,000 standard cubic feet per barrel of feed. The product of the second hydrogenation stage contained only 0.05% by weight of aromatic hydrocarbons and had a smoke number of 35. Other properties of this two-stage product, are listed in the table under the heading JP-5A. From the California Research correlation, a smoke number of 35, for the second stage product, corresponds to a luminometer number of 82.

Tar Sands Retorting and Refining Processes

Preparation of Jet Fuels

	Charge stock							
	JP-5					Propylene tetramer		
	Operation							
	Deep hydrogenation of aromatics			Moderate hydrogenation of aromatics		Saturation of olefins		
	2 stages							
Catalyst type	CoMo[1]	Ni[2]	Ni-W	Ni-W	CoMo	CoMo		
Reactor conditions:								
Operating pressure, p.s.i.g	750	500	1,800	750	750		750	500
Gas recycle rate, s.c.f./bbl	5,000	10,000	5,000	0	0		0	3,000
Temperature, °F	725	500	575	600	600		600	600
Liquid hourly space velocity	2	0.75	1	1.5	1		2	2
Inspection data	Charge							
Gravity, °API	43.9	45.3	44.8	44.4	44.1	52.1	54.2	54.1
Distillation (Engler) °F.:								
10%	393	392	393	388	396	358	360	363
50%	419	418	418	419	418	365	370	371
90%	465	452	444	449	448	380	383	384
Aromatics, weight percent	12.4	0.05	4.0		9.8			
Olefins, weight percent						92.4	6.4	3.8
Freezing point, °F		—54	—51	—58	—58		<—76	<—76
Flash point, (cc.), °F	154	148			146	136	136	138
Estimated Luminometer No.[3]		82		69	62		95	94
Smoke point	24	35		30	27		40	39
Aniline point, °F	149.5	164.6					175.0	176.4

[1] Desulfurization step.
[2] Deep hydrogenation step.
[3] Luminometer No. estimated from smoke point.

It can be seen from the charge properties listed in the table that this charge is a paraffinic kerosene. The table also lists, for purposes of comparison, runs made on the same straight run kerosene wherein only a single hydrogenation (or hydrodesulfurization) stage was used. Also shown, for comparison purposes, are similar runs made on propylene tetramer (which is a product obtained by the catalytic polymerization of propylene in the presence of a phosphoric acid on kieselguhr catalyst).

The hydrogenated propylene tetramer makes an excellent blending stock for incorporating with the two-stage hydrogenation products in order to make products having luminometer values above 85 (surprisingly, such hydrogenated acyclic olefins can be produced which have luminometer values of 100).

COMPANY INDEX

The company names listed below are given exactly as they appear in the patents, despite name changes, mergers and acquisitions which have, at times, resulted in the revision of a company name.

INVENTOR INDEX

Inventor Index

U.S. PATENT NUMBER INDEX

NOTICE

Nothing contained in this Review shall be construed to constitute a permission or recommendation to practice any invention covered by any patent without a license from the patent owners. Further, neither the author nor the publisher assumes any liability with respect to the use of, or for damages resulting from the use of, any information, apparatus, method or process described in this Review.

EPOXY RESIN HANDBOOK 1972
Blue Book No. 5

This book contains technical data and specifications of commercial epoxy resins and their curing compounds, as manufactured or sold in the United States.

Epoxy resins, based on ethylene oxide (oxirane) or its homologs or derivatives, and nearly always used with hardeners or curing agents, are classified as thermosetting resins. They offer excellent chemical resistance and good adhesive properties; they are strong and tough with low shrinkage during cure. They have excellent electrical properties and good heat resistance.

Consumption of uncured epoxy resins in the U.S. has increased from less than one million pounds in 1950 to about 140 million pounds in 1971.

Like the other volumes in our Blue Book Series, this book is intended as a guide to technical data of the following 69 U.S. companies with standard product lines:

Abbott Laboratories
Ablestik Laboratories
Adhesive Engineering Company
Ajinomoto Co., Inc.
Allied Products Corporation
American Cyanamid Company
Amicon Corporation
Amoco Chemicals Corporation
Amrez Corporation
Anderson Development Company
Apogee Chemical, Inc.
ArChem Company
Armstrong Products Co., Inc.
Bacon Industries Inc.
The Biggs Company
The Borden Chemical Company
Castall, Inc.
Celanese Resins
Ciba-Geigy Corporation
Daubert Chemical Company
Devcon Corporation
John C. Dolph Company
The Dow Chemical Company
Emerson & Cuming, Inc.
Emery Industries Inc.
The Epoxylite Corporation

Epoxy Technology Inc.
Fenwal Incorporated
Fluoro-Plastics, Inc.
Furane Plastics Incorporated
General Mills, Inc.
Hardman Incorporated
The Harshaw Chemical Co.
High Strength Plastics Corporation
The Homalite Corporation
Hughson Chemical Company
Hysol Division—The Dexter Corporation
Isochem Resins Company
Key Polymer Corp.
Kristal Kraft, Inc.
Leffingwell Chemical Company
The Lubrizol Corporation
The Marblette Corporation
Mereco Products
Miracle Adhesives Corporation
M-R Plastics & Coatings, Inc.
Pacific Resins & Chemicals, Inc.
Pennsylvania Industrial Chemical Corporation
Plastics Engineering Company
The Polymer Corporation
Polymer Research Corp. of America
Reichhold Chemicals, Inc.
Ren Plastics, Inc.
Rohm and Haas Company
W. S. Shamban & Company
Shell Chemical Company
Sterling Division of RCI
Talon Adhesives Corp.
Techform Laboratories, Inc.
Tescom Corporation
Tra-Con, Inc.
Transene Company, Inc.
Union Carbide Corporation
Uniroyal Chemical
U. S. Polymeric, Inc.
United States Steel
R. T. Vanderbilt Company, Inc.
Vebo-Chemie AG
Washburn-Lanson Company

All the information is taken directly from the manufacturers' hard-to-get data sheets and technical bulletins at no cost to, nor influence from, the manufacturers of the specified epoxy resins and compounds.

414 pages

$36

ACRYLIC AND VINYL FIBERS 1972
by M. Sittig
Chemical Process Review No. 62

Acrylic fibers are versatile materials whose popularity continues to grow. They are the most wool-like of the noncellulosic fibers. Modacrylic (modified acrylic) fibers have a silk-like feel with the added advantage of being strong and hard-wearing, plus the important property of being inherently flameproof.

There are other fibers derived from vinyl monomers which have outstanding properties of their own. Their manufacture and applications are reviewed here also. Altogether 123 processes are described in detail. A partial table of contents follows. Numbers in ( ) indicate a plurality of processes per topic.

1. ACRYLONITRILE MANUFACTURE
   From Propylene, NH₃ and O₂ (11)
   From Ethylene, HCN and O₂
   From Acetylene and HCN (3)
   From Acrolein Cyanohydrin
   By Dehydrogenation of Propionitrile (2)
2. ACRYLONITRILE POLYMERS
   Emulsion Polymerization (2)
   Solution Polymerization (8)
   Suspension Polymerization (2)
3. POLYACRYLONITRILE SPINNING SOLUTIONS
   American Cyanamid Process
   BASF Process
   Rhône-Poulenc Process
4. SPINNING ACRYLONITRILE-BASED FIBERS
   Dry Spinning
   Melt Spinning
   Wet Spinning (2)
   Composite Fiber Manufacture (2)
5. VINYL CHLORIDE MANUFACTURE
   Oxychlorination of Ethylene (2)
   Oxychlorination of Ethane (2)
   Sulfochlorination of Ethane
   Cracking of Ethylene Dichloride (4)
   From Acetylene & Hydrogen Chloride (4)
   Reaction of Methane + Chlorine
6. POLYVINYL CHLORIDE MANUFACTURE
   Emulsion Polymerization
   Suspension Polymerization (3)
   Fluidized State Polymerization (3)
   Solution Polymerization
   Mass Polymerization (3)
   Reactor Cleanup

7. PVC FIBER MANUFACTURE
   Dry Spinning
   Melt Spinning
   Wet Spinning
8. VINYL ACETATE MANUFACTURE
   Acetylene + Acetic Acid (4)
   Ethylene, Acetic Acid + Oxygen (9)
9. POLYVINYL ACETATE MANUFACTURE
   Emulsion Polymerization
   Solution Polymerization (2)
   Copolymerization with Ethylene
10. POLYVINYL ALCOHOL PRODUCTION
    From Polyvinyl Acetate (2)
    Ethylene-Vinyl Acetate Copolymers
11. POLYVINYL ALCOHOL FIBER PRODUCTION
12. ACRYLIC ESTER MANUFACTURE
    Propylene Oxidation
    Acrolein Oxidation
    Isobutane Oxidation
    From Methacrylaldehyde
    Hydrolysis of Acrylonitrile
    From Acetone Cyanohydrin
    From Alkyl Esters + Formaldehyde
    Cleavage of Polyacrylic Esters
    Carbonylation of Methylacetylene
    Esterification of Acrylic Acid
13. POLYACRYLIC ESTER MANUFACTURE
    Emulsion Polymerization (3)
14. VINYLIDENE CHLORIDE PRODUCTION
    Monomer Stabilization
15. POLYVINYLIDENE CHLORIDE PRODUCTION
    Emulsion Polymerization (2)
16. POLYVINYLIDENE CHLORIDE FIBERS
17. VINYL FLUORIDE PRODUCTION
    Acetylene + Hydrogen Fluoride (5)
    Vinyl Chloride + Hydrogen Fluoride
18. POLYVINYL FLUORIDE PRODUCTION
    Suspension Polymerization (3)
19. POLYVINYL FLUORIDE FIBER MANUFACTURE
    Wet Spinning Process
20. FUTURE TRENDS

331 pages

$36

NONCATALYTIC
AUTO EXHAUST REDUCTION 1972
by D. Post
Pollution Control Review No. 10

Deals with a broad range of systems and devices in the areas of noncatalytic or thermal combustion and physical separation of fumes and particles by filtration or cyclone-type centrifugal action. Chemical reactions not initiated or supported by any kind of catalyst are also described.

The book is a review of 87 U.S. patents of recent origin. Unburned hydrocarbons and carbon monoxide are the principal components sought to reduce the volume of patent literature, activity in this phase of pollution control is far greater than in other approaches.

Yet, a wide variety of separation processes are being considered, where efforts are toward absorption of pollutants by water and filtration of suspended particles, (particulates). A partial table of contents follows. Numbers in ( ) indicate the number of processes described under each heading.

I. COMBUSTION
   Initiation of Combustion (10)
   Secondary Air Supply (10)
   Combustion in or at an Engine Exhaust Manifold (7)
   Heat Exchange (11)
   Control of Exhaust Gas Flow (2)
   Combustion Aid Materials and Construction (4)
   Combustion Chamber Variations (10)
II. SEPARATION
   Sorption (7)
   Filtration (6)
   Inertial Separation (5)
   Condensation (2)
   Electrostatic Precipitation (1)
III. CHEMICAL REACTIONS OTHER THAN COMBUSTION
   Electrically Induced Oxidation (1)
   Removal of Lead with Phosphorus Compounds (1)
   Granular Chemical Treating Agents (1)
   Combustion and Electrostatic Precipitation (1)
   Electrically Charged Gold Plated Fibers (1)
   High Temperature Decomposition via Plasma Flame (1)

IV. OTHER METHODS
   ENGINE OPERATION (4)
   Ozone Injection, Combustion and Filtration
   Air-Fuel Mixture to Engine and Exhaust Gas Pressure Control
   Carburetor Design, Carburetor Controller, and Exhaust Gas Combustion
   Throttle Valve Positioning
   MISCELLANEOUS (3)
   Corrosion Resistant Muffler
   Fumes Collecting Tunnels Below Road Surface
   Galvanic Cells to Monitor Exhaust Gas Composition
To indicate the wealth of information found in each chapter, a selection of topics from Chapter I on Combustion follows:
   High Voltage Ignition
   Heated Baffles for Ignition
   Sequential Firing
   Electrostatic Aids
   Hot Wire Ignition
   Temperature Controlled Elements
   Tandem Aspirating Chambers
   Direct Flame in Constricted Area
   Exhaust Gas Ignition
   Free Radicals to Promote Combustion
   Secondary Air Compressor
   Multiple Port Aspiration
   Control of Secondary Air
   Secondary Air Aspirator
   Temperature Actuated Air Blower
   Speed-Regulated Secondary Air
   Combustion at Each Exhaust Port
   Circumferential Secondary Air Inlet
   Control of Back Pressure
   Combustion in Exhaust Manifold
   Preheated Secondary Air
   Annular Heat Exchange Passage
   Steady Flame to Initiate Combustion
   Periodic Flow Reversal
   Laminar Flow in Heat Exchanger
   Exhaust Gas Recycling
   Surface Combustion on Refractory Packing
   Mixing Devices
   Gold Plated Combustion Chamber
   Tangential Flow of Exhaust Gas

278 pages

$36

TOBACCO FLAVORING
SUBSTANCES AND METHODS 1972
by S. Gutcho

Domestic and oriental tobaccos are often combined to prepare a blend with pleasant flavors and aromas before and during smoking. When certain tobaccos are in short supply and the formulation of a natural blend becomes too costly, the manufacture of an equivalent product by addition of flavors (natural or synthetic) is required. The loss of aromatic substances within a filter also requires the addition of flavors or enhancers. 86 Processes. Numbers in ( ) denote numbers of processes per chapter or heading.

1. MENTHOL FLAVOR (10)
   Monomenthyl Esters of Polycarboxylic Acids
   Menthyl Acetals
   Menthyl Ethers
   Menthyl Esters of Aliphatic Keto Acids
   Menthyl Chlorocarbonate and Menthyl Linalool Carbonate
   Mentholated Cigar Tobacco
   Cyclohexanones & Cyclohexenones
   Carbonate Esters of Flavorants
   Polyhydroxy Compounds
   Inclusion Complexes
2. TOBACCO FLAVOR
   Naphthofuran-2-one & Naphthopyran-3-one
   Polyisoprenoid Hydrocarbons
   Lactic Acid Esters of Isoprenoid Alcohols
   Methyl & Ethyl Pyridines
   3,4-Substituted Maleimides
   2,5-Substituted Pyrroles
   1-Pyrrolidinecarboxyaldehyde
   Piperitenone
   cis-3-Hexen-1-ol
   3-(2-Hydroxycyclohexyl)Propionic Acid Lactone
   2-Methyl-5-Isopropyl-1,3-Nonadien-8-one
   5-Methylacetylfuran &
   5-Methylfuraldehyde
   Turkish Tobacco Flavor
   Tobacco Extract
3. OTHER FLAVORS
   MINT (4)
   Cyclohexylcyclohexanone as Enhancer
   Aliphatic Dicarboxylic Acids Polyvalent Metal Salts
   Diels-Alder Adducts
   Butyrolactones
   SPICY (5)
   Dimers of Cinnamic Acid
   Substituted Malic Acids

   Saturated & Unsaturated d'-Lactones
   Cyclohexen-1-one Derivative
   Butadiene Derivative
   WOODY (5)
   Naphthalenone Derivative
   Theaspirone + Cyclohexenylbutanol Derivatives
   Butyrolactones
   Naphthopyran Derivative
   Biphenyl and Cyclohexylcychexane
   CAMPHOR (3)
   Hexahydrotetramethylchromanone
   α-Keto Acids
   FRUITY AND FLOWERY (6)
   Methylpyrrole Derivatives
   Benzopyran Derivatives
   1-Methyl-2-Pyrrolecarboxaldehyde
   Maleic Anhydride Derivatives
   Butyrolactones
   Chemical Additives
   VARIOUS FLAVORS (3)
   By-products from Cocoa & Chocolate
   Pyrazine Derivatives
   α-,β-Unsaturated δ-Lactones
4. TECHNIQUES OF FLAVOR IMPROVEMENT
   USE OF ADSORBENTS (4)
   FLAVOR RETENTION (3)
   TOBACCO SMOKE IMPROVEMENT (3)
   FLAVOR ENHANCEMENT (2)
5. FLAVOR INCORPORATION
   USE OF MICROCAPSULES (3)
   Microcapsules in Tobacco Sheet
   Flavors for Encapsulating
   Microencapsulated Clove Flavor
   USE OF POLYMERS
   INCLUSION COMPLEXES (2)
   USE OF CHARCOAL
   UNUSUAL TECHNIQUES (4)
6. SYNTHESIS OF FLAVORS (10)
   Naphthofuranones & Pyranones
   Polyisoprenoid Lactic Esters
   Polyisoprenoid Hydrocarbons
   Tobacco Component Esterification
   Amino Acids + Carbonyl Sugars
   Alcoholyses of Saccharides
   Flavors from Fermentation Gas
   2-Hydroxyacetophenones
   Cyclohexenones
   Menthyl Carbonates + Polyhydroxy Compounds

161 pages

$24

Latest technology

ISOCYANATES MANUFACTURE RECENT DEVELOPMENTS 1972

by M. W. Ranney

Chemical Process Review No. 63

This book describes 127 recent processes related to improved methods of manufacture for toluene diisocyanate, polymeric isocyanates, aliphatic isocyanates, and some flame-retardant, halogen-containing isocyanates. Based on 172 U.S. patents issued since 1967, the book presents an advanced review of manufacturing methods for obtaining isocyanates. In the following partial table of contents, numbers in ( ) are numbers of processes per topic.

1. TOLUENE DIISOCYANATES
   - PHOSGENATION PROCESSES (8)
     - Rapid Phosgenations
     - Tubular Reactor
     - Elongated Reaction Column
     - Two-Stage High Pressure Process
     - Continuous Two-Stage Process
     - Hydrochlorination of Diamine
     - Hot Phosgenation Process
     - Nonvicinal Toluene Diisocyanates
   - DISTILLATION AND RECOVERY (8)
     - Rotating Mill-Type Evaporator
     - Distillation Processes
     - Separation of Ortho Isomers
     - Distillation with poly-OH Compounds
     - Crystallization and Distillation
     - Heating with Organotin Compounds
     - Phosgenation of Distillation Residues
     - Recovery of Toluenediamines
   - STABILIZATION AND CHLORIDE REMOVAL (5)
     - Dilauryl Thiodipropionate
     - Aromatic Amines
     - Stabilization at Elevated Temperatures
     - Metal Naphthenates for Chloride Removal
     - Copper Powder for Chloride Removal
   - OTHER PROCESSES AND MIXTURES (3)
     - Nitrogen Oxide-Urea Reactions
     - Xylylene Dichloride and Alkali Metal Cyanate
     - Polyisocyanate Blends
2. AROMATIC ISOCYANATES
   - POLYISOCYANATES (13)
   - CONVERSION OF NITRO COMPOUNDS USING CARBON MONOXIDE (8)
   - SULFONYL ISOCYANATES (4)
   - OTHER PROCESSES (11)
     - Hindered Isocyanates containing Hydroxyls
     - Isocyanatophenols
     - 1,4-Bis(Isocyanato)-1-Phenyltetrahydronaphthalene
     - Oxydi(p-Phenylene Isocyanate)
     - Conversion of Isonitriles
     - Decomposition of N-Haloamides
     - Decomposition of Cyclic Nitrile Sulfites
     - Terphenyl Triisocyanates
     - 4-Substituted-2,2-Toluene Diisocyanate
     - Isocyanatostilbenes
     - Tetramethyl-p-Xylylenediamine
4. NONAROMATIC ISOCYANATES
   - CYCLOALIPHATIC POLYISOCYANATES (8)
   - UNSATURATED DIISOCYANATES (5)
   - OTHER POLYISOCYANATES (6)
   - MONOISOCYANATES (6)
   - MISCELLANEOUS (3)
4. HALOGEN-CONTAINING ISOCYANATES
   - AROMATIC (12)
   - ALIPHATIC (6)
5. POLYUREAS AND SILICONES
   - POLYUREAS AND BIURETS (6)
   - SILICON-CONTAINING COMPOUNDS (2)
6. GENERAL PROCESSES
   - GENERAL SYNTHESIS (10)
     - Isocyanic Acid-Olefin Reactions
     - Decomposition of Cyclic Nitrile Carbonates
     - Conversion of Isocyanates to Isothiocyanates
     - Phosgenation in Presence of Weak Lewis Bases
     - Temperature-Controlled High Dilution Phosgenation Process
     - Phosgenation Using Amide Catalysts
     - Trialkyl Boranes as Color Stabilizers
     - 2,2-Dimethoxy Propane as Viscosity Stabilizer
     - Secondary Carbamoyl Chlorides as Intermediates
     - Diphenyl Carbonate-Amine Reaction Products
   - MISCELLANEOUS PROCESSES (3)

258 pages

$36

Manufacture and applications

WATER-SOLUBLE POLYMERS 1972

by Y. L. Meltzer

Chemical Process Review No. 64

Synthetic water-soluble polymers are making appreciable inroads into the traditional starch and natural gum market. Synthetics have a much lower Biological Oxygen Demand (BOD) than starch, which can be a big stream pollutant. In addition, synthetics can be designed for a specific end use much more so than modified starches and starch derivatives. Yet the latter are still less expensive to produce and for this reason the newest processes in this very active field have received ample treatment. 139 Patent-based processes. Numbers in ( ) indicate numbers of processes per chapter in the following much curtailed table of contents:

1. MARKET SURVEY
2. ACRYLAMIDE POLYMERS (9)
   - U.V. Hardening
   - Aqueous Slurried Explosive
   - Friction Reducing Compositions
   - Chromatographic Adsorbents
3. ACRYLIC AND METHACRYLIC POLYMERS (13)
   - Stabilized Suspension Polymerization
   - Spray-On Bandages
   - Siloxane-Acrylate Copolymers
   - Flocculating Agent
   - Wallpaper Coating
4. CELLULOSE ETHERS (8)
   - Sulfonamide Modification
   - Dissolution of Cellulose Ethers
   - Surface-Sulfonated Cellulose Ethers
   - Absorbent Cellulose Particles
5. CARBOXYMETHYL CELLULOSE (13)
   - High Viscosity CMC
   - Increasing Thickening Power
   - Low Cost Process for CMC
   - Uniformly Substituted CMC
6. HYDROXYETHYL CELLULOSE (5)
   - Low Sulfate Ash HEC
   - Improved Oxidative Aging
7. HYDROXYPROPYL CELLULOSE (4)
   - Water-Immiscible Dispersants
   - New HPC Compounds
   - Propylene Oxide for Etherification
8. METHYL CELLULOSE (2)
   - Continuous Process
   - MC as Starch Substitute
9. OTHER DERIVATIVES (3)
   - Hydroxyethyl Hydroxypropyl Cellulose With High Thermoplasticity
   - Ethyl Cellulose with Reduced Viscosity
   - Soluble Epoxy Derivatives
10. ETHYLENE OXIDE POLYMERS (8)
    - High Molecular Weight Polymers
    - Oxidation of Alkenes to Oxides
    - Oxidation to Nitriles
    - Butynediol-Polyalkylene Oxides and Sulfuric Esters as Antifog Materials
    - Fiber Lubricating Composition
    - Water-Soluble Alkylene Oxide Block Copolymer
11. POLYETHYLENIMINE (18)
    - Polyethylenimine Boranes
    - Water-Soluble Copolymers of Alkylenimine and Alkylene Sulfide
    - Aminocarboxylate Chelants
    - Selective Alkylation
    - Copolymer of Ethlenimines and Lactones
    - Sizing Paper
    - Leachproof Fire-Resistant Complex
    - Sequestering Ion Exchange Resins
12. POLYVINYL ALCOHOL (20)
    - Vinyl Ester Polymerization
    - Melt-Formable PVAs
    - Modified PVA Films
    - Predetermined Viscosity
    - Polymerization of PVC with PVA
    - Producing Coated Paper
    - Coating a Substrate with Capsules
    - Improved Water Repellency
13. POLYVINYLPYRROLIDONE (14)
    - Functional Polymers
    - Gelling Polar Liquids
    - Pharmaceutical Compositions
    - Coated Confections
    - Stabilization of Beer
    - Granulated Feed
14. STARCH, MODIFIED STARCH, AND DERIVATIVES (22)
    - Hydroxypropylated Potato Starch
    - Starch Conversion Products
    - Sulfite-Carbonyl Starch Complex
    - Obtaining Amylose
    - Starch Phosphonates
    - "Inhibited" Starches

323 pages

$36

Pollution prevention

ELECTROLESS PLATING AND COATING OF METALS 1972

by J. McDermott

Electroless plating contributes its share toward reducing the pollution of our environment.

The most troublesome contaminants resulting from electroplating are solutions of cyanides, copper salts, and chromium compounds plus the acidic "drag-out" solutions and the dumpings from the cleaning, plating, and pickling steps.

Much water pollution can be avoided by the judicious application of directions given in the 201 patented processes (most issued since 1965) described in this book. Obviously there is no water pollution in a process based on the condensation of metallic vapor on the substrate under conditions of moderate to high vacuum.

Numerous nonelectrolytic processes are available for the production of metallic coatings. Some of the more significant procedures include hot dipping, impregnation or cementation, plasma arc spraying, vacuum coating, mechanical plating, and chemical deposition by electroless bath techniques.

Electroless plating has been the subject of much research over the past few years. In general, this term covers processes in which a metal compound is reduced to the metallic state by means of a chemical reducing agent. Typically, using nickel as an example, the nickel ions are reduced to the metal by the action of sodium hypophosphite. Many proprietary processes involving catalysts, both formulations and application techniques, have evolved within the last few years.

Electroless copper formulations widely used in printed circuit board manufacture, and processes for gold, silver, palladium, platinum, and cobalt, have been developed.

The protection of ferrous surfaces by aluminum or zinc coatings involves the use of molten bath techniques with recent efforts being devoted to vapor phase and powder deposition. Zinc-rich coatings continue to be of interest and are growing in commercial importance.

Requirements in the aerospace industry have resulted in coating techniques for providing high temperature, oxidation-corrosion resistant materials using refractory metals, such as columbium. High performance nickel alloys are coated for use as jet engine turbine blades.

Briefly, the need for protective metal coatings is increasing not only because of the demands of the space age, but also for protection of equipment against corrosive environments including at times our own corrosive atmosphere.

In the following partial table of contents, numbers in ( ) indicate the number of processes per topic.

1. COPPER
   - General Bath Formulations and Additives (10)
   - Circuit Boards (6)
   - Application to Ferrous Substrates (6)
   - Miscellaneous Coating Methods (4)
2. NICKEL, CHROMIUM, COBALT
   - Nickel Bath Formulations (20)
   - Specific Substrates (5)
   - Chromium (9)
   - Cobalt and Nickel (6)
   - Nickel-Iron-Phosphorus (7)
3. ALUMINUM, ZINC, TIN
   - Aluminum Vapor Techniques (3)
   - Aluminum Powder Techniques (4)
   - Molten Bath Techniques (5)
   - Hydride Bath Techniques (6)
   - Zinc Galvanizing (10)
   - Zinc-Rich Coatings (6)
   - Tin (5)
4. PRECIOUS METALS
   - Gold (8)
   - Platinum (6)
   - Silver and Palladium (3)
5. COATING OF REFRACTORY METALS
   - Aluminum (3)
   - Titanium, Chromium Alloys (8)
6. COATINGS FOR HIGH PERFORMANCE NICKEL ALLOYS
   - Nickel-Iron-Cobalt Alloys (8)
   - Other Alloys (7)
7. FLAME SPRAY, MECHANICAL PLATING, GENERAL PROCESSES
   - Flame Spray (7)
   - Mechanical Plating (5)
   - General Processes—Steel Substrates (12)
   - Miscellaneous Coatings and Substrates (22)

300 pages

$36

Marketing and financial guide

PHARMACEUTICAL AND COSMETIC FIRMS U.S.A. 1972

Second Edition

This publication lists about 750 leading pharmaceutical and cosmetic firms in the United States of America. Their business falls into the following categories:

Prescription Drugs
Proprietaries (OTC drugs)
Biologicals
Veterinary Pharmaceuticals
Medical and Hospital Supplies (includes diagnostic reagents, kits, etc.)
Dental Supplies
Cosmetics and Toiletries
Custom Manufacture (Private Formulas) and/or packaging of the above.

The following useful information has been listed for each firm, wherever available:

Name
Address
Telephone Number
Parent Company or Headquarters
Category (see above)
Annual Sales (1971 where available)
Number of Employees
Executives (Names & Titles)
Plant Locations
Domestic Divisions, Subsidiaries and/or Affiliates
Foreign Subsidiaries
Types of Products and well known Brand Names of Proprietaries and Cosmetics

This guide puts much information that is difficult to obtain at your fingertips. Considerable effort at screening has been made to include only those firms that have a significant annual sales figure. Both the pharmaceutical and cosmetic industries include a large number of very small companies, making these fields difficult to assess. We have attempted to eliminate these very small firms from this book.

The pharmaceutical industry in the United States is a large, well-established, and affluent industry. The American cosmetic industry, although subject to greater financial fluctuations, is no less opulent.

Many of these companies maintain giant research complexes and are spending about $500 million yearly on research alone, while total annual sales exceed the $10 billion mark. These are two large industries which are growing rapidly, recession and inflation notwithstanding.

Since only the largest companies are listed, this guide allows you to concentrate your efforts in the most profitable direction:

Pinpoint your sales efforts toward the Big Buyers
Know whom to contact
Find out who owns whom
Prepare market reports
Increase sales effectiveness
Search for potential acquisitions
Use the book . . .
as a guide to employment and as a personnel guide.

Two indexes are included. The first index lists the names of all divisions, subsidiaries, and affiliates which are involved in pharmaceutical, cosmetic, and related businesses not listed separately in the book, with the name of the parent company.

The other index lists the best known trademarks and brand names of proprietary items, cosmetics, and toiletries.

270 pages

$24

Important technology

RELEASE AGENTS 1972

by M. McDonald

Release agents, also named parting agents, slip agents, or abherents, are defined as substances capable of forming more or less permanent solid or liquid films that prevent, or at least reduce, adhesion between two surfaces.

Pressure-sensitive labels, for instance, could not be marketed or handled and their paper backing could not be peeled off before use, were it not coated with a release agent.

It is safe to state that several industries, now considered as basic, could not have grown to their present greatness without release agents. Examples are polymer processing and plastics molding, rubber processing, metal casting and forming (especially continuous casting of steel), glass molding, printing, paper coating, pressure-sensitive adhesives (tapes, etc.) and the food industry (especially baking, frying, and wrapping).

This volume describes the most recent developments in release agents as revealed by the U.S. patent literature in 110 patents issued since 1960.

The numbers in parentheses indicate the numbers of processes or application techniques discussed under a given heading or chapter.

1. METAL CASTING OR FORMING
WATER-BASED COMPOSITIONS (17)
Resins + Carbohydrate + Acid
Calcium Fluoride Powder
Other CaF_2 Compositions
Synthetic Hydroxyapatite
Refractory and Binder Slurries
Polysiloxane + Thickener
Alkoxysilanes
Silica and Xanthomonas Colloid
Humic Acid in Continuous Casting (3)
Swelling and Lubricating Powders
Fireclay and Polysaccharide Gums
Cryolite + Molasses + Hexachloroethane
Alumina for Molding Copper
Silicas
Guar Gum
OIL-BASED COMPOSITIONS (7)
Aromatic Bitumen
Addition of Lecithin
With Carboxylic Acid
Carboxylic Acid + Dispersant
Acetylated Hydroxy Fatty Acid in Castor Oil
Suspended Refractory Materials
Carbon and Fatty Acid Foods
OLEFINS (2)
BORON COMPOUNDS (2)
SILICONES (2)
NAPHTHALENE (1)
POLYFLAVANOIDS (1)
FATTY ACIDS (1)

2. PLASTICS AND RUBBER PROCESSING
MOLDING RUBBER (8)
MOLDING PLASTICS (16)
FILAMENT MAKING (1)
EXTRUDING PLASTICS (2)
PLASTIC FILMS (1)
FLOOR AND WALL COVERINGS (1)

3. CONCRETE
EPOXY AND VINYL RESINS (1)
OIL-BASED COMPOSITION (7)
PVA AND LIGNITIC WASTES FROM PAPERMILLS (2)

4. TABLETS
POLYFLUOROCARBONS (1)
ADIPIC ACID (2)
FUMARIC ACID (2)
OIL IN MICROCAPSULES (3)

5. GLASS INDUSTRY
OIL-BASED COMPOSITIONS (4)
SODIUM SILICATE, UREA AND GRAPHITE (1)
LEAD COMPOUNDS (1)

6. FIBER MATERIALS
PRESSURE-SENSITIVE TAPES (5)
RELEASE PAPERS (4)
PAPERBOARD MANUFACTURE (1)
MOLDING CORK COMPOSITIONS (1)

7. FOOD PRODUCTS
MEAT (2)
CHEESE (1)
DOUGH AND BAKED GOODS (1)

8. ICE
ICE CUBE TRAYS (2)
ATMOSPHERIC ICE (2)

9. MISCELLANEOUS
POWDERED MATERIALS (3)
OVEN COATINGS (1)
BEESWAX CANDLES (1)
PLASMA SPRAYING (1)
POLYSILOXANE EMULSIONS (1)

253 pages

$36

FOOD

AGGLOMERATION PROCESSES IN FOOD MANUFACTURE 1972
by N. D. Pintauro
Food Processing Review No. 25

In an agglomeration process several particles are caused to adhere to each other, resulting in a porous, open structure aggregate with new characteristics, such as increased flowability, wettability, and dispersibility. 108 Patent-based processes.

1. Nonfat Dry Milk
2. Chocolate Drink Powders
3. Whole Milk and Other Dairy Products
4. Sugars and Other Sweeteners
5. Soluble Coffee and Tea
6. Flour and Cake Mixes
7. Other Agglomeration Processes
Beverage Mix Products
Dried Egg Products
Monosodium Glutamate in Agglomerates
Colored Agglomerates
Dispersibility with Surfactants
All Purpose Processes

270 pages. $36

SAUSAGE PROCESSING 1972
by Dr. E. Karmas
Food Processing Review No. 24

A patent-based review of sausage production technology, with numbers of specific processes indicated in ( ).

Cured Color (18)
Additives (3)
Forestalling Rancidity (4)
Fermented Flavors (3)
Texturizing Agents (13)
Emulsion Stabilizers (5)
Defatting (6)
Demeating Bones (4)
Composition Control (2)
Ingredients Identification (2)
Stuffing (10)
Linking & Tying (13)
Forming & Shaping (3)
Smoking & Pumping (4)
Hot Air Cooking (6)
Cooking in Liquids (3)
With Heat Exchange
Electrical Cooking (14)
Casing Release & Removal (5)
Fresh Pork Sausage (3)
Dry Sausage (8)
Various & Novelty Products (4)

136 Processes. 218 pages. **$36**

ENZYMES IN FOOD PROCESSING AND PRODUCTS 1972
by H. Wieland
Food Processing Review No. 23

Commercial availability of enzymes has increased considerably. Enzymes applicable to food processing are now plentiful, and the alert food processor is urged not to miss this opportunity to improve his products in many ways. 101 Processes. The numbers in ( ) indicate the number of processes allocated to each topic.

FRUIT & VEGETABLE PROCESSING (13)
STARCH & SUGAR CONVERSION (9)
BAKED GOODS APPLICATIONS (12)
CHEESE MAKING (11)
MEAT TENDERIZATION (18)
SPECIAL APPLICATIONS (13)
FLAVORS THROUGH ENZYMES (13)
DEOXYGENATING AND DESUGARING (6)
ENZYME STABILIZATION (6)

269 pages. **$36**

SEAFOOD PROCESSING 1971
by M. Gillies
Food Processing Review No. 22

Describes 84 processes based on U.S. patents issued since 1960. Numbers in ( ) denotes numbers of processes in each chapter.

1. PRESERVATION (13)
On Fishing Vessels
Chemical Methods
Edible Coatings
Various Preservatives
2. CANNING PROCEDURES (11)
Tuna and Similar Fish
Sardines
Forestalling Struvite
3. PROTEIN CONCENTRATES (14)
Mechanical Means
Chemical Means
Biological Means
Stickwater Proteins
4. MOLLUSKS & SHELLFISH (18)
Squid
Bivalves
Crustaceans
5. CONSUMER PRODUCTS (17)
6. ANIMAL FOODS (11)

206 pages. **$36**

FRUIT PROCESSING 1971
by M. Gutterson
Food Processing Review No. 21

All 140 processes (mostly developed since 1960) were selected with the purpose of providing fruits and fruit products retaining the characteristics of freshly picked fruit, yet capable of being shipped the world over and being highly acceptable by organoleptic tests. Preventing the growth of microorganisms with a minimum of chemicals and processing equipment was another goal.

1. GENERAL TECHNIQUES (34 processes)
Heat Treatments, Increasing Cellular Permeability, Inhibiting Discoloration, Ripening, Dehydration
2. TREATMENT OF POMES (23)
3. CITRUS FRUITS (18)
4. BERRIES (20)
5. DRUPES (16)
6. DRIED FRUITS (10)
7. OTHER FRUITS (19)
Flavor Improvement, Delaying Senescence, Use of Enzymes and Freezing Techniques. 223 pages. **$36**

POULTRY PROCESSING 1971
by G. H. Weiss
Food Processing Review No. 20

Poultry is the most efficient and effective means for converting grain to protein. This book discusses in detail the different methods devised to assure excellent flavor, texture and tenderness concomitant with easy preservation, maximum storage time, easy handling, and consumer acceptance. 55 processes in 8 chapters:

1. **Preservation (11 processes)**
2. **Chilling and Freezing (6)**
3. **Enhancing Palatability (10)**
4. **Stuffed Products (3)**
5. **Molded Rolls and Loaves (19)**
6. **Batter-Coated Products (2)**
7. **Cooking Procedures (2)**
8. **Poultry Concentrates (2)**

168 pages. **$24**

FOOD

VEGETABLE PROCESSING 1971
by M. Gutterson
Food Processing Review No. 19

Shipping vegetables from one continent to another has become a normal means of supply. But such transporting is possible only by adequate processing of the perishable vegetable goods. Many of the 184 process descriptions in this book are concerned with just such treatments. Processes for improving the stability of vegetables in regard to time, temperature and moisture are numerous. So are those where the emphasis is in making vegetables more digestible and more acceptable to children and adults:

1. **General (27 processes)**
2. **Potatoes (59)**
3. **Other Roots (12)**
4. **Bulbs (13)**
5. **Leaves & Stems (8)**
6. **Tomatoes & Others (30)**
7. **Corn (6)**
8. **Legumes (23)**
9. **Olives & Mushrooms (6)**

335 pages. **$36**

FLAVOR TECHNOLOGY 1971
by Dr. N. D. Pintauro

Scientific and trade journals contain only limited information on practical and applied flavor research and technology. Industry and commercial operators wish to keep such information confidential. This book reviews such technology from U.S. patents since 1960. There are 99 processes in 9 chapters:

1. **Spice Technology** (11)
2. **Peppermint & Citrus** (11)
3. **Fruit Essences** (9)
4. **Dairy Flavors** (6)
5. **Bread Flavors** (8)
6. **Vanilla** (9)
7. **Meat Flavors** (17)
8. **Meat Seasonings** (10)
9. **Fixation** (18)

228 pages. **$35**

MILK, CREAM AND BUTTER TECHNOLOGY 1971
by G. Wilcox
Food Processing Review No. 18

In these days of heightened consumer awareness, the alert dairy processor cannot afford to bypass the latest developments in his field. Much emphasis now is on modified milk products which contain numerous proteins of high nutritional value. The even distribution of essential amino acids bestows on modified milk a great enticement for use with otherwise deficient diets. Methods for low sodium milk products, hypoallergenic dietary prepns. and infant milk products are given special attention. 181 Processes are described: 1. Pasteurization and Sterilization (15 processes). 2. Removal of Radioactive Contaminants (8). 3. Buttermilk and Allied Products (10). 4. Modified Milk Products (21). 5. Dehydration of Skim Milk (28). 6. Dehydration of Whole Milk, Whey and Milk Blends (47). 7. Concentrated Milk (19). 8. Cream (22). 9. Butter (11).
313 pages. **$35**

EGGS, CHEESE AND YOGURT PROCESSING 1971
by G. Wilcox
Food Processing Review No. 17

One route to discovering the latest technology is via this Food Processing Review which serves to bring you timely, useful information. Brought to you in this one easy-to-use, comprehensive volume is commercial research and development done in the field from 1960 to 1970, gathered from the U.S. patent literature.

The Table of Contents shows the processes discussed in this book. The numbers in parentheses indicate the number of processes covered for each particular process, equipment or product.

Section I—Eggs: Whole Eggs (18); Egg Yolks (7); Egg Whites (27); Egg Products (10). Section II—Cheese and Yogurt: Cottage Cheese (26); Cheddar Type and Process Cheeses (45); Cream Cheese and Bakers' Cheese (8); Mozzarella, Provolone and Parmesan Cheeses (8); Miscellaneous Cheese Processes (17); Manufacture of Yogurt (5).

280 pages. **$35**

RICE AND BULGUR QUICK-COOKING PROCESSES 1970
by R. Daniels
Food Processing Review No. 16

This salient report in our Food Processing Review series summarizes with detailed process information the pertinent U.S. patent literature relating to quick-cooking processes for both rice and bulgur. The information provides needed know-how concerning processing of raw rice and wheat to obtain the more desirable refined forms.

63 specific processes covered. The numbers in ( ) indicate their distribution.

Rice Milling—Extraction—Polishing (13)
Quick-Cooking Rice (17)
Special Rice Processes (6)
Brown and Parboiled Rice (6)
Specialty Products with Rice (9)
Quick-Cooking Wheat Bulgur Products (12)

267 pages. **$35**

FRUIT JUICE TECHNOLOGY 1970
by M. Gutterson
Food Processing Review No. 15

This publication deals with the technology of the noncarbonated fruit juice industry from 1960 through 1970 as covered in the U.S. patent literature. Modern technology has studied and overcome many processing problems, resulting in a vast output of new and improved processing methods. It is oftentimes difficult to keep up with the latest technology. This book is designed to offer you such help.

In the abbreviated Table of Contents shown below, you can see the large amount of valuable material included. The numbers in ( ) indicate the number of processes discussed.

1. Manufacturing Techniques (23), 2. Concentration of Fruit Juices (37), 3. Stabilization Processes (19), 4. Dehydration (18), 5. Freeze Drying (24), 6. Flavors from Fruit Juices (10), 7. Miscellaneous Processes (9).
206 pages. **$35**

FOOD

MEAT PRODUCT MANUFACTURE 1970
by Dr. E. Karmas
Food Processing Review No. 14

This Review concerns latest technology in preparing packaged meats in ready-to-cook and ready-to-eat forms.

The Table of Contents below indicates the many areas covered in this survey.

General Processing: Curing Methods and Ingredients, Increased Water Binding and Yield, Improved Curing Formulations, Integral Meats, Smoking, Thermal Processing and Sterilization, Miscellaneous Processing Methods.

Products: Bacon Production, Patty Type Products, Dehydrated Convenience and Snack Products, Modified and Novel Products.

273 pages. **$35**

MODERN BREAKFAST CEREAL PROCESSES 1970
by R. Daniels
Food Processing Review No. 13

Describes in detail production processes and equipment for the manufacture of modern breakfast cereals. These include both ready-to-eat and quick-cooking products.

Offers detailed practical information for the manufacture and production of these cereal products based on the U.S. patent literature. 61 processes included. Abbreviated Table of Contents follows.

Dough Cooking and Extrusion Processes
Treatment Prior To Puffing
Puffing Processes
Processes For Whole Cereal Grains
Cereal Shaping Processes
Sugarcoating Process
Fruit Incorporation and Nutritional Enrichment
Quick Cooking Cereal Products

217 pages. **$35**

STARCHES AND CORN SYRUPS 1970
by Dr. A. Lachmann

This report covers the field of starch production from many standpoints.

Wet milling is the primary method of starch production, therefore much of the material is concerned with this route to starch. Dry milling processes are also covered.

In addition, coverage of the current technological progress in hydrolyzing starches into dextrins, corn syrups and dextrose and starch fractionation into amylose is covered.

Contains 139 processes covering: The Manufacture of Starch, Treatment of Starch, Modified Starch, Pregelatinized Starch, Acid Hydrolysis of Starch to Sweeteners, Starch Hydrolyzing Enzymes, Enzymatic Starch Hydrolysates, Starch Hydrolysates Produced by Acid and Enzyme Treatments, Starch Fractionation.
275 pages. **$35**

FRESH MEAT PROCESSING 1970
by Dr. E. Karmas
Food Processing Review No. 12

This Food Processing Review, deals with 106 detailed processes covering essential developments in the fresh meat processing industry since 1960. The book provides a well-organized tour through the field; the processes included are well researched and presented as an easy-to-use guide to what is being done in this vital field today.

The material has been divided into two parts; processes for enhancing palatability, and preservation processes. The numbers in ( ) after each heading indicate the number of processes for each entry.

A. Palatability: Tenderness (33), Flavor and Tenderness (8), Flavoring (12), Color (13), Integral Texture (6). B. Preservation: Moisture Retention (9), Antimicrobial Treatment (10), Ionizing Radiation (7), Other Methods of Preservation (8). 236 pages. **$35**

SOLUBLE TEA PRODUCTION PROCESSES 1970
by Dr. N. Pintauro
Food Processing Review No. 11

This book describes production processes for producing soluble tea and offers a wealth of detailed practical information based primarily on the U.S. patent literature. Describes 73 specific processes in this field with substantial background information. The Table of Contents is listed below. The numbers in ( ) indicate the number of processes in that category.

Withering and Rolling (4)
Fermentation, Firing and Sorting (8)
Extraction (13)
Recovery of Aroma (10)
Tannin-Caffeine Precipitate (Cream) (15)
Filtration and Concentration (8)
Dehydration Process (6)
Agglomeration and Aromatization (9)

Illustrations. 183 pages. **$35**

BAKED GOODS PRODUCTION PROCESSES 1969
by M. Gutterson
Food Processing Review No. 9

This book describes 201 recent processes for the production of baked goods. Based on the patent literature, it offers an up-to-date comprehensive publication of manufacturing processes.

There is a substantial amount of information in this book relating to the use of various chemicals and related additives.

Contents: Bread, Yeast Leavened Products, Chemically Leavened Products, Leavening Agents, Air Leavened Products, Non-Leavened Products, Refrigerated Doughs, Emulsifiers and Dough Improvers, Miscellaneous, Indexes. Illustrations. 353 pages. **$35**

FOOD

SOLUBLE COFFEE MANUFACTURING PROCESSES 1969
by Dr. N. Pintauro
Food Processing Review No. 8

This book describes significant manufacturing processes for producing soluble coffee, and offers a wealth of detailed practical information based primarily on the U.S. patent literature. Describes 114 specific processes in this field with substantial background information.

Introduction: Roasting, Extraction, Filtration and Concentration, Recovery of Aromatic Volatiles, Spray Drying and Other Dehydration Processes, Freeze Drying Processes, Aromatization of Soluble Coffee Powder, Agglomeration Techniques for Soluble Coffee, Decaffeinated Soluble Coffee, Packaging of Soluble Coffee. Illustrations, Indexes, 254 pages. **$35**

ALCOHOLIC MALT BEVERAGES 1969
by M. Gutcho
Food Processing Review No. 7

The traditional brewing process is a batch operation, costly and time consuming. There would be economic advantages to improved continuous processes which would require less capital investment for plant and equipment, give savings in labor, better use of raw materials, shorter processing time, and a more uniform product.

Detailed descriptive process information is found in this review, based on 157 U.S. Patents in the brewing field, issued since 1960. The 157 processes are organized in 7 chapters which tend to follow the steps in the brewing process.

Contents: Malting, Wort, Hops, Fermentation, Freeze Concentration and Reconstitution of Beer, Chillproofing, Preservation against Microbiological Spoilage, Foam, Indexes. Illustrations. 333 pages. **$35**

CONFECTIONARY PRODUCTS MANUFACTURING PROCESSES 1969
by M. Gutterson
Food Processing Review No. 6

This book is of technological significance in that it details over 200 processes for producing confections, based on the U.S. patent literature since 1960.

Based solely on new technology, this book offers substantial manufacturing information relating to this field. The wide scope of detailed data can be seen by the chapter headings indicated below:

Candy
Chocolate Products
Whipped Products
Icings
Gels
Coatings and Glazes
Gums and Stabilizers
Egg Products
Marshmallows and Meringues
Puddings
Frozen Confections
Chewing Gum
Other Confections
Indexes
Illustrations. 321 pages. **$35**

FOOD

DEHYDRATION PROCESSES FOR CONVENIENCE FOODS 1969
by R. Noyes
Food Processing Review No. 2

Describes 236 up-to-date dehydration processes for producing specific foods. Most detailed body of information ever published.

The detailed, descriptive process information in this book is based on 236 U.S. patents in the food dehydration field—issued between January 1960 and May 1968. This book serves a double purpose in that it supplies detailed technical information, and can be used as a guide to the U.S. patent literature on dehydration of foods. By indicating only information that is significant, and eliminating much of the legal jargon in the patents; this book then becomes an advanced commercially oriented review of food dehydration processes.

Dry Milk Products, Cheese and Yoghurt, Eggs, Fruit and Vegetable Juices, Fruits, Potatoes, Vegetables, Coffee, Tea, Miscellaneous. Many illustrations. 367 pages. **$35**

CHEMICAL

ANTIFOAMING AND DEFOAMING AGENTS 1972
by T. G. Rubel
Chemical Process Review No. 60

Describes 105 patent-based processes.

1. **Foam Control in Aqueous and Nonaqueous Systems**
2. **Mechanical Means of Foam Control**
3. **Foam Inhibition in Lubricants, Fuels, Hydraulic Fluids, and Organic Liquids**
4. **Antifoamers for Wax Coatings**
5. **Foam Prevention in Pulp and Paper Production**
6. **Foam Reduction in Paints**
7. **Controlling Foam in Drilling Fluids**
8. **Phosphoric Acid Foam**
9. **Antifoamers for Gases**
10. **Breaking Detergent Foams**
11. **Foam Depressants for Dyes**
12. **Antifoaming of Proteins**
13. **Foam in Antifreezes**
14. **Defoaming Steam**
15. **Polymer Foam Suppression**
16. **Foam Prevention in Photoengraving Solutions**

251 pages. **$36**

SYNTHETIC LUBRICANTS 1972
by M. W. Kanney
Chemical Process Review No. 59

A review of 205 patent-based processes.

1. **Organic Esters**
   General Syntheses
   Inhibited Fluids
   Extreme Pressure Additives
   Greases
2. **Silicones**
   Fluid Syntheses
   Grease Formulations
   Solid Lubricants
3. **Polyglycols, Phosphates and Silicates**
4. **Polyphenyl Ethers**
   Additives
   Halogen-Containing Ethers
5. **Fluorocarbons**
   Grease Formulations
   Fluorinated Esters
   Thread Sealants
6. **Petroleum**
   Viscosity Index Improvers
   Dispersants
   Extreme Pressure Additives
   Grease Formulations
   Metalworking Formulas

245 pages. **$36**

EDIBLE OILS AND FATS 1969
by Dr. N. E. Bednarcyk
Food Processing Review No. 5

This book describes in detail 225 recent process developments.

Shortenings; Fluid, Plastic, Miscellaneous: Margarine and Spreads; Margarine Oils, Highly Nutritional Oil Blends, Antispattering Agents, Fluid and Whipped Margarines, Flavor, Color, and Texture Modifications, Low Calorie Spreads: Salad Oils, Mayonnaise and Emulsified Dressings; Crystallization Inhibitors, Emulsified Dressings, Flavored Salad Oils, Low Calorie Dressings: Frying and Cooking Oils; Equipment, Breakdown Inhibitors, Antispattering Additives, Other Additives: Hard Butters; Preparation by Fractional Crystallization, Preparation by Ester Exchange, Miscellaneous: Oil Processing; Antioxidants and Stabilizers; Emulsifiers and Emulsions; Mixed Ester Emulsifiers, Dried Emulsion, Miscellaneous: Peanut Butter and Spreads; Chocolate Products; Indexes. Illustrations. 404 pages. **$35**

SNACKS AND FRIED PRODUCTS 1969
by Dr. A. Lachmann
Food Processing Review No. 4

The sales of snack foods in the U.S. may reach the two billion dollar mark soon. Many companies are actively working on new snack foods or on improved processes. The patent literature on french fried potatoes, potato chips, corn chips and other crisps is continually growing and it is the purpose of this book to present this literature in easy readable form.

French fried potatoes and their methods of production are described in the second chapter. The next chapter deals with potato chips, still the most popular product of the snack food industry. The U.S. market for potato chips is estimated to be approximately 600 million dollars in 1969. In Chapter Four the processes for corn chips are covered; in Chapter Five, apple crisps. Chapter Six describes processes for expanded chips and some specialty items; and the last chapter deals with batter mixes. Many illustrations. 181 pages. **$35**

PROTEIN FOOD SUPPLEMENTS 1969
by R. Noyes
Food Processing Review No. 3

The 126 Processes in this book are organized in 8 chapters by raw material source including the important newer processes for producing protein by fermentation of hydrocarbons. Another chapter on textured foods describes in detail a number of processes for producing these products that simulate meat. Indexes by company; inventors and patent number help in providing easily obtainable information.

This book is based upon the patent literature and serves a double purpose in that it supplies detailed technical information and can be used as a guide to the U.S. Patent literature on processes to obtain protein materials.

Contents: Hydrocarbon Fermentation, Fish-Based Protein, Soybeans, Cottonseed, Other Oilseeds and Legumes, Wheat and Gluten, Milk-Based Protein, Textured Foods, Miscellaneous, Indexes. Many illustrations. 412 pages. **$35**

ANTISTATIC AGENTS 1972
Technology and Applications
by K. Johnson

Antistatic agents described in 160 U.S. patents since 1965 are covered in this book with specific sections devoted to two large volume applications—Plastics and Textiles.

Antistatic agents are used in plastics such as phonograph records, bottles, and film wraps to reduce pickup of dust and dirt.

In the textile industry, charged fibers interfere with the spinning process, and the attraction of dust particles produces marks and soiling in weaving.

1. **Polyolefins (27)**
2. **Records and Films (17)**
3. **Fibers & Fabrics Treatment (29)**
4. **Further Fibers & Fabrics (27)**
5. **Techniques of Treatment (22)**
6. **Softener & Lubricant Formulations (20)**
7. **Other Applications and Syntheses (18)**

307 pages. **$36**

OPTICAL BRIGHTENERS 1972
Technology and Applications
by T. Rubel

Describes synthesis and use of fluorescent dyes that have the property of absorbing ultraviolet radiant energy and emitting energy in the visible range.

To the unaided human eye the fluorescence is not noticeable. Its presence, however, has the effect of brightening colors and making things whiter than white.

Based on 136 U.S. patents issued since Jan. 1965:

1. Optical Brighteners Added to Natural Materials (6 Processes)
2. To Synthetic Polymers (52)
3. To Natural & Synthetic Substances (42)
4. To Detergents (8)
5. To Fabric Softeners (5)
6. Brighteners for Papers and Photographic Materials (19)
7. Other Applications (4)
   Company Index
   Inventor Index
   U.S. Patent Number Index.

281 pages. **$36**

CHEMICAL

LIQUID FUELS FROM COAL 1972
by G. K. Goldman
Chemical Process Review No. 57

1. **Extractive Solvents (15)**
2. **Solvation (4)**
3. **Deashing (4)**
4. **Dual Solvent Systems**
5. **Multistage Systems (4)**
6. **Microwave and Ultrasonics (2)**
7. **Thermal Liquefaction**
8. **Separation of Suspensions**
9. **Noncatalytic Hydrogenation (4)**
10. **Catalytic Hydrogenation (13)**
11. **Hydroconversion Catalysts (13)**
12. **Ebullated Bed Processes (11)**
13. **Hydrocracking**
14. **Quadriphase Hydrogenation**
15. **Refining (2)**
16. **Jet Fuel Production**
17. **Underground Hydrogenation**
18. **Thermal Cracking (16)**
19. **Catalytic Depolymerization**
20. **Pyrolysis (5)**

101 Processes. 228 pages. **$36**

HYDROFLUORIC ACID MANUFACTURE 1972
by S. Weiss
Chemical Process Review No. 58

Reviews 166 U.S. patents pertaining to HF manufacture, including a chapter on fluosilicic acid.

The current expansion in HF capacity appears to stress the traditional fluorspar-sulfuric acid route in foreign (esp. Mexican) plants built or planned. Domestic producers, squeezed by rising costs and shrinking supplies of U.S. fluorspar, are becoming increasingly interested in HF recovery from waste products of phosphate fertilizer plants.

1. **HF from Fluorspar (38 processes)**
2. **HF from Waste Gases (26)**
3. **HF from Other Sources (11)**
4. **Refining by Distillation (25)**
5. **Purification in Solution (12)**
6. **Refining by Formation of Reversible Complexes (21)**
7. **Purification by Chemical Reactions (18)**
8. **Fluosilicic Acid Manufacture (15)**

254 pages. **$36**

SULFURIC ACID MANUFACTURE AND EFFLUENT CONTROL 1971
by M. Sittig
Chemical Process Review No. 55

102 processes of manufacture and 39 pollution control measures are outlined in this encyclopedic survey:

SO_2 from Sulfur (11 processes)
SO_2 from Waste Gases (11)
SO_2 from Hydrogen Sulfide (2)
SO_2 from Sulfide Ores (8)
SO_x and H_2SO_4 from Sulfates (12)
H_2SO_4 from SO_2 HCl (2)
The Chamber Process (4)
Conversion of SO_2 to SO_3 (9)
SO_3 to H_2SO_4 and Oleum (5)
Integrated Contact Processes (14)
Unconventional Processes (2)
Concentration of H_2SO_4 (2)
Dilution of H_2SO_4 (1)
Purification of H_2SO_4 (2)
Recovery of Spent H_2SO_4 (17)
Removal and Recovery of SO_x from Tail Gases (30)
Recovery of Acid Mists (9)
Future Trends

423 pages. **$48**

CHEMICAL

ION EXCHANGE RESINS 1970
by C. Placek
Chemical Process Review No. 44

This report on ion exchange resins provides detailed information on 126 U.S. patents issued since 1960 concerning the composition and manufacture of ion exchange materials. This Review, by its organization, also provides a guide to these ion exchange resins by grouping them according to physical form, behavior characteristics, etc.

1. Anion Exchange Resins
2. Cation Exchange Resins
3. Resins For Removing Metals
4. Resins Having Mixed Properties
5. Specific Use Resins
6. Unconventional Materials
7. Process Emphasis
8. Properties of Ion Exchange
9. Ion Exchange Membranes
10. Emphasis on Shapes

329 pages. **$35**

RADIATION CHEMICAL PROCESSING 1969
by R. Whiting
Chemical Process Review No. 41

This book surveys the radiation processing field and is based on the U.S. patent literature since 1960. Over 250 separate processes are described.

Contents: Polyolefins, Other Polymers, Elastomers, Hydrocarbons, Organic Chemicals, Inorganic and Organic-Metallic Compounds, Other Processes. 377 pages. **$35**

PHOTOCHEMICAL PROCESSES 1969
by B. Albertson
Chemical Process Review No. 36

Describes 210 photochemical production processes in detail.

Introduction, Photohalogenation, Photonitrosation, Organic Photochemical Reactions, Inorganic Photochemical Reactions, Photopolymerization, Indexes. Illustrations. 185 pages. **$35**

CHLORINE AND CAUSTIC SODA MANUFACTURE RECENT DEVELOPMENTS 1969
by Dr. R. Powell
Chemical Process Review No. 33

Brine Electrolysis
Diaphragm and Mercury Cells
Recovery of Mercury
NaOH Production
Titanium Anodes
Sea Water Electrolysis
Cl_2 Production
Deacon Process Modifications
Numerous Illustrations,
48 processes, 265 pages. **$35**

AMINES, NITRILES AND ISOCYANATES PROCESSES AND PRODUCTS 1969
by M. Sittig
Chemical Process Review No. 31

Material covered includes: Manufacture of Amines, Manufacture of Mono-Nitriles, Acrylonitrile Derivatives, Isocyanate Manufacture, Future Trends. 62 illustrations. 201 pages. **$35**

TRIMELLITIC ANHYDRIDE AND PYROMELLITIC DIANHYDRIDE 1971
by P. Stecher
Chemical Process Review No. 53

Trimellitic anhydride (TMA) being an anhydride and a carboxylic acid, can undergo many useful reactions; it can form esters and polyimides. Demand is rising sharply. Pyromellitic dianhydride (PMDA) yields polyimides and cured epoxy resins having very high temperature stability. This book gives 61 manufacturing processes and all the technology involved in making TMA and PMDA:

1. TM-Acid Synthesis (17)
2. TM-Acid Purification (3)
3. TMA Preparation (8)
4. TMA Purification (2)
5. TM-Double Anhydride (2)
6. PM-Acid Synthesis (6)
7. PMDA Preparation (5)
8. PMDA Purification (4)
9. Non-Hazardous Oxidations (1)
10. Derivatives of TMA & PMDA (13)

233 pages. **$35**

PHTHALOCYANINE TECHNOLOGY 1970
by Y. L. Meltzer
Chemical Process Review No. 42

Advances in phthalocyanine technology have been truly explosive during the past few years. New phthalocyanine products, processes and applications have poured forth from industrial, governmental and academic laboratories at a rapid pace. These advances in technology have made themselves felt in the market place and in government programs, and have contributed to corporate sales and profits. At the same time, however, competition has become more intense in the phthalocyanine field making it imperative to keep up with the latest technological advances.

Examines recent developments in phthalocyanine technology as reflected in U.S. patents and other literature. The first 23 chapters discuss up-to-date manufacturing processes for phthalocyanine pigments and dyes. Chapters 24 through 31 discuss unusual new applications for phthalocyanines. 390 pages. **$35**

SYNTHETIC PERFUMERY MATERIALS 1970
by M. Gutcho
Chemical Process Review No. 45

This Review shows you how to produce synthetic perfumery materials. It contains a valuable odor index.

The 152 U.S. patents included in this book are distributed among the 11 areas as shown below:

From Terpenic Materials (28)
Alcohols (11)
Esters (18)
Ethers (19)
Aldehydes (10).
Ketones (18)
Lactones, Pyrones, Substituted Phenols and Quinones (12)
Other Structures (7)
Naphthalene and Indene Derivatives (17)
Compounds with Scent of Ambergris or Irone (9)
Product Application (13)

273 pages. **$35**

CITRIC ACID PRODUCTION PROCESSES 1969
by R. Noyes
Chemical Process Review No. 37

Detailed descriptions of production processes for citric acid, based on the patent literature.

The Table of Contents is indicated below:

Processing, Iron Impurities Other Microorganisms, Recovery and Purification, Other Processes. Indexes. 157 pages. **$24**

NITRIC ACID TECHNOLOGY RECENT DEVELOPMENTS 1969
by Dr. R. Powell
Chemical Process Review No. 30

Ammonia Oxidation Process, Wisconsin Thermal Process, Nitrogen Fixation by Shock Waves, Nitrogen Fixation in a Nuclear Reactor, Absorption of Nitrogen Oxides in Water, Concentration of Dilute Nitric Acid Solutions, Direct Production of Concentrated Nitric Acid, Purification of Nitric Acid, Stabilizers for Nitric Acid. Numerous illustrations. 245 pages. **$35**

AROMATICS MANUFACTURE AND DERIVATIVES 1968
by M. Sittig
Chemical Process Review No. 17

Contents: Introduction, Production of Aromatics, Separation of Aromatics, Purification of Aromatics, Reactions giving Hydrocarbon Products, Other Reactions, Phenol Production, Styrene Manufacture and Derivatives, Future Trends. 73 illustrations. 232 pages. **$35**

CATALYSTS AND CATALYTIC PROCESSES 1967
by M. Sittig
Chemical Process Review No. 7

Contents: Hydrocarbon Conversion Processes, Hydrocarbon Polymerization Processes, Hydrocarbon Oxidation Processes, Future Trends. 109 illustrations. 303 pages. **$35**

INDUSTRIAL GASES MANUFACTURE AND APPLICATIONS 1967
by M. Sittig
Chemical Process Review No. 4

This book discusses conventional cryogenic air separation and purification techniques in considerable detail.

This book also discusses newer techniques such as adsorption using molecular sieves, and permeation using various membrane materials. 313 pages. 103 illustrations. **$35**

CHEMICAL

POLYMETHYLBENZENES 1969
by H. W. Earhart

Presents physical property data. Discusses the chemistry of the PMB's established chemical reactions, relative kinetic rate data, yields, etc. Known as well as suggested end-uses for numerous PMB's and derivatives are given, e.g. for benzene, toluene, xylene, mesitylene, pseudocumene, hemimellitene, durene, isodurene, prehnitene, penta-and hexamethylbenzene. 63 tables. 549 references. 158 pages. **$20**

ORGANIC CHEMICAL PROCESS ENCYCLOPEDIA
by M. Sittig

Second Edition 1969

A handy desk-top reference to organic chemicals and their industrial manufacturing processes.

Gives the key processing facts for instant reference to 711 industrial organic chemical processes—with 711 large flow diagrams. 712 pages—8½" x 11"—hard cover. **$35**

INORGANIC CHEMICAL AND METALLURGICAL PROCESS ENCYCLOPEDIA 1968
by M. Sittig

This book is organized in an unusual format. There is one inorganic chemical or metallurgical process on each page. At the top of the page an equipment drawing or flow diagram is shown, and underneath a description of the process is given. 883 pages—8½" x 11"—hard cover. **$35**

POLYMERS AND ADHESIVES

ABS RESIN MANUFACTURE 1970
by C. Placek
Chemical Process Review No. 46

ABS (acrylonitrile-butadiene-styrene) resins make up one of the most rapidly growing segments of the polymer industry. **Straight ABS Materials; ABS Modified with Acrylic Derivatives; ABS from Alpha-Methylstyrene; Miscellaneous Modifiers; Modification of Properties; Process Variations.** 233 pages. **$35**

CELLULAR PLASTICS RECENT DEVELOPMENTS 1970
by K. Johnson

Describes 189 processes:
Polyolefins (15)
Polyvinyl Chloride (15)
Polystyrene (22)
Rubber (15)
Polyurethanes (71)
Polyesters and Epoxides (15)
Urea-Formaldehyde and Phenolic Resins (9)
Other Cellular Products (27)

280 pages. **$35**

FLUOROCARBON RESINS 1971
by Dr. M. W. Ranney
Chemical Process Review No. 51

1. Polytetrafluoroethylene (42). 2. Vinylidene Fluoride Elastomers (38). 3. Vinyl Fluoride. 4. Trifluorochloroethylene (15). 5. Fluorodienes (16). 6. Fluoroethers (13). 7. Fluorinated Nitroso Polymers (6). 8. Others (23). 9. General Processing Techniques (14). 226 pages. **$35**

COMPATIBILITY AND SOLUBILITY 1968
by I. Mellan

Normally, it requires laborious testing to determine compatibility of polymers, resins, elastomers, plasticizers, and solvents. Predictions made without testing or literature searching, are usually unreliable.

This book helps you evaluate proper materials by the use of 224 tables. 304 pages. **$20**

ETHYLENE-PROPYLENE-DIENE RUBBERS 1970
by Dr. M. W. Ranney
Chemical Process Review No. 49

Summarizes patent literature relating to: Polyene Monomers—Polymer Synthesis; Catalysts and Activators; MW Regulators; Process Technology; Recovery Techniques; Modified Terpolymers; Adhesives; Miscellaneous Vulcanizates; Cross-Linking Agents. 272 pages. **$35**

COATINGS

POLYURETHANE COATINGS 1972
by K. Johnson

Reviews 157 U.S. patents issued mostly since 1960 related to paint vehicles, wet look, highly glossy fabric coatings, microporous products, etc.

1. COATING VEHICLES
   Isocyanates (9 processes)
   Carboxyl, Polyols (16)
   Modified Resins (13)
   Aqueous Systems (9)
   Catalysts & Crosslinking (5)
   Miscellaneous (17)
2. MICROPOROUS MATERIALS
   Solvent Processes (22)
   Pore-Forming Agents (9)
   Suede Substitutes (3)
   Others (3)
3. COATED FABRICS & PAPERS
   Water Repellency & Ability to Dryclean (8)
   Coated Fabrics (13)
   Papers (3)
4. MAGNETIC TAPES & OTHER SUBSTRATES
   Magnetic Tapes (6)
   Wire Coatings (3)
   Other Applications (18)

338 pages. **$36**

POWDER COATINGS AND FLUIDIZED BED TECHNIQUES 1971
by Dr. M. W. Ranney

Describes 166 processes. Due to the actuality of the subject all have been developed very recently. Numbers in ( ) indicate number of processes per chapter.

1. FLUIDIZED BED—SPRAY-POURING TECHNIQUES (27)
   Fluidized Bed Designs
   Spray-Powder, etc.
2. ELECTROSTATIC PROCESSES (8)
3. EPOXIES (19)
   Curing Agents
   Modified Epoxies
   Powdering Techniques
4. POLYOLEFINS (10)
   Primers & Surface Treatment
   Use of Copolymers
5. VINYLS (6)
6. OTHER RESINS (10)
7. PIPE COATINGS (28)
8. ELECTRICAL COMPONENTS (19)
9. OTHER APPLICATIONS (24)
10. INORGANIC & PARTICLE COATINGS (15)

249 pages. **$36**

PAPER COATINGS BASED ON POLYMERS 1971
by K. Johnson

178 Processes for coating paper stock elaborated during the last 10 years. Pigment binder and barrier coatings are discussed in detail e.g. acrylics give high gloss and good ink holdout, while silicone and solvent-based coatings allow considerable latitude in formulations.

1. POLYETHYLENE ETHYLENE COPOLYMERS—HOT MELTS (34 processes)
2. POLYVINYLIDENE CHLORIDE BARRIER COATINGS (10)
3. WATER-SOLUBLE COATINGS (30)
4. STYRENE-BUTADIENE ETHYLENE-PROPYLENE LATICES (27)
5. VINYL ACETATE LATICES (13)
6. ACRYLIC LATICES (23)
7. SILICONE AND SOLVENT-BASED COATINGS (24)
8. SPECIALTY COATINGS (17) Photographic Paper Coatings, Opaque Coatings, Metallized Coatings, Chemical Watermark Paper, Coatings for Erasable Paper, Mulch Sheets.

313 pages. **$36**

WIRE COATINGS 1971
by D. J. De Renzo

The good insulating properties of many thermoplastic and thermosetting polymers make them suitable for coating wires to be used as conductors in electrical apparatus. Other properties include abrasion resistance, impact strength, flexibility, solvent resistance, and high temperature stability.

The U.S. patent literature of the past ten years provides an excellent description of the many types of processes for organic wire coatings. Numbers in ( ) indicate the number of processes described in each chapter. 180 processes in all.

Acrylics (12), Epoxy Resins (9), Fluorinated Resins (4), Polycarbonates (5), Polyesters (31), Polyimides and Polyamides (26), Polyolefins (41), Polyspiranes (5), Polyurethanes (8), PVA Resins (15), Silicones (7), Vinyl Chloride Polymers and Copolymers (13), Other Resins (4).

232 pages. **$35**

PAINT ADDITIVES 1970
by H. Preuss

This publication surveys the field of paint additives offered for sale by manufacturers in the United States. It gathers together for you in one useful volume a series of articles written by Mr. Preuss for METAL FINISHING from 1965 through 1970. It is designed to help lead the paint formulator through the maze of modern additives; placing at his fingertips needed information about their chemistry, properties, specifications, uses and applications.

Additives form an integral part of a coating. Some of the additives discussed in this book are: antiskinning ,antifoaming, antifouling, antifreezing, dispersing, destaticizing, antiliverning, antisagging, curing, antisettling or suspension and moisture resistant agents; plasticizers; antioxidants; fire retardants; corrosion inhibitors; odorants and deodorants; and many others. 249 pages. **$18**

METAL COATING OF PLASTICS 1970
by Dr. F. Lowenheim

Describes 125 processes for applying metallic coatings to plastic articles on a production basis with reasonable reliability, and in such fashion that the metal is acceptably adherent to the substrate, and that the resulting products are useful for decorative or functional purposes. 254 pages. **$35**

ELECTRODEPOSITION AND RADIATION CURING OF COATINGS 1970
by Dr. M. W. Ranney

The advantages of electrodeposition: Pinhole-free coating, eliminating of fire hazards and air pollution problems, automated operation and fast throughput make this an attractive method. Radiation curing is quick, eliminates ovens and uses solvent-free vehicles. 96 Patent-based process on 170 pages. **$35**

POLYMERS AND ADHESIVES

PLASTICIZERS GUIDEBOOK AND DIRECTORY 1972
Blue Book No. 4

This book contains technical data and specifications of commercial plasticizers manufactured in the United States by 52 companies.

The U.S. market has plasticizer sales of about $250 million per year.

Like the other volumes in our Blue Book Series, this book is intended as a guide to U.S. manufacturers with standard product lines.

All the information is taken directly from the manufacturers' hard-to-get data sheets and technical bulletins at no cost to, nor influence from, the manufacturers of the specific plasticizers.

In each case enough information is presented to enable the researcher or chemical processor of plastics to judge from the data presented whether or not a given plasticizer type or grade will do the job for the intended application to the resin on hand. 282 pages. **$36**

POLYOLEFIN RESINS 1972
Blue Book No. 3

This informative date book on olefin polymers and their producers is the third volume in our comprehensive Blue Book Series. In keeping with our policy, this book attempts to provide a complete listing of commercially available, standardized resins offered by 22 U.S. producers.

The book describes the readily available higher-molecular-weight polymers of ethylene and propylene. Some elastomeric copolymers are also listed. Included are product specifications and applications.

All the information in this volume is taken directly from the manufacturers' hard-to-get data sheets and technical bulletins. In each case enough information is provided to enable the researcher to judge from the data presented whether or not a given polyolefin type or grade will do the job for the intended applications. 291 pages. **$36**

ADHESIVES 1972
Blue Book No. 2

The second volume in our comprehensive Blue Book Series. In keeping with our policy, this book attempts to provide a reasonably complete listing of commercially available, standardized products offered by American industry. The book describes the "on the line" adhesive products of 121 U.S. manufacturers arranged according to company names.

All the information was selected from the manufacturers' hard-to-get data sheets at no cost to, nor influence from, the manufacturers of the adhesives.

A primary purpose of the book is to present the significant, first line information about adhesives all in one place—saving you many hours of work trying to obtain specific information and facts. 407 pages. **$36**

POLYMER ADDITIVES 1972
Blue Book No. 1

Perhaps the most comprehensive listing of commercially available, protective additives ever offered to the plastics industry. Gives products of 86 U.S. manufacturers arranged according to company name. Each product is carefully indexed by chemical, generic, trivial, and trade name or registered trademark in the "one alphabet" index at the end of the book.

Abounds with antioxidants and stabilizers plus countless other protective aids. By listing the intended uses and physical properties, as well as the manufacturers and suppliers, this book intends to furnish a real service to the advancing polymer technology.

The data appearing in this book were selected by the publisher from manufacturers' literature at no cost to, nor influence from the manufacturers of the materials. 472 pages. **$36**

SYNTHETIC TURF AND SPORTING SURFACES 1972
by M. S. Casper

High labor costs have made natural turf surfaces almost prohibitively expensive. Increased interest in spectator sports make it desirable to provide sport surfaces which can be used despite weather conditions and seasonal variations. This review of 84 U.S. patents describes the present state of the art.

1. **Turf Substitutes (8)**
2. **Golf Installations (4)**
3. **Tennis Courts (2)**
4. **Race Tracks (2)**
5. **Resilient Surfaces (7)**
6. **Installation Aids (3)**
7. **Skiing Surfaces (29)**
8. **Golf Surfaces (22)**
9. **Skating Surfaces (4)**
10. **Tobogganing Slide**
11. **Aircraft Landing Pads**
12. **Lawn Elements**

260 pages. **$36**

RIGID FOAM LAMINATES 1972
by M. G. Halpern

This book concerns itself with the manufacture of rigid foam laminates, in which the foam cores are bonded to a great variety of outer coatings. 134 processes from U.S. patents.

1. Chemical Processes for the Preparation of Plastic Foams (7)
2. Nonplastic Expanded Materials (5)
3. Plastic Skin—Plastic Foam Laminates (15)
4. Polyurethane Foam Compositions (10)
5. Nonplastic Skin and Foamed Plastic Core Laminates (9)
6. Paper & Foam Compositions (6)
7. Containers & Packaging Materials (9)
8. Refrigerated Containers (9)
9. Acoustical Panels (5)
10. Roofing Applications (12)
11. Structural Panels (14)
12. Internal Reinforcements (12)
13. Adhesive Techniques (8)
14. Embossing & Decorating (4)
15. Miscellaneous (9)

271 pages. **$36**

POLYMERS AND ADHESIVES

SEALING AND POTTING COMPOUNDS 1972
by J. A. Szilard

Sealing and potting compounds are used to protect against ingress or egress of liquids or gases. In most cases the desired protection is against the pentration of moisture. Describes 166 sealant manufacturing processes based on polymer technology including silicones.

Products intended for:
General Use
Soil Treatment
Highways and Runways
Building Construction
Aircraft Construction
Pipe Joint Sealing
Automotive Use
Shoemaking
Swimming Pool & Aquarium Sealing
Shafts & Stuffing Boxes
Carton & Container Sealing
Electrical & Electronic Instruments

Also discusses special sealants for extremely high and low temperatures, lubricating sealants, encapsulants for printed and high frequency circuits, and many more. 288 pages. **$36**

REINFORCED COMPOSITES FROM POLYESTER RESINS 1972
by Dr. M. W. Ranney

1. POLYESTER INTERMEDIATES
   Hydroxy Intermediates (9)
   Carboxylic Acids-Anhydrides (14)
   Diels-Alder Adducts (8)
   Others (10)
2. ADDITIVES
   Catalysts (9)
   Accelerators-Promoters (12)
   Inhibitors (12)
   Thickeners (16)
   Color Controllers (10)
   Miscellaneous (3)
3. FLAME RETARDANTS
   Acid-Anhydrides (9)
   Hydroxy Intermediates (6)
   Other Reactants (16)
4. FORMULATIONS
   Acrylics (3)
   Nitrogen Compounds (4)
   Other Thermoplastics (6)
   Reactive Solvents (4)
   Low Profile Shrinkage (3)
5. PROCESSING
   Glass Fiber Treating (4)
   Other Processes (8)

166 Patent-based Processes on 324 pages. **$36**

PLASTIC PRINTING PLATES MANUFACTURE AND TECHNOLOGY 1971
by M. G. Halpern

Shows easy adaptation to traditional letterpress practice and automated equipment for plastic 3-dimensional relief plates.

1. PHOTOPOLYMERIZED PRINTING PLATES (2)
2. CELLULOSE POLYMERS (5)
3. OTHER POLYMERS (6)
4. ANCHOR LAYERS (6)
5. PHOTOINITIATORS (10)
6. MODIFICATIONS (22)
   Afterexposure Treatments
   Calendering Aids
   Speed & Contrast Aids
   Increasing Sensitivity
7. PHOTOCHEMICAL CROSSLINKING (9)
8. POLYAMIDE PLATES (12)
   Sensitizers
   Photomechanical Processes
9. PHOTOREPRODUCTION LAYERS (20)
10. INTAGLIO IMAGES AND ETCHABLE PLASTIC PLATES (7)
11. MOLDED PLATES (4)

294 pages. **$36**

VINYL AND ACRYLIC ADHESIVES INCLUDING PRESSURE SENSITIVES 1971
by K. Johnson

Includes 123 processes.

1. ACRYLICS (51)
   Pressure Sensitives
   Laminates
   Tire Cord Adhesives
   Anaerobics
2. POLYVINYL ACETATE (14)
   Hot Melts
   Wood Bonding
3. POLYVINYL ALCOHOL (10)
   Paper and Corrugated Board
   Water-Soluble Pressure Sensitives
   Cement Compositions
4. ETHYLENE COPOLYMERS (13)
   Hot Melts
   Atactic Polypropylene
5. OTHER VINYL POLYMERS (25)
   Iron-On Adhesives
   Fabric Bonding
   Pressure Sensitive Phenol-Aldehyde Resins
6. PRESSURE SENSITIVE TAPES (10)
   Release Coatings

287 pages. **$36**

FLEXIBLE FOAM LAMINATES 1971
by M. McDonald

Reviews the U.S. patent literature on the technology of flexible foam laminates from 1960 through early 1971. Altogether 101 processes in 6 chapters. In 1970 about 75 million pounds of polyurethane foam in the U.S. alone were bonded, mostly to fabrics, to form flexible laminates.

1. THERMAL METHODS (16 processes)
2. ADHESIVE METHODS (15)
3. FOAM-IN-PLACE METHODS (19)
4. FABRIC TO FOAM (17)
5. FLOOR COVERINGS (14)
6. MISCELLANEOUS (20) Packaging Materials, Foam on Cardboard, Sealing Strips, Sound Insulation, Polyester Foam Laminates, Polypropylene Foam to Metal, Deforming Foam Surfaces, Stretchable Foam Laminates.

265 pages. **$36**

POLYMERS IN LITHOGRAPHY 1971
by D. J. De Renzo

About 50% of all printing today is done by lithography, also named the planographic method. This has led to an extensive use of polymers for making the base plates and the sensitized plate coatings. Polymers are used also in etching solutions, lacquers, deletion fluids, inks, etc. 145 processes from the U.S. patent literature since 1965.

1. DIAZO TYPE PRESENSITIZERS (46 processes)
2. NONDIAZO PHOTOSENSITIVE LAYERS (17)
3. BASE PLATES AND COATINGS (32)
4. OTHER POLYMERS FOR PLATES (9)
5. LACQUERS, ETCHANTS, ETC. (18)
6. THERMOGRAPHIC PROCESSES (13)
7. ELECTROPHOTOGRAPHIC PROCESSES (9)
8. THE DRIOGRAPHIC PROCESS.

216 pages. **$36**

POLYMERS AND ADHESIVES

URETHANE FOAMS TECHNOLOGY AND APPLICATIONS 1971
by Y. L. Meltzer

Urethane foam production is growing at about twice the annual growth rate of the overall plastics industry. Rigid foams are used in refrigerators and freezers, and in sophisticated and efficient types of food processing and preserving equipment. By far the largest consumer is the building and construction industry; while flexible foams are leading the demand in the furniture, aviation and automotive industries. The book contains descriptions of 148 manufacturing processes of which 42 deal with application technology:

Raw Materials (39)
Special Additives (30)
Product Types (29)
Processing (8)
Applications (42)

448 pages. **$36**

EPOXY AND URETHANE ADHESIVES 1971
by Dr. M. W. Ranney

An ever increasing demand for epoxy adhesives makes them the leader of the industry. Urethane polymers and intermediates are also augmenting the adhesives market. Isocyanate monomers are applied to textile fibers, metals, and elastomers as primers for adhesion. Polymethylene polyphenyl isocyanates are used in formulations for bonding glass, metal, elastomers and wood to a variety of substrates. Polyurethanes with polyesters, polyamides, and elastomers meet many high performance requirements. 111 processes in 7 chapters:

Metal to Metal (25)
Fiber to Rubber (22)
Glass & Ceramics to Metal (18)
Polymer to Polymer (12)
Plastic to Metal (10)
Paper and Wood (13)
General Purpose Adhesives (11)

280 pages. **$36**

POLYIMIDE MANUFACTURE 1971
by Dr. M. W. Ranney
Chemical Process Review No. 54

The U.S. patent literature of the past ten years provides an excellent description of the many types of polyimides and their syntheses. This book is an attempt to collate and summarize those processes pertaining to the manufacture of polymers containing an imide grouping. Emphasis has been placed on practical, technically useful information. About 90 distinct processes of manufacture are described in eight chapters.

1. Polyamide Acids (20)
2. Polyimide-Esters from TMA (7)
3. Polyimide-Amides (11)
4. Modified Polyimides and Cross-Linking (11)
5. Specialty Intermediates (15)
6. Silicone-Fluorocarbon-Polysulfone Modifications (11)
7. Cellular Polyimides (5)
8. General Processing Techniques (9)

243 pages. **$35**

HOT-MELT ADHESIVES 1971
by M. McDonald

Reviews the U.S. patent literature from 1950 through early 1971. Hot-melts set fast enough to accommodate high-speed machinery in shoemaking, paper converting, bonding textiles (replacing hand and machine sewing), metal container sealing, etc. 63 processes:

1. **Hot-Melts for Shoemaking** (14)
2. **Bonding Paper & Paperboard** (23)
3. **Bonding Metals** (7)
4. **Bonding Plastics** (6)
5. **Bonding 2 or more Materials** (7)
6. **Textiles and Coated Substrates** (6)

238 pages. **$35**

FLAME RETARDANT POLYMERS 1970
by M. Ranney

Summarizes selected process technology for the use of fire retardant imparting additives and reactive intermediates for major polymeric plastic materials, with particular emphasis on recent technology in the areas of polyesters, polystyrene and polyurethane foam. There are 144 separate processes included, all based on the U.S. patent literature.

An abbreviated Table of Contents is listed. The numbers in parentheses indicate the number of processes included for each entry.

Polyethylene and Polypropylene (15)
Polystyrene (19)
Polyurethanes (50)
Polyesters (13)
Other Polymer Systems (26)
General Utility Additives (21)

263 pages. **$35**

POLYSULFIDE MANUFACTURE 1970
by C. Placek
Chemical Process Review No. 50

This report covers 73 processes dealing with polymers possessing the disulfide (-SS-) group. Basic Processes (14); Modified Polysulfide Polymers (13); Curing (12); Process Control (4); Physical Form (3); Single-Package Compositions (6). 141 pages. **$35**

POLYCARBONATES—RECENT DEVELOPMENTS 1970
by K. Johnson
Chemical Process Review No. 47

Part I—Aromatic Polycarbonates: Synthesis and Polymerization (17); Halogen-Containing Polycarbonates (9); Processing (20); Modified Polycarbonates (23); Applications (5). Part II—Aliphatic Polycarbonates: Cycloaliphatics (8); Linear Aliphatics (6). 298 pages. **$35**

ENVIRONMENT AND POLLUTION

NITROGEN OXIDES EMISSION CONTROL 1972
by A. A. Lawrence
Pollution Control Review No. 9

Principal sources of air-polluting nitrogen oxides (NOx) are power plants and automobiles. How to control these emissions is shown in 79 patent-based processes of recent origin.

1. **Catalytic Conversion of Stack Gases**
2. **Adsorptive Techniques**
3. **Liquid Scrub Processes Purification of Waste Gases from Nitric Acid Processes**
4. **Combustion Techniques**
5. **Recovery and Utilization of NOx**
6. **Catalytic Conversion of Auto Exhaust NOx**
7. **Noncatalytic Means of NOx Reduction**
8. **Health Devices Removing NOx from Tobacco Smoke**

212 pages. **$36**

POLLUTION ANALYZING AND MONITORING INSTRUMENTS 1972

All together 157 companies are represented. About 350 instruments or other analytical equipment pieces are described. The major listings include:

1. **Diagrams of the apparatus with a description of its components and accessory equipment.**
2. **Technical discussion of the analytical reactions involved.**
3. **Specifications.**
4. **Brief statement about the specific and all-around uses of the apparatus.**

The data appearing in this volume were selected by the publisher from each manufacturer's literature at no cost to, nor influence from the manufacturers of the equipment.

Supplies detailed technical data on the types of pollution measurements and analyses which can be made and lists the companies providing such instrumentation. 354 pages. **$36**

WASTE TREATMENT WITH POLYELECTROLYTES 1972
by S. Gutcho
Pollution Control Review No. 8

Polyelectrolytes are high-molecular-weight polymers. They are water soluble or water dispersible and may be anionic, cationic or nonionic. They are now being used in the treatment of sewage, the clarification of industrial waste water, and the purification of contaminated rivers and lakes. 144 Processes based on U.S. patents.

1. **Anionic Polyelectrolytes** (26 processes)
2. **Cationic Polyelectrolytes (52)**
3. **Nonionics (10)**
4. **Polyelectrolytes from Natural Sources (25)**
5. **Aspects and Methods (12)**
6. **Types & Syntheses (12)**
7. **Sewage Treatment (7)**

Attention is focused on phosphate removal, low ash sewage sludge formation, and on recycling of waste water for acceptable purity. 237 pages. **$36**

DETERGENTS AND POLLUTION 1972
Problems and Technological Solutions
by H. R. Jones
Pollution Control Review No. 7

Thanks to a complicated series of scientific disputes over alleged deleterious effects on environment and human health, there is probably more confusion about how to properly satisfy this market, than there is about any other class of chemical products.

188 Processes:
Manufacture of Linear Olefins
Purification Thereof
Manufacture of Linear Paraffins
Their Purification
Routes to Linear Alcohols
Their Purification
Alkylaromatic Hydrocarbons
Their Purification
Other Raw Materials
Sulfation and Sulfonation
Detergent Formulations
The "Builder" Problem
Removal from Sewage
Future Trends
268 pages. **$36**

ENVIRONMENTAL CONTROL IN THE INORGANIC CHEMICAL INDUSTRY 1972
by H. R. Jones
Pollution Control Review No. 6

Inorganic pollution control is still a field that must receive greater attention and action. Be greater attention. Because of the nature of the industry obsolete units remain sufficiently profitable to continue in use.

Provides helpful directions for adequate pollution control. Commercial processes are shown, as well as detailed technology from the U.S. patent literature:

1. Wastewater Characteristics
2. Water Pollution Problems in the Manufacture of 33 Specific Chemicals
3. Actual Pollution Control Processes for Specific Wastewaters
4. Air Pollution Problems in the Manufacture of 15 Specific Chemicals
5. Actual Pollution Control Processes for Atmospheric Emissions
6. Awareness and Future Trends.

249 pages. **$36**

ENVIRONMENTAL CONTROL IN THE ORGANIC AND PETROCHEMICAL INDUSTRIES 1971
by H. R. Jones
Pollution Control Review No. 3

1. WASTE SOURCES
2. WATER USE
3. WATER POLLUTION
4. RECEIVING WATERS
5. REUSE OF WATER
6. PHYSIOLOGICAL EFFECTS
7. POLLUTION PARAMETERS
8. MONITORING
9. CHEMICAL CLASSIFICATION
10. SPECIFIC PRODUCTS
11. WASTE WATERS
12. INDUSTRIAL-MUNICIPAL TREATMENT PLANTS
13. INTERNAL IMPROVEMENTS
14. PHYSICAL TREATMENTS
15. CHEMICAL TREATMENTS
16. BIOLOGICAL TREATMENTS
17. OTHER DISPOSAL METHODS
18. WATER ECONOMICS
19. AIR POLLUTION
20. AIR POLLUTANTS REMOVAL
21. IMMEDIATE RECOMMENDATIONS
22. REFERENCES-INDEXES

257 pages. **$36**

ENVIRONMENT AND POLLUTION

HYDROGEN SULFIDE REMOVAL PROCESSES 1972
by P. G. Stecher
Pollution Control Review No. 5

Furnishes reliable and efficient methods of H_2S removal from gases, air, and liquids. 80 Patent-based processes.

1. **ABSORPTION FROM GASES WITH INORGANICS**
2. **WITH ORGANICS**
   Alkanolamines
   Other Amines
   Esters and Ethers
   Other Compounds
   Recycling Absorbents
3. **REMOVAL FROM GASES BY OTHER METHODS**
   Oxidation
   Adsorption
   Hydrotreating
   Use of Electrolysis
   H_2S Recycle in White Liquor Regeneration
   Ion Exchange Resins
   Molecular Sieves
   Adsorption plus Oxidation
4. **REMOVAL FROM LIQUIDS**
   From Fluid Hydrocarbons
   From Aqueous Solutions

288 pages. **$36**

SULFUR DIOXIDE REMOVAL FROM WASTE GASES 1971
by A. V. Slack
Pollution Control Review No. 4

Reviews the problems of smelter operators, power plants, refineries, sulfur acid plants, and Claus process sulfur plants.

1. THE PROBLEM
   Alternatives of Control
2.-3. THROWAWAY PROCESSES
   Dry Systems
   Wet Systems
4. ECONOMIC FACTORS IN RECOVERY
5. RECOVERY PROCESSES
6. ALKALIS AS ABSORBENTS
7. ALKALINE EARTH ABSORBENTS
8. METAL OXIDE SORPTION
9. ADSORPTION PROCESSES
10. CATALYTIC OXIDATION & REDUCTION
11. OTHER RECOVERY METHODS
   Organic Sorbents
   Fuel Gasification
   Gas Cleaning

200 pages. **$36**

PAPER RECYCLING AND THE USE OF CHEMICALS 1971
by M. McDonald

Paper accounts for almost half of our solid waste (ca. 40 million tons per year accumulate in the U.S. alone). But paper can be reused. Treatment is mechanical and chemical, using many substances for removing printer's ink, plastic coatings, wax, adhesives, etc. The secondary fibers industry, on the threshold of an era of expanded growth, is consuming a steadily increasing amount of solvents, bleaches, and other chemicals discussed in this book. 68 processes.

Removing Ink (23)
Removing Coatings and Impregnants (19)
Dispersing Coatings (11)
Repulpable Adhesives and Coatings (5)
Miscellaneous (10)

304 pages. **$36**

CATALYTIC CONVERSION OF AUTOMOBILE EXHAUST 1971
by J. McDermott
Pollution Control Review No. 2

The need for controlling the exhaust gas emissions from gasoline, diesel, and jet engines is becoming increasingly urgent. The emission of carbon monoxide, nitrogen oxides, lead compounds, reactive olefins, and even of carcinogens such as benzopyrene, has become the concern of almost every legislature.

This book summarizes the U.S. patent literature relating to combustion catalysts, such as various metal oxides, platinum, and palladium. In general, the catalytic unit, mounted after the exhaust manifold, completes the oxidation of unburned hydrocarbons and converts the carbon monoxide to carbon dioxide. 94 processes and devices are described.

Catalytic Converter Design (31)
Catalyst Bed Design (17)
Catalysts (32)
Catalytic Units (14)
208 pages. **$36**

CORROSION RESISTANT MATERIALS HANDBOOK 1971
Second Edition
by I. Mellan

Corrosion, always an urgent and persistent problem, bothers and baffles us even more today, because of the quantity and complexity of chemicals in our polluted biosphere. This book will help you cut losses by enabling you to choose the proper commercially available corrosion resistant material. The index lists thousands of corrosive substances and refers you to specific recommendations in the 147 tables:

Synthetic Resins (90 tables)
Elastomers (17 tables)
Cements (11 tables)
Glass & Ceramics (4 tables)
Wood (3 tables)
Metals & Alloys (22 tables)

487 pages. **$25**

MERCURY POLLUTION CONTROL 1971
by H. R. Jones
Pollution Control Review No. 1

In 1970 mercury pollution hit the headlines. Mercury ions were expected to react with other inorganic ions in the water, form precipitates, and sink harmlessly to the bottom. But when organic molecules from sewage or dead organisms are present, mercury reacts with these molecules to form toxic methyl mercury compounds which are excreted very slowly by fish and man. This book explains in detail what measures can be taken to prevent further pollution and to remove existing contamination. 13 Chapters: 1. The Fish Episode. 2. Production of Mercury. 3. Its Properties. 4. Uses of Mercury. 5. Its Toxicology. 6. Detection and Determination. 7. Air Pollution by Mercury. 8. Cleanup of Spilled Mercury. 9. Removal from Gases. 10. From Liquids. 11. From other Materials. 12. Legislation. 13. Trends and Problems. 251 pages. **$35**

ENVIRONMENT AND POLLUTION

HAZARDOUS CHEMICALS HANDLING AND DISPOSAL 1970
The Institute of Advanced Sanitation Research International

This publication is the record of a symposium of hazardous chemicals handling and disposal.
Hygiene Control—Handling Certain Hazardous Chemicals
Hazardous Chemicals Handling in "The Pharmaceutical Chemical Industry"
Effects of Hazardous Chemicals on Biochemical Oxygen Demand Tests of Stream Water Samples
Pesticide Handling in an Industrial Plant
Thermal Method for the Disposal of Hazardous Wastes
Land Disposal of Hazardous Chemicals
Hazardous Chemicals Disposal in a Large Chemical Complex
Research, Development and Application of New Biological Methods for Toxic Wastes Degradation and Disposal
Design and Tests of a Portable Cask for Explosive Chemicals
130 pages. **$15**

HAZARDOUS CHEMICALS HANDLING AND DISPOSAL 1971
The Institute of Advanced Sanitation Research International

This is the record of the Second Symposium.
Pesticide Container Decontamination
Fate and Effects of Pesticides
Separation of Organic and Inorganic Chemicals in a Waste Stream
Vector Problems in Waste Disposal
Plants Poisonous to Livestock
Land Application and Anaerobic Lagoon Disposal of Waste
Reverse Osmosis for Reclamation and Reuse of Chemical and Metal Waste Solutions
Thermal Methods for Destruction of Chemical Waste
Specialty Gases and Hazardous Wastes
Education of the Public
Hazardous Chemicals from Natural Sources
Maximum Allowable Concentrations and Water Quality
Biochemical Oxygen Demand and its Meaning
163 pages. **$20**

DESALINIZATION BY REVERSE OSMOSIS 1970
by J. McDermott

Summarizes 71 U.S. patents relating to reverse osmosis with emphasis on membrane technology. Chapters on Membrane Preparation; Equipment Design; Modified Reverse Osmosis Techniques; Vapor Permeation; Energy Sources; Solution Modifications; Submerged Units; Special Units; Detailed Engineering Outlays and Drawings. 209 pages. **$35**

DESALINIZATION BY DISTILLATION 1971 RECENT DEVELOPMENTS
by J. McDermott

The prospect of revitalizing arid areas, together with the problem of providing increased quantities of potable water has produced considerable research. In the past two years, over one hundred patents relating to distillation processes have been issued in the U.S. 194 pages. **$35**

DESALINIZATION BY FREEZE CONCENTRATION 1971
by J. McDermott

This volume is the second of a series of three, dealing with the major desalinization processes. The information contained will provide needed knowhow concerning the renewed interest in freeze concentration processes, such as vacuum freezing, surface freezing, hydrate processes and crystal washing. 207 pages. **$35**

SOUNDPROOF BUILDING MATERIALS 1970
by Dr. M. W. Ranney

There is increasing public awareness of the health menace of excess noise. The Walsh-Healy Act regulates noise in factories with government contracts. These factors, added to the current interest in other forms of pollution abatement, signify a rapidly growing market. Describes 100 patent-based processes. 217 pages. **$35**

POLYAMIDE FIBER MANUFACTURE 1972
by M. Sittig
Chemical Process Review No. 61

The polyamides or nylons are the oldest wholly synthetic fibers. This is a book about the actual production of nylon fibers based on no less than 223 U.S. patents.

1. Introduction
2. Polyamide Compositions
3. Adipic Acid Manufacture
4. Higher Dibasic Acids
5. Alternate Acid Types
6. Adiponitrile Manufacture
7. Diamine Manufacture
8. Nylon Salt
9. Caprolactam—Conventional Routes
10. Caprolactam—Alternate Routes
11. Higher Lactam
12. Polylactam Processes
13. Polyamide Production
14. Fiber Production
15. Waste Recovery and Pollution Problems
16. Future Trends

262 pages. **$36**

FLOCKED MATERIALS 1972
Technology and Applications
by E. L. Barden

Demand for flocked materials and articles covered with fibers or similar substances is increasing. Fibers and flakes are used to flock walls and ceilings, because the flocking is decorative, soundproofs, waterproofs, acts as a thermal insulator and is highly durable.

Plush toys, velvet greeting cards, good quality carpeting, even battery plates and synthetic turfs can be produced by flocking. 111 processes:

Electrostatic Methods (23)
Mechanical Flocking (4)
Types of Flock (3)
Flock Treatments (8)
Adhesives (13)
Decorative Effects (12)
Wearing Apparel (16)
Home Furnishings (11)
Automobiles (7)
Others (14)

294 pages. **$36**

POLYESTER FIBER MANUFACTURE 1971
by M. Sittig
Chemical Process Review No. 56

In 1970 polyester became the number one U.S. fiber, surpassing the consumption figure for nylon by another 100 million pounds. Predictions are that continuous processing will be common in 1975. A total of 116 processes is given.

1. INTRODUCTION
2. ECONOMICS
3. VARIOUS POLYESTER COMPOSITIONS (6)
4. RAW MATERIALS AND PURIFICATION (9)
5. DIMETHYL TEREPHTHALATE (8)
6. INTEGRATED POLYESTER PRODUCTION (5)
7. BIS (HYDROXYETHYL) TEREPHTHALATE (23)
8. PREPOLYMERS (8)
9. POLYCONDENSATION (28)
10. POLYMER AFTER-TREATMENT (2)
11. SCRAP RECOVERY (3)
12. FIBER PRODUCTION (24)
13. FUTURE TRENDS

214 pages. **$36**

SPANDEX MANUFACTURE 1970
by M. McDonald
Chemical Process Review No. 48

This book covers methods of making spandex fibers, that is, the conversion of polyurethanes into fibers, as described in the U.S. patent literature. The U.S. patent literature has the most complete and comprehensive process information available, and as such, this publication will give you key processing information for this fast-growing fiber. The Table of Contents below gives the scope of this volume. The numbers in ( ) represent the number of processes included.

Wet Spinning Processes (13), Solvent Spinning Processes (19), Melt Spinning Processes (3), Chemical Composition and Raw Materials (19), Improving Resistance to Ultraviolet Light and Oxidation (9), Improving Dyeability of Spandex (9), Miscellaneous (8).

191 pages. **$35**

SOIL RESISTANT TEXTILES 1970
by Dr. M. W. Ranney
Textile Processing Review No. 5

Ideal soil release finishes must be capable of releasing stains readily and preventing redeposition of soil during laundering. Treatments should render manmade fibers and durable press reactants less attractive to oily stains and should be more easily wetted.

This report summarizes the developments in soil retardant and soil release finishes in both the carpet industry and in textile manufacture. It includes the newest technology associated with the use of acrylates and fluorochemical treatments. The numbers in ( ) following each treating agent indicate the number of processes covered for that particular compound.

Introduction: Metal Oxides and Salts For Carpet Treatment (15), Acrylic and Vinyl Polymers (10), Silicones (6), Fluorochemical Compounds (72), General Treatments (14). 216 pages. **$35**

WATERPROOFING TEXTILES 1970
by Dr. M. W. Ranney
Textile Processing Review No. 4

This Textile Processing Review summarizes the technology of water resistant treatments for textiles and fabrics as described in the U.S. patent literature since the early 1950's. 246 waterproofing processes are included—64 relate to use of fluorochemicals.

The numbers in ( ) after each entry in the Table of Contents, where the treatment processes are organized by the agent used, indicates the number of production processes for each agent.

Production Processes for Waterproofing Textiles using the following Agents: Metal Salts and Wax-Containing Formulations (44), Silicones and Alkyl Polysiloxanes (53), Organofunctional Silicones and Fluorosilanes (20), Acrylics (8), Nitrogen Containing Compounds (30), Fluorochemical Compounds (64), Elastomer, Vinyl, Polyolefin Vapor Permeable Fabrics (27), Miscellaneous Treatments (9). 353 pages. **$35**

SYNTHETIC PAPER FROM SYNTHETIC FIBERS 1971
by K. Johnson

This book provides a summary of the U.S. patent literature through 1970, relating to 74 processes for producing synthetic papers on conventional papermaking machinery:

1. **Cellulosics** (37 processes)
   - Cellulose Derivatives (15)
   - Cross-Linked Cellulose (4)
   - Blends with Other Fibers (10)
   - General (8)
2. **Polyamides** (8)
   - General (5)
   - Nylon + Cellulose (3)
3. **Polyacrylonitrile** (13)
   - Bonding (7)
   - General (4)
   - Blends (2)
4. **Synthetic Fibers** (16)
   - General Processing (10)
   - Specialty Papers (2)
   - Polytetrafluoroethylene (3)
   - Polyester (1)

236 pages. **$35**

NONWOVEN FABRIC TECHNOLOGY 1971
by M. McDonald

Nonwovens are structures produced by bonding or interlocking of fibers, accomplished by mechanical, chemical, thermal, or solvent means. Low cost is the primary advantage over woven or knitted products, resulting in a wide variety of disposable items from flush-away diapers to industrial uniforms. U.S. hospitals and other medical organizations bought over $100 millions worth of disposable hospital gowns and other nonwovens in 1970 of what is thought to be a $800 million market. This book emphasizes those processes that turn out materials for making garments, draperies, upholstery, sheets, etc. 121 processes are described:

1. Resin Bonding (22 processes). 2. Spunbonding (23). 3. Needle Punching (28). 4. Fluid Pressure (13). 5. Heat Bonding (10). 6. Web Formation (7). 7. Miscellaneous (18). 240 pages. **$35**

MULTICOMPONENT FIBERS 1971
by C. Placek

Discusses processes for producing multicomponent fibers, that is, those fibers that consist of two or more polymeric compounds spun together. The spinning of multicomponent fibers is one method used to produce bulked or crimped fibers. The difference in physical properties of the two filaments results in a bulked yarn.

This report covers 106 patents issued since 1960. The processes range over a wide spectrum of fiber technology—composition, properties, physical forms and spinning techniques. Numbers in ( ) indicate the number of processes described in each chapter.

Variations of the Same Polymer (24), Chemically Unrelated Components (10), Spontaneous Crimp (2), Permanent Crimp (12), Specific Properties of Fibers (8), Production of Sheath-Core Structures (10), Side-by-Side Components (7), Spinning Technology (33).

225 pages. **$35**

CREASEPROOFING TEXTILES 1970
by Dr. M. W. Ranney
Textile Processing Review No. 2

Summarizes detailed process information relating to textile creaseproofing agents used to obtain wash and wear, or permanent press fabrics. Over 300,000 words, describes 343 processes in this field. Shows you chemical agents used, and processes by which they are applied.

Dimethylolethylene Urea and Related Compounds, Aldehyde-Urea Condensates, Uron Resins, Aminoplasts—Catalyst Performance, Melamine Derivatives, Triazones, Carbamates, Other Nitrogen-Containing Compounds, Phosphorus-Amino Compounds—Aziridines, Aminoplast-Thermoplastic Resin Compositions, General Processing Techniques and Formulations, Aldehydes, Acetals, Epoxies, Epihalohydrins, Sulfones, Sulfonium Salts, Cross-Linking Agents, Miscellaneous, Polymeric Coatings—Rubber, Vinyl, Silicones, Radiation Curing, Wool, Nylon, and Others. Indexes. 460 pages. **$35**

FLAME RETARDANT TEXTILES 1970
by Dr. M. W. Ranney
Textile Processing Review No. 3

Describes 177 commercial processes to produce flame retardant textiles and fabrics.

Most activity is based on chemical modification of cellulose through hydroxyl groups. Use of phosphoric acid, urea-phosphates, and other phosphorylating agents all confer flame retardant properties to cellulose. A significant portion of this book is devoted to the latest in application of phosphorus containing materials.

Numbers in ( ) indicate the number of processes described.

Ammonium Salts, Borates (12); Antimony, Titanium Metal Oxides (25); Amine-Phosphorus Products (21); Aziridines, APO, APS (21); Methylol-Phosphorus Polymers, THPC (27); Phosphonitrilic Chlorides (9); Triallyl Phosphates and Phosphonates (26); Silicones Isocyanates, Miscellaneous (10); Nylon, Acrylics (18). 373 pages. **$35**

U. S. MARKETS

OVERSEAS MARKETS

OVERSEAS MARKETS

POLLUTION CONTROL COMPANIES U.S.A. 1972

Provides a marketing guide to the U.S. pollution control industry.

The first section is an alphabetical listing of ca. 1,500 companies or company units (divisions, subsidiaries, etc.) which manufacture or supply products useful in the areas of air, water, noise, and radiation pollution control and waste management.

The second section lists more than 500 companies and company units which provide such professional services as consulting, design engineering, and analyses of air or water pollutants.

The address and telephone number of each company is listed together with a brief description of the company's pollution control products or services, although these may constitute only a small portion of the company's business. 239 pages. **$24**

CHEMICAL GUIDE TO THE UNITED STATES 1971
Sixth Edition

Describes over 400 of the largest chemical firms in the U.S.: Those who actually carry out chemical syntheses in their plants. Companies and factual data about them are listed in alphabetic order, followed by an index which gives companies, subsidiaries and divisions, again by strict alphabetic arrangement.

Whenever available the following information is given in detail:

Name and Address with Zip Code
Ownership
Annual Sales
Number of Employees
Principal Executives and Titles
Plant Locations
Products
Subsidiaries and Affiliates
Internal Structure

Also gives information on closely held firms, joint ventures, and others that do not publish annual reports. 191 pages. **$20**

TEXTILE GUIDE TO EUROPE 1972
Second Edition

This improved edition describes about 2,600 of the leading yarn, fabric, knitwear and hosiery manufacturers in 18 countries of Western Europe.

Each chapter is preceded by a resume of the textile industry in the country concerned.

Where available the following information is given for each company:

Full Name
Complete Address
Telephone Numbers
Telex Numbers
Ownership
Sales
Number of Employees
Plant Locations
Principal Executives
Range of Products
Domestic Subsidiaries
Foreign Subsidiaries

In each section the salient features are pinpointed through the expedient of a statistical analysis. 290 pages. **$24**

FOOD GUIDE TO EUROPE 1972

Describes 1,600 of the leading food processing companies located in 18 countries of Western Europe. Where available and pertinent, the following information is given:

Name
Address
Telephone Number
Telex Number
Ownership
Sales
Number of Employees
Plant Locations
Principal Executives
Products
Domestic Subsidiaries
Foreign Subsidiaries

Each chapter includes a short resume of the food industry in the country concerned, giving the salient features of the industry and production and trade statistics. Prepared in our London office. 325 pages. **$24**

WORLD PHARMACEUTICAL FIRMS 1972

Lists alphabetically by country the names and full addresses of over 6,000 manufacturers of ethical drugs, pharmaceutical specialties and basic pharmaceutical materials in all the major producing areas of the world.

For easy reference the 52 countries are arranged in geographical areas:

North America
South America
Western Europe
Eastern Europe
Africa
Australasia
Asia
North Africa and Middle East

This book will enable companies dealing with the pharmaceutical sector to mail sales literature, help plan and evaluate area representation, assist in the preparation of market reports and provide useful references.

Prepared in our London office. 122 pages. **$24**

EUROPEAN PAINT MANUFACTURERS 1971

Developing technology in the field of polymer-based and solventless coatings has resulted in European acquisitions and mergers. Describes about 1,000 of the most important paint manufacturers in 17 countries of Western Europe. Entries are listed alphabetically by country and the following data are presented as fully as they were obtainable:

Name
Address
Telephone Numbers
Telex Numbers
Number of Employees
Principal Executives
Products
Plant Locations
Domestic Subsidiaries
Foreign Subsidiaries
Sales Volume

Prepared in our London Office. 155 pages. **$24**

FOOD AND BEVERAGE PROCESSING INDUSTRIES 1971

The usefulness of this book derives from its organization. It is divided into 2 sections. The first section is an alphabetical listing of approximately 3,500 U.S. food firms giving the correct name, address and zip code. Also concise, pertinent information (where available) such as:

(a) Annual Sales
(b) Number of Employees
(c) Name of Chief Executive
(d) Product Types

The second section is arranged numerically according to zip code with the companies once again listed alphabetically within their proper zip code numbers, thereby providing you with an easy-to-use geographical index to the U.S. food industry.

It is a great help in marketing efforts by providing the means for forward geographical planning.

169 pages. **$20**

ELECTRONICS INDUSTRY OF JAPAN 1972

Aimed at giving you a concise but detailed picture of the present state of this important industry. The first section gives details of 145 major companies.

Complete Name
Address
Founding Date
Capital & Assets
Sales & Profits
Executives
No. of Employees
Major Stockholders
Bankers
Agreements
Products

The second section gives more limited data on a further 714 companies. The third section gives statistics. The book is completed by an alphabetical list of Japanese brand names. Prepared in Japan. 147 pages. **$24**

EUROPEAN CHEMICAL DISTRIBUTORS 1971

A considerable proportion of the sales of the world's major chemical companies are made through distributors, particularly in foreign countries. The book is divided into a main section, arranged by European distributors, and an index of worldwide companies the 1,300 distributors are representing.

Includes:

Austria	Luxembourg
Belgium	Netherlands
Denmark	Norway
Finland	Portugal
France	Spain
Germany	Sweden
Greece	Switzerland
Iceland	Turkey
Ireland	United Kingdom
Italy	

The chemical companies represented by the distributors are cross-referenced in the index. 264 pages. **$24**

EUROPEAN PHARMACEUTICAL MARKET REPORT 1971
Second Edition

Gives statistical information from 1960 to the end of 1969 on the 5,000 million dollar drug industry of the EEC (European Economic Community) and of the EFTA (European Free Trade Association). Type of information included:

General and Historical
Growth Potentials
Production and Sales
Domestic and Foreign Trade
Distribution—Pricing
Market Structure
Structure of the Industry
Names and Addresses of Trade Associations and of over 1,000 Manufacturers
Research and Development
Government Legislation
Health Service Expenditures

This book, a greatly expanded version of the earlier successful study, will bring you up to date with the European pharmaceutical scene and will give you a coherent picture of this complex market. 158 pages. **$36**

TEXTILE INDUSTRY OF JAPAN 1971

Relates significant developments of nearly 900 companies:

Name and Address
Principal Officers
Employees
Capital and Sales
Total Assets
Bankers & Stockholders

Statistically analyzes the whole Japanese textile industry:

Production
Trade
Raw Materials
Consumption
Employment Pattern
Wages & Productivity
Important Trademarks

Increasing pressures from expanding developing countries and restricted imports by the U.S. are producing many changes evaluated here.

205 pages. **$35**

OVERSEAS MARKETS

CHEMICAL GUIDE TO EUROPE 1971
Fifth Edition
Prepared in our London Office to give on-the-spot coverage. Describes ca. 1,100 companies in the 19 countries of Western Europe which together constitute a market almost as large as that of the U.S. Includes all major European Chemical Companies. Gives this information (where pertinent and available):

Name and Address
Telephone and Telex Numbers
Ownership
Plant Locations and Products
Internal Structure
Local Subsidiaries and Affiliates
Foreign Subsidiaries and Affiliates
Principal Executives
Annual Sales
Number of Employees

Also companies which are predominantly non-chemical, but have important chemical interests, are included. 288 pages. **$20**

KEY EUROPEAN INDUSTRIALS 1970
This important new directory describes 1,000 leading manufacturers in 19 countries of Western Europe. Prepared by our London office, it will provide the hard-pressed executive with a unique, on-the-spot guide to the activities of Europe's key industrial companies and groups. Find out who owns whom.

Full name and address
Telephone and telex numbers
Share capital, sales, profit
Number of employees
Principal executives
Range of products and activities
Domestic and foreign subsidiaries

Volume I — (EFTA) — Austria, Denmark, Finland, Iceland, Ireland, Norway, Portugal, Sweden, Switzerland, United Kingdom. 180 pages.
Volume II — (EEC) — Belgium, France, Germany, Greece, Italy, Luxembourg, Netherlands, Spain, Turkey. 182 pages.
2 Volumes—**$35**

PETROCHEMICAL INDUSTRY OF JAPAN 1970
The bulk of the book is a detailed guide to the 205 manufacturers in the industry. Companies are listed alphabetically, giving their address, capital, sales, number of employees, president and, where relevant, ownership. For every company, the existing and planned capacity of each product is listed, together with its plant location and expected completion date. 147 pages. **$35**

EUROPEAN FOOD MARKET RESEARCH SOURCES 1970
Enables you to pinpoint publications most likely to be of assistance.
References are classified by Government statistics and reports, other statistics and reports, trade associations, food trade journals; other newspapers and periodicals, directories, advertising statistics, bank reviews. 111 pages. **$19**

ELECTRONICS MANUFACTURERS OF WESTERN EUROPE AND U.S.A. 1970
A comprehensive guide to names and addresses of electronics manufacturers in 16 countries.
Enables you to mail sales literature and promotional material as effectively as possible; helps to plan and evaluate area representation more accurately; is a useful day-to-day work of reference. 131 pages. **$19**

ELECTRONICS GUIDE TO EUROPE 1969
Contains company profiles of over 600 leading electronics manufacturers in 14 countries. Arranged for easy comparison: Full name and address, ownership, principal executives, product range, domestic and overseas subsidiaries, plant location, latest sales figures, number of employees. 150 pages. **$20**

EUROPEAN KNITWEAR AND HOSIERY MARKET REPORT 1970
17 countries included. Trend of activity established. Size structure of domestic market determined. Information on yarn consumption, knitwear and hosiery production, foreign trade, number of companies and employees engaged in manufacture. Comprehensive selection of statistical material. 166 pages. **$35**

PHARMACEUTICAL AND COSMETIC

X-RAY CONTRAST AGENTS 1971
by M. Gutcho
Describes 55 processes suitable for the preparation of new x-ray contrast agents.
1. Polyiodobenzoic Acid Derivatives (16). 2. Polyiodophthalic Acid Derivatives (5). 3. Iodophenyl Derivatives (12). 4. Radiopaque Formulations (9). 5. Miscellaneous Contrast Media (4). 6. Process Improvements (9). 7. Other Uses for Radiopaque Materials. 130 pages. **$20**

ARTIFICIAL KIDNEY SYSTEMS 1970
by M. Gutcho
Contains significant, detailed technical data, based on the patent literature relating to manufacturing, assembly, and operation of artificial kidney systems.
Dialyzers in Artificial Kidney Systems (17); The Design of Dialyzer Parts (9); Dialysate Modifications (12); Lung and Kidney Machines (6); Dialyzers (6); Blood Purification Processes (2). 320 pages. **$35**

SUSTAINED RELEASE PHARMACEUTICALS 1969
by A. Williams
To ensure a long lasting, continuous and not too intensive action of a therapeutic agent in the human body, it is necessary to delay the absorption.
Aside from chemical alterations of the drug in question, the problem can be solved by the preparation of the so-called sustained release medicaments for which 89 processes are given here. 273 pages. **$35**

ANTIOBESITY DRUG MANUFACTURE 1970
by Dr. B. Idson
Describes 162 processes for drugs or compounds proposed or employed for the reduction of body weight. The majority of the preparative processes is for sympathomimetic drugs of the pressor amine or amphetamine type. These substances, sometimes in connection with carboxymethylcellulose, produce a diminution of the desire for food intake. 193 pages. **$35**

COSMETIC FILMS 1970
by M. Gutcho
The abbreviated Table of Contents indicates the four major films and the distribution of the patents within each area — the numbers in ( ).
Powders (21)
Creams and Lotions (12)
Nail Preparations (19)
Lipsticks (14)
143 pages. **$20**

NUCLEOTIDES AND NUCLEOSIDES 1970
by S. Gutcho
Organic Synthesis of Nucleotides in General, and of Specific Nucleotides, Fermentation Procedures for Nucleotides in General and for Specific Nucleotides, Enzymatic Digestion of Nucleic Acids, Nucleotides Coenzymes, Cyclic Nucleotides, Dinucleoside Phosphates, Purification Techniques, General Procedures, Nucleotides as Flavor Enhancers. 200 pages. **$35**

TETRACYCLINE MANUFACTURING PROCESSES 1969
(2 Volumes)
CTC, Oxytetracycline, TC, DMTC and DMCTC, 2N-Derivatives, Position 4 Derivatives, 6-Methylene Derivatives, 6-Deoxy Derivatives, Anhydrotetracyclines, 7-and/or 9-Derivatives, 11a-Halo Derivatives, 5a, 11a-Dehydrotetracyclines, 12a-Derivatives, Epimers, Mechanism Study intermediates. Indexes. 931 pages. **(2 Volumes) $45**

DENTIFRICES 1970
by T. Jefopoulos
A guide to information available from U.S. Patent literature to therapeutic and cosmetic agents in dentifrices.
The numbers in ( ) indicate the number of processes covered.
Cleaning Agents (17)
Polishing Agents (14)
Prophylactic Compositions (27)
Fluorides (30)
Dentifrices for Dentists (6)
Other Dentifrices (30)
Improved Processing (2)
191 pages. **$35**

HAIR PREPARATIONS 1969
by A. Williams
Provides a detailed technological summary of recent developments based on 138 U.S. patents, since 1960, covering all aspects of hair preparations for the head, beard, eyelashes, and eyebrows.
Introduction, Dyeing, Bleaching, Waving, Setting, Shampoos-Rinses, Grooming-Tonics, Shaving Assistants, Other, Indexes. 208 pages. **$35**

FIBRINOLYTIC ENZYME MANUFACTURING 1969
by T. Rubel
Chemical Process Review No. 38
Methods for production and purification of fibrinolytic agents, their precursors and activators. Emphasis is on urokinase and streptokinase which activate plasminogen to form plasmin.
Plasminogen and Fibrinolysin, Urokinase, Streptokinase and Streptodornase, Other Fibrinolytic Enzymes. Indexes. 139 pages. **$24**

VITAMIN B_{12} MANUFACTURE 1969
by R. Noyes
Chemical Process Review No. 40
Vitamin B_{12} active substances are important therapeutic products for treatment of pernicious anemia. Also used for treatment of various other human ailments, and as a veterinary growth factor. This book offers various methods of producing vitamin B_{12} active substances. 327 pages. **$35**

VITAMIN E MANUFACTURE 1969
by T. Rubel
Chemical Process Review No. 39
This review relates the known methods for the preparation of tocopherols from natural products or by synthetic means, and conversion of non-alpha tocopherols.
Introduction; Tocopherols From Deodorizer Sludge, Conversions to Alpha Tocopherol, Synthesis of Tocopherols, Miscellaneous Related Processes, Indexes. 114 pages. **$24**

AGRICULTURAL

AGRICULTURAL CHEMICALS MANUFACTURE 1971
by M. Sittig
Chemical Process Review No. 52
Agricultural chemicals, properly used, are essential for supplying the food requirements of the world's evergrowing population. Current attacks on the toxicity of today's pesticides notwithstanding, our agriculture saves about 5 dollars worth of produce for every dollar spent on the war against harmful pests. 172 manufacturing process and product descriptions are given:

1. **Environmental Control in Manufacture**
2. **Manufacture of Intermediates** (4)
3. **Insecticides** (80)
4. **Herbicides** (48)
5. **Fungicides** (25)
6. **Nematocides** (5)
7. **Plant Growth Regulators** (9)
8. **Fertilizer Additives** (1)
9. **Future Trends**

264 pages. **$35**

HORMONAL AND ATTRACTANT PESTICIDE TECHNOLOGY 1971
by Y. L. Meltzer
The need for non-chemical pesticides which are highly selective, nonpolluting and nontoxic, is urgent. Encouraging results are being obtained with insect hormones and hormonelike substances that interfere with the life cycle of noxious insects. 23 chapters based on the world's patent literature and technical articles: 1. Scope of the Problem. 2. Insect Hormones as Pesticides. 3. Insect Development and Hormones. 4. Juvenile Hormone. 5 Ecdysone. 6. Brain Hormone. Attractants for 7. Insects. 8. Bees. 9. Boll Weevils. 10. Cabbage Looper Moths. 11. Cockroaches. 12. Bombyx mori. 13. Flies. 14. Gypsy Moths. 15. Pink Bollworms. 16. Termites. 17. Yellow Jackets. 18. 10,12-Hexadecadiene Derivs. 19. Aliphatic Hydroxy Attractants. 20. Polyenols. 21. Review Articles. 22. Regulations. 23. Future Trends. 281 pages. **$35**

AQUATIC HERBICIDES AND ALGAECIDES 1971
by J. H. Meyer
There is a growing need for control of aquatic weeds and algae. This vegetation destroys natural waterways and water supplies. The most effective control is by chemicals. This book gathers the latest technology for producing or using aquatic herbicides and algaecides, based on U.S. patent literature. Numbers in ( ) indicate the number of processes described, 108 in all.
Metal Compounds (22)
Chlorinated Hydrocarbons (7)
Other Halogenated Compounds (16)
The Halogens Themselves (4)
Sulfur-Containing Materials (12)
Quaternary Ammonium Compounds (8)
Amides and Imides (10)
Amines (6)
Acids and Their Derivatives (8)
Miscellaneous Organic Compounds (9)
Carriers (6)
177 pages. **$35**

AMMONIUM PHOSPHATES 1969
by Dr. M. W. Ranney
Chemical Process Review No. 35
This book describes recent processes for production of ammonium phosphates.
Introduction; Ammonium Orthophosphates, Diammonium Orthophosphates, Ammonium Polyphosphates, Metal Ammonium Phosphates, Ammonium Phosphate—Ammonium Nitrate Mixtures. Many illustrations. 278 pages. **$35**

NEW FERTILIZER MATERIALS 1968
by C. I. E. C.
Ureaform, Crotonylidene & Isobutylidene Diurea, Triple Superphosphate, Ammonium Phosphates, Nitrophosphates, Nitrate of Potash, Potassium Phosphates and Metaphosphates, Magnesium, Sulfur Fertilizers, Oxamide, Urea Nitrate and Phosphate, Hydrides of Phosphorus, Red Phosphorus. Applications. 430 pages. **$35**

CONTROLLED RELEASE FERTILIZERS 1968
by Dr. R. Powell
Chemical Process Review No. 15
This book offers you complete technical data on numerous processes and products in this field. The two major approaches are (a) compounds of low solubility, and (b) coated granules.
Introduction; Compounds of Low Solubility, Coated Granules, Prevention of Nitrogen Losses, Rapid-Release Fertilizer. 279 pages. **$35**

FERTILIZER DEVELOPMENTS AND TRENDS 1968
by A. V. Slack
R&D Trends, Ammonia, Ammonium Nitrate, Sulfate, Urea, Slow Release Nitrogen, Other Nitrogen Fertilizers, Phosphoric Acid, Ammonium Phosphate, Nitric & Superphosphates, Thermal and Other Phosphate Processes, Potassium Fertilizers, Fluid Fertilizers, Bulk Blending, Minor Nutrients. 98 illustrations. 406 pages. **$35**

OTHERS

INDUSTRIAL MEMBRANES 1972
Design and Applications
by J. McDermott

1. **REVERSE OSMOSIS MEMBRANES**
Cellulose Acetate (18)
Other Cellulosics (5)
Unit Fabrication (13)
2. **OTHER DEIONIZING MEMBRANES**
Nylon Membranes (4)
Other Polymers (8)
Discrete Particles (5)
3. **ION EXCHANGE MEMBRANES**
Preparations (22)
Inorganic Membranes (4)
Separation Processes (5)
4. **FILTER MEDIA**
For Fluids (9)
For Gases (3)
Ultrafiltration (3)
Other Applications (4)
5. **SOLVENT SEPARATION**
Hydrocarbons (4)
Water Removal (2)
6. **MEDICAL & OTHER USES**
Medical & Biological (5)
Other Uses (4)

118 Processes. 246 pages. **$36**

INDUSTRIAL SOLVENTS HANDBOOK 1970
by I. Mellan
A handbook with complete, up-to-date, pertinent data regarding industrial solvents.
821 tables contain pertinent data concerning physical properties of solvents and degrees of solubility of materials in these solvents. Numerous graphs included giving a great deal of data concerning various parameters. Also includes phase diagrams for multi-component products.
The vast amount of information contained in this book is shown in the abbreviated Table of Contents in the next column. The numbers in ( ) after each entry indicate the number of tables.
Hydrocarbon Solvents (14); Halogenated Hydrocarbons (130); Nitroparaffins (5); Organic Sulfur Compounds (5); Monohydric Alcohols (122); Polyhydric Alcohols (150); Phenols (6); Aldehydes (10); Ethers (53); Glycol Ethers (79); Ketones (44); Acids (18); Amines (124); Esters (61). 478 pages. **$25**

MICROENCAPSULATION TECHNOLOGY 1969
by M. W. Ranney
Based on 81 U.S. patents describing encapsulating techniques for particles and droplets.
Phase Separation Methods; Interface Reactions—Polymerizations. Physical Methods (Multi-Orifice Centrifugal, etc.) and Applications (transfer sheets, etc.) are the chapter headings.
There is considerable potential for future application of microencapsulated products. 275 pages. **$35**

CONTINUOUS CASTING OF STEEL 1970
33 Magazine
This volume of highly technical and economic data and information on continuous casting originally appeared as a series of articles over the years in 33 Magazine. Continuous Casting of Steel 1970 is as current as the World Continuous Casting Round/Up of August-September 1970. 341 pages. **$20**

FIRE RETARDANT BUILDING PRODUCTS AND COATINGS 1970
by Dr. M. W. Ranney
The value of this report is indicated by the number of building materials here.
1. **Wood Impregnation**
2. **Fiberboard**
3. **Ceiling Tile and Panels**
4. **Asphaltic Products**
5. **Intumescent Coatings**
6. **General Formulations**
7. **Adhesives**
186 pages. **$35**

ELECTRON BEAM WELDING 1971
by Dr. R. Bakish
The material has been arranged for easy use in the seven broad areas shown, with the number of developments indicated. 1. Processes and Equipment (41), 2. Alternate Beam Generating System (8), 3. Beam Control (20), 4. Moveable Chambers (8), 5. Beam Protective Devices (6), 6. Viewing Devices (10), 7. End Products (13). 150 pages **$35**

SUPERCONDUCTING MATERIALS 1970
by P. Conrad
Electronics Materials Review No. 11
Gives 99 detailed manufacturing and fabrication processes. Superconductive materials can improve long distance transmission of electric power, provide more compact memories for computers, improve magnets for physics research and thermonuclear power reactors.
135 pages. **$35**

PHOTOCONDUCTIVE MATERIALS 1970
by M. Sittig
Electronic Materials Review No. 8
Photoconductors have a number of important applications, such as television camera tubes, solar cells, photoelectric cells, solid state light amplifiers, electrophotographic copying machines. 86 processes. 288 pages. **$35**

BATTERY MATERIALS 1970
by P. Conrad
Electronics Materials Review No. 10
Describes 162 processes useful in the manufacture of modern batteries:
Aqueous Battery Systems (89)
"Dry" Battery Systems (29)
Inorganic Electrolyte Systems (6)
Organic Electrolyte Systems (6)
Solid Electrolyte Systems (18)
Molten Electrolyte Systems (11)
Radioactive Batteries (3)
171 pages. **$35**

RESISTOR MATERIALS 1971
by P. Conrad
Electronics Materials Review No. 12
A helpful guide to new resistor materials.
Metals and Other Elements and Alloys (48)
Metal-Metal Oxide Mixtures (9)
Inorganic Oxide Compositions (32)
Other Inorganic Compounds (21)
Organic Compositions (12)
217 pages. **$35**